THE Harrowsmith
R E A D E R III

Edited by James Lawrence

The Third Anthology from
Canada's National Award
Winning Magazine of
Country Life and
Alternatives to Bigness

A permanent reference edition
with material selected from
Issues Number Thirty to
Number Fifty-Four

Camden House Publishing Ltd.

CAMDEN
◆HOUSE◆

PUBLISHING

© 1984 by Camden House Publishing Ltd.

All rights reserved. The use of any part of this publication reproduced,
transmitted in any form or by any means, electronic, mechanical,
photocopying, recording or otherwise, or stored in a retrieval system
without the prior consent of the Publisher is an infringement of the
copyright law.

Canadian Cataloguing in Publication Data
Main entry under title:
The Harrowsmith reader, volume III
Includes index.
ISBN 0-920656-32-3
1. Country life - Canada. 2. Agriculture - Canada.
I. Lawrence, James. II. Harrowsmith.
S501.2.H373 1984   630'.971   C84-099456-7

Trade distribution by Firefly Books, Toronto

Printed in Canada by
Friesen Printers, Altona, Manitoba, for
Camden House Publishing Ltd.
7 Queen Victoria Road
Camden East, Ontario
K0K 1J0

Cover illustration by Roger Hill

THE Harrowsmith
R E A D E R III

Editor & Publisher
James M. Lawrence

Associate Editors
Jennifer Bennett, Pamela Cross, Michael Webster

Assistant Editor
John Archibald

Copy Editors
Charlotte DuChene, David Archibald, Mary Patton
John Giesbrecht, Sharon McFadzean

Graphic Artists
Linda Menyes, Judith Goodwin, Philip Wood, Pamela McDonald

Assistant to the Editor & Publisher
Kathryn MacDonald

Editorial Assistant
Denise Fisher

Contributors
Ron Allensen, John Barber, Lamont Bassett, John Bianchi
Anne Borella, Tom Daly, Frederick Doe, Blair Drawson
Stephen Errington, Gordon Flagler, Adrian Forsyth
Charmaine Gaudet, Kit Gifford, Ian S.R. Grainge
Mary Preus Hamilton, Eric Hayes, Anna Johnson, Robert Kaufman
Charles Long, Elizabeth Long, Tim Matson, Helen Molitor
Patrick Morrow, R.A.J. Phillips, Graham Pilsworth, Annie Proulx
Bart Robinson, Marta Scythes, Ernie Sparks, David Stone
Bob Suzuki, James Tughan, Alasdair G.B. Wallace

Cohorts
Janet Baker, Peggy Baker, Dianne Bartlett, Pamela Conway
Douglas Cordingley, Susan Dickinson, Linda Dillon, Cheryl Dowhaluk
Frank B. Edwards, Cheryl Empey, Bonnie Golomb
Wayne Grady, Linda Grant, Patti Ann Herrington
Margaret Hewitt, Rose Howard, Alice Z. Lawrence
Janice McAvoy, Edith McQuay, Mariella Morrin, Jane Murphy
Brian Parker, Brian C. Patterson, Alice Pitt, Marilyn Skinner
Patsy Skinner, Wayne Skinner, Glenda Smith, Eileen Whitney

Contents

Introductions

With the appearance of this book, *Harrowsmith* has just completed its eighth year of publication — eight years, it might be added, more than certain Canadian publishing moguls confidently predicted when the magazine first appeared. Immediately perceived by many as a publication for barefoot hippies or plain dirt farmers, *Harrowsmith* went on to demonstrate an unexpected appeal in Canada and the northern United States, but the problem of identifying just who would want to subscribe to such a magazine remains an enduring vexation in the minds of many media and advertising observers.

"What kind of person reads *Harrowsmith*?" is a question we have heard from the day the magazine appeared; it is not an unreasonable question, but we believe it is one that defies any easy response. Unlike the magazines that readily reduce their audiences to simplified, stereotypical readers — the Milwaukee Milkman or the Rosedale Matron — *Harrowsmith* has steadfastly professed the inability or disinclination to tuck our "typical" reader into some sort of artificial conceptual pigeonhole.

This derives from the fact that this magazine has an astonishingly diverse following of readers. Among them are hold-over hippies and traditional farming families, but one also finds an ex-Governor-General of Canada, retired professors of biology, corporation presidents, CBC personalities and hundreds of thousands of people who can hardly be said to conform to any standard of dress, political outlook, profession or background.

What we do know is that a typical issue of *Harrowsmith* today is received by about 150,000 primary readers (paid subscribers and newsstand buyers), whose copies are, in turn, read by an average of 2.06 other interested parties. The total audience, as tallied by the survey organization that measures such things in Canada, is thus approximately 450,000 per issue — a far cry from the several hundred charter subscribers who helped launch *Harrowsmith* in 1976.

We also know that the magazine is equally well received by men (51 percent) and women (49 percent) and that 58 percent of *Harrowsmith*'s readers are between 25 and 49 years of age. More than half have been to university, and 64 percent have household incomes of $25,000 per year or more.

None of these statistics, however, really distinguishes *Harrowsmith* from other leading magazines such as *Maclean's, Time* or *Saturday Night*. Only when one begins to delve into the special interests of the readers do the unique qualities of the *Harrowsmith* audience begin to emerge. An amazing 91 percent have a garden, with 87 percent growing vegetables, 56 percent raising fruit and berries, 78 percent planting flowers and 35 percent cultivating herbs. Fully 94 percent preserve produce by freezing, 71 percent by canning and 30 percent in a root cellar. The average *Harrowsmith* reader spends 8.4 hours per week in his or her garden during the growing season. (Significantly, this typical gardening reader passes on things he has learned in the magazine to an average of 4.3 other people during the past year. Extrapolated over the full 450,000 readers, this fact means that gardening information from *Harrowsmith* makes its way to more than 1.9 million people each year.)

The home also appears to play significantly in the lives of these readers: 80 percent own their own residences, a third of these have built their own homes, and another 32 percent are planning to build a new home in the future. They are serious about home improvement and renovation, spending almost eight hours per week on do-it-yourself projects, and they are actively putting energy conservation measures in practice. Some 67 percent of *Harrowsmith* readers heat their homes with wood, either as a primary or secondary source, while 5.4 percent currently use solar energy collection systems. More than half plan to add on a greenhouse to their homes.

Now, some of this is confounding to certain media analysts. Why, they ask, would anyone with a university education and a good income want to spend time chasing and hoarding sticks of firewood, staking tomato vines or blanching kettles of green beans? Did not all of this back-to-the-landism fade from the trendy heights it enjoyed in the late '60s and early '70s?

John Bianchi

Clearly not, if one judges by the collection of articles within this anthology and the strong positive reaction with which readers have greeted them. This material represents what we consider to be some of the most useful and lasting information published by *Harrowsmith* during the past three years. For those of us who talk and correspond with the magazine's readers and contributors each day, it is obvious that the demand for this highly pragmatic material is still very much in evidence today.

What is not clear, however, is the motivation each reader may have in pursuing the apparently arcane arts of self-sufficiency in an age when the essentials of life have never been more readily accessible.

Consider the lawyer who can be found spending his weekends cutting maple firewood in the back reaches of his rural property. Surely thrift is not a major consideration for the well-to-do professional, yet he will note with quiet glee the prices others are paying for wood of lesser quality. Traditionally, accountants have disparaged this sort of thinking, pointing out that the cord of firewood the lawyer perceives as costing little or nothing actually carries a price tag of several hundreds —

or thousands — of dollars, depending on the solicitor's regular hourly fee structure.

For most of us, this sort of accounting appears blatantly faulty, if not laughable. Rarely do we read of the same rules being applied to time spent golfing or sailing. In the case of many pursuits covered in this book, one finds activities that blend, in a unique and gratifying way, a mixture of necessity, thrift and recreation. For many of us, planting a garden or stocking the pantry with a year's worth of bayberry candles is far more appealing than the prospect of an afternoon of golf — with the added satisfaction of asserting our survival skills and our sense of economical independence, if only temporarily, from the consumer economy.

For dedicated *Harrowsmith* readers, we hope that this selection of articles will serve as a permanent reference, while newcomers may find in these pages motivation to try their hands at the new and unknown. In the end, we offer no new characterizations of our "typical" reader, but we think these articles speak eloquently for the sort of people who read *Harrowsmith* and stand as proof that the notions of self-sufficiency and self-reliance are still very much alive and expanding in 1984.

— *JL*

The Genial Hermit

"I'll tell you one thing," says the sane trapper of Sheep Rock, Yukon Territory. "You sure develop a great sense of the absurd up here."

By Bart Robinson with photography by Patrick Morrow

Below Dawson City, the Yukon is a monumental river. Three hundred miles north of its alpine headwaters and 1,700 miles south and east of its final debouchment at the Bering Sea, it is already more than a quarter mile wide and running at 200,000 cubic feet per second. Under the flat light of noon, it is a powerfully rolling sluice of sand-choked water; at dawn and dusk, with the sun working the pale peaks of the Ogilvie Mountains, it is a wondrous golden-scaled serpent whispering arcanum to the land through which it passes. The aboriginal Athabascan Indians considered it "the mightiest of rivers," and named it so.

For all its grandeur, though, the Yukon is but a river to match that which cradles it, a topography of prodigious mountains, unending forests and immense, ever-changing skies. It is a land of resonant silence, isolated and adverse, and is known to its inhabitants simply as "the country" — much in the sense that many native North American populations knew themselves as "the people." Once part of it, it is difficult to imagine anything else. Because it is remote and often inhospitable, because extraordinary events have occurred there and because it has always demanded much of those who have lived or tried to live there, the Yukon has achieved a mythic status among those of a southerly rearing. Raised on the prose of Jack London and the verse of Robert Service, they ponder "the last frontier," "the great beyond," and "the land of the midnight sun," and are quick to people the region with characters untouched since the days of '98. The few stalwarts who do live there, and particularly those who live alone in the bush, often find themselves cast in roles not of their own choosing. At best, they are regarded as colourful eccentrics; at worst, as misanthropic malcontents prowling the far peripheries of civilization.

A trapper-hermit-turned-artist, John Lodder contemplates the North in transition from his vantage point alongside the Yukon River. "Nothing is black and white; I dabble in the grey areas."

This is also the stomping ground of Ken Killkrazy, a bushman as broad as an axe, strong as an ox and tough as frozen moose hide. He drinks like a fish, smokes like a chimney and looks like 40 acres of bad news from the Russian front. Despite his 60-odd years, Ken is still going strong, the sort of man who will mush 50 miles with frozen feet at 60 below, take an un- cleaned hunting knife to his own appendix and still be back in town for last call at the Snake Pit to knock back shots of overproof rum with Effluvia Pale beer chasers, roll up a chain's worth of Old Rope cigarettes and trade four-letter invectives with the boys. He shoots fast, usually straight, and is indiscriminate in his targets.

Killkrazy, of course, is pure Yukon fiction, the comic protagonist created by John Lodder, who him- self might be described as a contemporary sort of her- mit, neither malcontent nor misanthrope and only slightly eccentric. One of a generation who headed for the far wilderness during the seventies, Lodder still lives in a small cabin across from Sheep Rock, a Yu- kon River landmark near the U.S.-Canadian border, 65 miles downstream from Dawson. Except for the company of four sled dogs, he has lived there alone for seven years. His life, however, is not that of a hide- bound recluse or ascetic: Despite his solitary ways, he genuinely enjoys people, and once every three or four months, Lodder makes his way to Dawson for sup- plies and socializing. Out at Sheep Rock, he keeps in touch via the network of people who live and travel

Isolation and economy have inspired Lodder's architectural pursuits: his sedge and log cabin, **left,** *and animal-proof cache,* **above.**

on his reach of the river. His friends describe him vari- ously as "an ordinary person living an extraordinary life," and as "a genius hiding out under a bush." Lod- der thinks of himself as "an ordinary person living out under an extraordinary bush." He is a trapper, a fish- erman, a painter and a writer; and he is well-read, ar- ticulate and possesses a finely honed sense of humour which he uses scalpel-like on the irritations in his life — such as Northern stereotyping.

"Well, hell yes! Of course we're all redneck morons up here, mad trappers and loser loners who live to kill. Why else would we be up here?" His eyes ignite like lightning-struck spruce snags, and he laughs maniac- ally, slipping into a bit of personal theatre. "You know what I do on a Sunday afternoon, boy? Drink beer — three, four cases — and run down innocent river trip- pers in a 30-foot aluminum river boat with twin Merc 75s on the back. I shoot the ones that don't drown. Damn, but I *love* doin' that!" He slaps his leg and laughs again, quietly this time, relaxing, and shakes his head gently, as if to clear it. "I'll tell you one thing: you sure develop a great sense of the absurd up here after a while."

The bush life, as actually practised by Lodder, is a Spartan one. He earns little and owns little, and there is little that separates him from the realities of the encircling geography. It is a physically demanding existence, and his appearance bespeaks as much. In his mid-thirties, he is a tall man, several inches over six feet, and his years in the bush have pared him to the dimensions of a thin plank whip-sawn from a particularly gnarly fir. His features are strong, chain-saw sculpted, and his dark eyes glitter behind a perpetually smudged pair of dark brown horn-rimmed glasses. His river clothes, tatters in which, by his own admission, he would "be humiliated in town," are impregnated with sand, grime, grease, gas and fish guts. A pair of ragged Levis wrap around a blown-out pair of size 14 boots, and when he is caught out on the river at night and the wind comes up, he dons successive layers of soot-grey mackinaws, the whole cloth in one covering the holes in another. A coachman's cap of similar colour and repair is tugged hard down over a thick shank of black hair.

If it is unlikely that Lodder will ever find his way into an Eddie Bauer catalogue, it is inconceivable that his cabin will appear in any smart four-colour brochure designed for urban-dwelling wilderness-vacation-home seekers. Lodder's cabin is made of logs, but resemblances end there. Twelve by 18 feet, it stands 13 logs high, granting a six-foot clearance. The roof is an unkempt profusion of grass and sedge; soil and duff lie piled against the lower logs as insulation and rodent-proofing. Three small windows allow particularly determined rays of light to penetrate the cabin interior, illuminating an uneven floor of rough planks, a plank bed, a frightfully battered but immensely personable barrel stove, a few barren shelves and a small plank table with a pole purlin support rising through its centre. All told, it is a rude affair, the overall effect heightened by Lodder's approach to housekeeping, which could most generously be described as lackadaisical.

The cabin lies on a rocky spit jutting out into the river, and would command a striking prospect if it were not for a claustrophobic tangle of 20-foot willows which surrounds it. An hour with a chain saw would salvage the view, but Lodder prefers the security (and the windbreak) proffered by the willows. "If I want to look at the river," he says flatly, "I'll walk down to the river and look at it."

Such is the voice of the seasoned pragmatist, and it but faintly resembles that of the young romantic who wandered into Dawson nearly a decade ago, an aspiring artist in search of a statement. Raised in Salmo, in southern British Columbia, Lodder attended the University of British Columbia for a year after high school, then moved to Alberta to pursue a fine arts diploma in Calgary. "The instructors told us anyone could learn technique," he recalls, "but without something to say, the technique would be useless." Taking the lesson to heart, Lodder headed east once again, this time to Toronto, "where it was all supposed to be happening." A quick survey of the city, however, convinced him otherwise, and he decided to become a latter-day nomad, "a gatherer of odd jobs, living the sort of life I read about on the dust jackets of the beat-generation literature I was reading then." Two

years on the road found him fighting forest fires just outside Mackenzie, British Columbia, on the Parsnip River, an experience which persuaded him that the good life lay outdoors in the western wildlands. "I discovered I was truly enjoying all the things everyone else hated — cooking over open fires, sleeping outdoors, getting lost in the forest and working hard for long hours."

Later, thumbing his way out of Mackenzie, John was picked up by a man driving to Alaska, and he decided he would tag along, at least as far as the Yukon. He was particularly interested in Dawson, which he had wanted to visit ever since reading Pierre Berton's *Klondike* as a teenager. Dawson was the heart of the last great North American gold rush, a boom town of 30,000 people in 1898, and Lodder was eager "to talk to some of the old ghosts and get a feel for the last frontier." The town, now a collapsing relic of drunkenly swaying false-front buildings, ankle-deep mud, and 700 feisty year-round residents, captivated his imagination and he settled nearby, spending his first winter in a tent, cutting wood for a living. The season became one of the cruellest on record — 60 below F in January and 40 below through March — and again Lodder found himself revelling in adversity. "I loved the challenge. I cut 185 cords of wood that winter, and I saw it as a great adventure. Every morning I would step outside, sniff the air and say, 'John old boy, this is really it.' " He stayed on, enamoured of the North and its people, soaking up the mystique of the Yukon, acquiring new skills.

During his second winter Lodder met Peter Beatty, a trapper who used a dog team to run a line not far from Dawson. Beatty became a close friend and major influence: "He was a walking demonstration of the quiet contentment that might come from a successful life in the bush, and I decided to try it." With an assistant's trapping licence, he learned the rudiments, and then, with the winter of 1975 approaching, he picked up a lease of his own and made the downriver plunge. He spent the season working a short line on snowshoes, taking lynx, wolverine, marten and the occasional fox and wolf. It was another exceptionally cold winter, and before it was over, Lodder found that he was devoting considerable amounts of time talking himself into doing whatever had to be done. On the most frigid mornings, with the fire in the stove gone dead and the trees outside splitting like cannon shot from the cold, he would find himself in earnest dialogue with a little voice that surfaced from the back of his mind. It was inevitably the same.

"What's wrong? Can't take it?"

"Of course I can, but I think it might be wise to wait until it warms up a little. A person could get in trouble out there."

" A person could get in trouble out there anytime, fool. And if you wait for it to warm up, you'll be in bed till June."

The Yukon River, top, is an artistic inspiration to Lodder. After seven years on the river, he finds his art an escape from such humdrum preoccupations as small-engine repair.

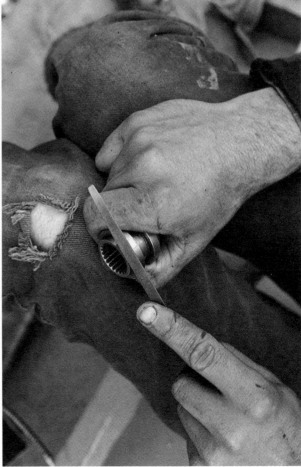

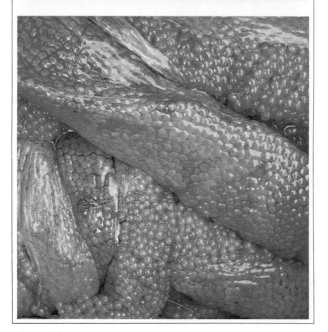

Lodder got up, every time, and when he walked into Dawson just before breakup the following spring, he discovered his winter's take was just enough to see him through to the next season. He also knew he had found a life which challenged him physically and psychologically. With little ado, he packed up a few more supplies and headed back downriver.

"There was no great soul-searching," he says. "What there was, was a gut feeling that life in the bush would mesh with the way I felt about things. It made sense. I knew if I lived simply I'd be able to support myself at something I was interested in and still have time for other pursuits."

Living simply is a dominant theme in Lodder's conversation. " 'The love of economy,' " he preaches, quoting Shaw, " 'is the root of all virtue.' " Necessity is unquestionably a large part of his frugality, but more than that, Lodder thoroughly enjoys the exercise of discovering just how little he needs in order to survive. The contents of the cabin reflect both the priorities of a life on the river and John's belief in the elemental life. On the shelves are an easy inventory of two boxes of Red River cereal, a box of Red Rose tea, a can of peanut butter, a can of red kidney beans, a sack of split green peas and a sack of brown sugar. On the table lie a box of matches and a bowl filled with lumps of salt. Behind the door are a metal jerry can, a Stihl D41 chain saw, cans of fibreglass resin, Coleman fuel, oil, assorted nuts, bolts, tools and fishing tackle. There are also two rifles, well-worn, but freshly oiled, swabbed and recently sighted. Last summer wolves came to the cabin at night and carried off a promising sled pup, and just downstream from Dawson, three people working a fish camp were mauled by a grizzly.

The only evidence in the cabin to suggest an inner life is a full shelf of books, a catholic collection ranging from *Jude the Obscure* to *Small Engine Maintenance*, and a crumpled watercolour tacked to the pole rising out of the table.

The finest, most visible statement to date of Lodder's thrift is his river boat, a flat-bottomed, square-nosed, chlorophyll-green, 16-foot plywood craft. A no-frills model, it was handcrafted with the benefit of few tools, and looks it: weary, well-used and decisively utilitarian. The oarlocks are whittled stakes set into the thwarts; the oars, two poles with slabs of plywood tacked to the ends. The engine is whichever of two 25-year-old Evinrudes Lodder has cajoled into running on any given day. He admits to spending more on outboard parts than he did to purchase the motors, but vows he will continue to use them until they cough themselves off their mounts in a final, fatal explosion of black smoke and rusted rubble. In the meantime, he looks for more 1955 Evinrudes "because they damn well made 'em better in those days." Lodder is a master scavenger and

Cleaning king salmon, **right,** *Lodder supplements his trapping income; his annual harvest can fetch $2,000 after filleting and smoking,* **top and centre left.** *He and his dogs share the feast of roe,* **bottom left,** *that is too perishable to be preserved for sale in Dawson.*

an indefatigable bargain seeker. Hunting and fishing provide moose, bear and salmon for his table, welcome additions to his staple diet of nonperishables. "Occasionally, in midwinter," he confesses, "I dream of fresh fruit."

In exchange for his retrenchment, Lodder says he wins the right to make his own decisions, take responsibility for his actions and divide his energies and hours as he sees fit. It is not an idle existence — "a solo life in the bush is very good for bringing on confrontations with any idleness your soul may harbour" — and the same restless energy that brought him to the river fuels an impulse to experiment with new approaches to old tasks and to move on to new endeavours. He recently exchanged his snowshoes for skis, and is presently training a dog team. And two years ago, he began to explore the possibility of fishing commercially for king salmon. His operation, characteristically, is a modest one. Using a single net 60 feet long, 12 feet deep, with 8-inch-diagonal mesh, Lodder limits his catch to five or six fish a day, even though the eddy where he sets his net will yield that many and more in an hour during the height of the run. Because there is no way to move whole, fresh fish to market, Lodder smokes his catch. It takes him an hour to process each of the 30- to 40-pound kings. Lodder believes he can make maybe $2,000 with his "just-keeping-busy" approach.

The king salmon are followed upriver by the chum, and Lodder, like many others on the river, puts more value on the chum than the king, even though they have less commercial worth. Chum are also known as dog salmon, and are the universal dog food along the river. A good-sized team will consume 1,000 fish a winter, and as dogs become part of his life, the fish become an important part of his economy.

Although Lodder is unquestionably knowledgeable in the ways of river living, he steadfastly maintains he is no bushman, a person he defines as one who has thoroughly mastered all the skills necessary for a successful life in the Yukon wilds.

"I've learned what I've had to to get by. In some cases, if it's something I'm very interested in, like certain aspects of trapping, I'll put a lot of time and effort into it, but in other areas, such as engine repair, I'll learn just enough to scrape by. My first couple of years were totally preoccupied with learning how to stay alive here, but now I've got the basics down and find my energies divided increasingly between the bush and some other pursuits not usually associated with the bush."

The "other pursuits," in fact, have John questioning his commitment to the river. After seven years, he finds himself devoting a disproportionate amount of time to writing, reading and painting: The artist, it seems, has found something to say. The work is of the North and Northern life, but his two chosen modes of expression are so divergent as to be surprising. One is the Yukon Komix, a crudely drawn and rudely satirical publication bearing his own Anarchist League Seal of Approval; the other, a series of quietly contemplative watercolours, softly glowing landscapes which belie any notion of an ex-urban barbarian run amok in the woods. Between the two, he expresses both his appreciation of the country and his considerable fascination with the residents.

"I use the watercolours to pin down the inner impact of certain moments and places: the magic of a sunrise in the Ogilvies, that first second when the light hits the rock and water." He cites as major influences Georgia O'Keefe and J.M.W. Turner, and he likens his approach to that of an Oriental painter who wanders the mountains by day, recording images and emotions to paint at night. Lodder believes the subtlety of watercolours to be perfect for his work, and when he talks of them, he might well be talking about one side of himself. "They're a meditative medium, requiring spontaneity and risk. You can change them, but in so doing, you lose the original impulse."

And then there is Ken Killkrazy who is, according to Lodder, the man most outsiders expect to find loose in the streets of Dawson. Other Lodder characters include Sid Blithers, a forestry official who adorns his office walls with posters of wolves and the inscription "Zap It," and the humane society lady who fights with a sharpened umbrella. "Good satire," Lodder believes, "holds nothing sacred," and he positions himself in a far corner, watching pipeliners, native activists, Greenpeacers, developers and bush people play out their roles. "Nothing is black and white; I dabble in the grey areas, peer over my glasses at these strident creatures and decide they're *all* crazy."

Lodder's work, especially the watercolours, has been well received, and its success has left him pondering the future. "I feel like I'm performing a balancing act, and it's a difficult one to maintain. The art is a bit frightening; I'm worried it will become so engrossing that the trapping and fishing will become secondary elements, and I'd hate to see that happen. They've been the source of my work." Nevertheless, he left the bush this winter, putting aside his traps for paintbrush and easel in the relative comforts of Dawson. Waving a long arm awkwardly at the river, he says, "This is just too big a chunk of me to walk away from forever, but maybe it's time to sample something else. Who knows? Maybe I'll even try a year in the South. It couldn't be much more mad than when I left it." He smiles, rubbing the side of his bearded jaw, and stretches his legs out toward Sheep Rock. "I wonder. Do you suppose a sane trapper from the back side of yonder might get a free lunch or two down there? Damn! Now that would be something just about as much fun as running down river trippers, don't you think?" ■

In his exploration of the Yukon landscape, Lodder treks past the Tombstone Range.

Bart Robinson is the managing editor of EQUINOX *magazine and is a longtime contributor to* Harrowsmith.

Rural Malaise

Exploring the emotional pitfalls of the pastoral life

A Harrowsmith Staff Report

That there is more to country life than the sensual tang of wood smoke, the sibilant lowing of contented cattle and the warm conviviality of a general store is clear to anyone who has ever broken free of mainstream urban living.

"I have no relish for the country," wrote Sidney Smith, a 19th-century British clergyman and essayist. "It is a kind of healthy grave." Even countryman Nathaniel Hawthorne warned that rural life was not all new-mown hay and happiness: "A man's soul may be buried and perish under a dung heap in a furrow of the field, just as under a pile of money."

The pastoral existence, obviously, does not prove equally stimulating to all who attempt it. The lack of ready employment opportunities and the hardscrabble economics combine to defeat some, while others find the motherlode of hard work at the end of the back-to-the-land rainbow more than their bodies — or minds — can bear. Still others complain of boredom, a sense of isolation or simple, unshakeable culture shock. Cut off from the constantly available stimulations of city life, unknown numbers of newcomers to exurbia find themselves unable to cope with the tranquillity of the country.

While the initial symptoms of emotional rural malaise tend to be vague, the outcomes may be painfully obvious: dreams broken, marriages strained or dissolved, homes or farms suddenly For Sale. Henry David Thoreau, in the last chapter of *Walden*, alluded to the pitfalls that await those who venture into the unknown:

"There is a solid bottom everywhere," wrote Thoreau. "We read that the traveller asked the boy if the swamp before him had a hard bottom. The boy replied that it had. But presently the traveller's horse sank up to the girths, and he observed to the boy, 'I thought you said that this bog had a hard bottom.'

" 'So it has,' answered the latter, 'but you have not got halfway to it yet.' "

Hoping to chart some of the boggier areas of rural life, *Harrowsmith* asked a number of contributors to explore the emotional challenges which face anyone who moves to — or already lives in — the country. Fortunately, while the tales of agrarian woe may do nothing to dispel the mid-winter doldrums, we find cheer in the ability of people to adapt, to survive and, perhaps most difficult of all, to grow beyond too-simple expectations of what a new style of life will hold. We are reminded of Einstein's verdict on the subject:

"I have lived in the solitude of the country and noticed how the monotony of quiet life stimulates the creative mind." ∎

Blair Drawson

Stranger In a Familiar Land

Life without roots: country newcomers as human transplants in rocky soil

By Frederick Doe

I should have known it would be like this. I grew up in a rural community. One of those spare, amorphous, rag-tag collections of humanity that belongs to a place out of a fear of leaving rather than any sense of being. You know the kind. You're driving down a back-country stretch of numbered road, past half-abandoned farms and faded strips of old election posters, when you become aware that the houses have hunched a little closer.

Sometimes there is even a sign, complete with epitaphs to say it mattered:

"Eden Falls pop. 406
Home of the Falcons —
'62 Junior Champs!"

Those are the big ones. Further down the road, in time if not in miles, is the empty store, thistles growing through the porch and an untrimmed board nailed crosswise over the Dr. Pepper sign that covers the one big window. You'll never know, but you're sure it must say "Salada" underneath — a slice of Norman Rockwell, decomposed.

Those places always have a sense of leaving about them, a communal tension that lifelong urbanites will only find in the waiting room of a bus station . . . where arrivals quickly melt away, but those who wait forever to leave can fill the air with their collective melancholy. That same tension is in the eyes of the young men who lean against Camaros, or jam their fists into their jeans and talk about maybe going up to Ottawa, or Edmonton, or wherever a brother-in-law happens to be who can get them a job.

At 18, I stood there with them. Except that the star attraction then was a '52 Ford, chopped and channelled, with flames painted on the fenders. Waiting. Waiting for jobs, waiting for girls, waiting for the bomb to fall, waiting for anything to happen. And sometimes — not often, but sometimes — a strange car might stop. Someone we didn't know. When strangers approached, the air got very still, expectant. The slouches became more casual — a studied casual where the chest swells out even as you slump back harder against the Camaro, or the Shake 'n' Burger, or whatever they're leaning on in Eden Falls these days. The thoughts at those times were of myths, easy city girls or toughs in search of a fight. The reality was almost always someone lost and looking for directions. And when the reality was announced, there was some relief, some embarrassed banter and always polite compliance.

"Yes, sir . . . ."

"No, sir . . . ."

"Make the second left, and it'll take you straight back up to the highway, sir."

We knew (as if we had seen it in a movie) that when the strangers drove away, they would be saying, "What polite young men! People are so much more friendly in the country." We thought of ourselves as friendly people. We basked in that image. Nurtured it. But these strangers weren't our real friends. And they never could be. Never.

And yet it didn't take many years in the city to find that the leaving was not complete. October pavements

Graham Pilsworth

other Edens and finding the natives friendly. Sadly, they are almost always city people, born and bred, who have simply mistaken that forelock-tugging politeness for friendship.

Country people are not unfriendly. It's just that real acceptance — whatever lies beneath that polite veneer — takes so blessed long when the social order is amended only over the span of generations.

I have often thought that it would be easier if we could all be seven again. As the new kids in school, we could endure the stares and giggles of the morning class, go out at recess to face the shoving tournament that would reestablish all our places on the hierarchy, wipe noses all around and get on with being pals. Seven-year-olds are smart enough to get it over with in half a day. Older strangers wait through a lifetime of forelock tugging to put down roots in the country.

Beneath the surface courtesy, there is an almost impenetrable barrier between those who come back to the land and those who have never left it. Deeply rooted, strongly felt and never expressed, the quiet gulf between "us" and "them" isolates the newcomer in an affable solitude that can be hard to recognize at first, especially by those newcomers who initially welcome rural solitude as a relief from the press of urban society. At some point, peace and quiet become social isolation, and the newcomer begins to wonder what he might have done wrong.

BOOTS BY THE DOOR

Our first mistake involved sexual mores — not ours, which are exemplary of course, but someone else's. Unfortunately, none of the handbooks on buying a place in the country mentions the importance of understanding the neighbours' sexual habits and longings. They go on at tiresome length over testing the soil and checking rights-of-way, but nowhere do they warn the would-be homesteader to beware of the local libidos. Our down payment put us on a patch of earth that straddled a no-man's-land between a middle-aged bachelor of unquestioned virtue and a lonely lady with somewhat wider experience. The incipient conflict was between a Catholic sexual outlook and a catholic one; and pent-up feelings had begun to smoulder when we landed in the crossfire. We weren't even there when the explosion came. It was a nomadic acquaintance of ours (another stranger to the area, who *ipso facto* "belonged" to us). He set it all off by arriving at the nascent homestead in our absence and innocently going to the neighbour's door — the wrong neighbour as it happened. One thing led to another, and, well . . . . The bachelor of virtue went courting and found our friend's boots by the door. While the neighbour had been saving himself, the bank had gone belly up. The indignation was righteous, loud and instantly spread to the remotest corner of the community.

Wandering Stranger got off with a slap on the wrist for not behaving like a gentleman. "A gentleman," said Virtuous Bachelor, "would have hidden his boots in the closet where callers couldn't see them."

"A gentleman," replied the Wandering Stranger,

didn't rustle underfoot, the snow was grey instead of white, and having a hundred city friends was not enough to compensate for the loss of starlight and those who understood the feeling without having to explain it.

We came back to smell the earth again. Only the name of the place was different, and this time we were the strangers. We weren't around when the Falcons won in '62. We had to ask where the dump was. No one had ever known my mother or could remember the smell of her hair. We weren't related to anybody. The social fabric of this new Eden was complete. We were welcome to drift along its fringes or even to stay and admire it awhile, but we could never be a part of this society. Never.

This new Eden, like the old one I remember, is a social womb where leaving is the expected thing, and entry is a violation of the natural order. A good place to come from, but not a place to go. I am sometimes falsely heartened to hear of other strangers moving into "should have seen my boots by the door and retreated instead of barging in." As was his habit, he soon wandered off and wasn't seen again.

Lonely Lady had a brand new rash of callers, from the elderly husbands of infirm wives to the pimply adolescents who parked their cars where they couldn't be seen and carried mints to cover up the smell of beer.

The Virtuous Bachelor stretched out the period of mourning and public sympathy for another six months and then went back to seeing the Lonely Lady — this time on the sly and for different reasons.

We, however, were held responsible for causing that epic upheaval in the social order. *Les agents provocateurs*, so to speak.

So cursed were we with the taint of inferior city morals that the local works department diligently removed every twig of the dense hedge that had screened us from the road. The better to see what was going on . . . or off.

CROSSED SIGNALS

One of the first bizarre rites that the neighbours observed was the erection of a clothesline. I spent most of the morning assembling the two t-shaped posts: each a simple eight-foot upright, with a crosspiece near the top, wide enough to hold three lines. When they were bolted and braced, I dragged them each across the lawn and was struggling to raise them into position when I became aware of a silent line of cars watching from the bottom of the yard (where the hedge used to be). Unnerved, I retreated to the house to consider whether we ought to invite them in for tea or ask for a hand with the clothesline. "Better not ask them to help," said my legal spouse (sorry, I have to put it that way — there have been rumours to the contrary). "It is, after all, a Sunday, and they may not be willing to work on Sunday." I looked at the calendar on the kitchen wall, and it was, indeed, a Sunday . . . Easter Sunday! Hoping to explain the crosses over a cup of tea, I approached the cars to invite the people in. They hurried off in a shower of gravel before I was halfway there.

From that point on, we have been avoided by the drinking crowd on the grounds of religious fanaticism, and by the church groups who consider us apostates at best, since none of them has seen us in his own congregation.

For those of you who have never lived in the country, it is important to understand the role that religion plays. It is not essential to be religious, or even to attend a church. It is important to choose your side and stay there. Most communities have a sufficiently diverse mix of denominations that differences are easily tolerated. The Anglicans, Catholics and variegated Gospel groups have not had a violent quarrel in this new Eden for nearly a hundred years. That may be because there are so few potential converts to compete for, but I suspect it has more to do with the balance of power. There could be no clear winner in any resurgence of hostilities as long as the sides remain even.

Depending on the birth rate and other natural factors, power in its various forms is shared among the groups in orderly fashion. The exception is the United Church, which handicapped as it is with an overambitious name, remains the smallest of the congregations. One Gospel group controls the maintenance of roads, the Anglican realm is the community hall and the card parties, the RCs are big in agriculture, and the boozers are allowed to run the fair.

How does a stranger fit into all that? About like a Muslim in Belfast, equally ignored by all sides.

COUSIN DREW

Politics in rural Canada has little to do with issues, ideology and elections. It has a lot to do with roads — whose road gets fixed and who gets paid to fix it. Our political isolation was clearly established in April of our first year here. My legal spouse, coming home with the pickup, slowed down before turning into the lane and promptly sank bumper deep into the centre of the township road. I'll spare the horrible details of two hours' work with an axle jack, in a roadbed that was more like icy chocolate pudding than *terra firma*, but suffice it to say that we were less than jolly at that point when a neighbour pulled up. Unable to pass, and safely parked on the *firma* side of the *terra*, he shut off the motor and came out to perch on the hood of his truck. I was halfway under our sunken wreck, groping for the jack like an upended duck and surfacing only to breathe and curse. On my next trip for air, the neighbour and I exchanged the usual pleasantries and comments on the weather. I dove under again while he settled back to wait and watched from his comfortable perch. Legal Spouse, who knew that said neighbour had a tractor sitting a few hundred yards away, dumped another load of stone in the mire beside Titanic and muttered in my ear, "Ask the son of a bitch to pull us out."

"Bad form," I whispered, being more mindful of rural protocol than she. "He's supposed to offer." She smiled at the neighbour, said something unpleasant about the weather and went back to hauling stone offerings for the swamp god.

When she returned, the smile on the face of Legal Spouse was as icy as the raw spring wind. "If you don't ask him, I will," she hissed through gritted teeth.

The neighbour somehow sensed that he might have been involved in the whispers. "Reckon you'll have to get drew out," he chuckled.

Not about to let the opening pass, Legal Spouse fairly jumped at the neighbour's suggestion. "Drew? Who's Drew? Where can we get hold of him? Does he have a tractor?"

(I should explain, for the benefit of practising urbanites, that all township officials, from the reeve to the weed inspector, are commonly referred to by their Christian names. This is to avoid confusion, since all elected and appointed officials have more or less the same last names. The "cousin party" is a powerful force in rural politics and a spot of nepotism is not unknown.)

The neighbour looked confused. Legal Spouse was plainly agitated and primed for confrontation. "Drew.

I want to know who Drew is," she demanded.

I took her gently by the arm and whispered softly in her ear, " 'drew,' as in I draw, you drew, he has drew; draw out the truck, drew out the truck, get the truck drew out."

We drove the truck out (much later) and resolved to get the road repaired, a political act that demands attendance at a meeting of the township council.

The local council meets one afternoon a month, whether or not the press of public business demands it. There was some suggestion once to have the meeting in the evening so working people could attend. The consensus was, however, that the only ones who ever attended were retired farmers, and afternoons suited them just fine.

So I downed tools to get to the next monthly meeting. The Township Hall is not imposing: two flags, an older portrait of a younger queen, and a roll of honour listing the names of the three young locals who died for king and country. Two privates and a corporal. The room is dim and musty, with the faintest odour of something from childhood — the Grade Two cloakroom, perhaps, or the old church basement when the furnace had been running.

BUSINESS AS USUAL

The meeting had already started. The councillors, still in their outdoor clothes, were seated around the table in the centre of the room. A half dozen metal folding chairs were set up against the far wall, under the eye of fading young Elizabeth. Business came to a standstill as the door banged shut behind me and the echoes clattered around the barren space. I tiptoed across the wooden floor, grimacing when the narrow boards squeaked. Although, in retrospect, I can't imagine why I was so concerned about being silent, since not a word was spoken until I was seated. Even then, the hush continued until I nodded once. They all nodded back, the reeve cleared his throat, and the business of government resumed.

There were two other supplicants there before me. The first (the one I had interrupted) asked for a sign at the end of his road, so visitors would know where to turn. The reeve thanked him politely and told him they would let him know. When it was obvious that no one would discuss the matter as long as he was there, Supplicant One left the hall.

"Who the hell was he?" asked the eldest councillor. He cupped his hand around his ear and leaned toward the reeve.

"Smith!" the reeve shouted into the old man's ear.

"Who?"

"Smith!"

"Is that George Smith's boy?"

"No. He's over in New Glasgow. That was Willard Smith here."

"Who's he related to?"

"Nobody."

"What's he want?"

"Wants a sign on his road."

"A what?"

"A sign!" the reeve shouted again.

"What for?"

"To show the name of the road."

"What road's he live on?"

"The 3rd Line . . . the old Stilton place."

"Everybody knows the name of that road, don't they?"

They all nodded sagely at one another while this sank in.

"No need for a sign as far as I can see," the old man concluded.

The reeve turned to Supplicant Two, beside me. "And what can we do for you, Donald?"

Donald, apparently, needed a larger culvert. His front field wasn't draining fast enough, and a bigger culvert under the road would — he reckoned — dry things up a little sooner next spring. My ears perked up.

The reeve turned to the road superintendent. "Have we got any bigger culverts around?" he asked.

The road superintendent, a portly and pious man who had inherited the job from his uncle, hemmed and hawed awhile and finally allowed as how there was a larger culvert under the Wolf Lake Road. It was quickly decided to dig up the Wolf Lake culvert and swap it for Donald's smaller one. Donald thanked them all, asked after the reeve's wife (his own wife's sister, I later learned) and left.

They all turned to me. I nodded. They nodded back. And waited.

I started to explain that, like Donald, I was also having a drainage problem. The eldest councillor interrupted.

"What did you say your name was?" He leaned forward and cupped a hand behind his ear.

I hadn't said, but the reeve told him anyway.

"You any relation to the Does from over in North Seneca?" the old man asked.

"No," I answered, "I'm afraid not."

He thought about that for a minute. "Just as well. They're a god-awful bunch of crooks." He started to tell me about the North Seneca Does, but the reeve cut him off.

"Do you know everybody here?" the reeve asked me.

"I'm afraid not." In truth, I didn't know a soul; and I didn't know whether to be worried or encouraged that the reeve seemed to know who I was.

The reeve went around the table with names. The same three names that appeared on the roll of honour, with several repetitions. We all nodded at one another until the names were over, then observed a one-minute silence before I remembered the business at hand.

"About this drainage problem —"

They thanked me politely when I had finished and told me they would let me know. It was obvious that they wouldn't discuss the matter as long as I was there. I left. They still haven't let me know what was decided; and the meeting was four years ago.

In the meantime — and especially when the road begins to thaw in spring — we ponder the myth of friendly country people and wonder if we will ever be accepted as equal members of the community. We wonder if the land we paid for will ever be known as ours, or will we always be "the city people living on the old Murphy place," the usurpers, the outsiders, the people you can wave to on the road or nod to in the store, share a drink, or a joke, or a chore, or a complaint about the weather, but never, never, never accept as full-fledged friends — not in this generation.

As human transplants in a barren soil, we felt the lack of roots as a handicap in the present rather than any nostalgia for the past. Nevertheless, like much of North America, I went looking for roots, looking for a community where one of us must have once *belonged* in the sense that my neighbours here *belong*.

DEJA VU

I had to go back a long way, five generations, to a little village in Ireland, before I managed to find an ancestor who hadn't severed his roots, who had endured from birth to death in more or less the same locale. The connection was too remote to touch the people or stir any ancient memories with the prodigal approach. I simply wanted to see the place and so arrived alone and unannounced on a local backwater bus.

The village was a single street, with (at most) 400 people hunched together in a quarter-mile strip of shops and houses. I arrived on a rainy afternoon in spring. The grey cobbled street was empty. I started at one end and walked slowly through the centre until the solid wall of houses gave way again to an overgrown field. I turned and retraced my steps through the town, trying to absorb some familiar feeling. My mother's name was on the door of several shops. I picked out the smell of smoke and manure hanging faintly in the drizzle, but the only feeling that was as sure and real as the green of the grass was the certain sense that I was being watched through a score of curtains. The fleeting sense of *déjà vu* went back, not to some earlier, Irish incarnation, but to the day they cut our hedges down.

I picked a tiny pub, whose proprietor (according to his signature on the window) had also claimed my mother's maiden name. I stood alone at the bar, nursing a pint and soaking up the idle talk that washed around me like the eddies of a stream. The drizzle became a soaker, and the bar began to fill up as darkness filled up the street. Farmers, past and present, the butcher with his bloodied cuffs, a knot of younger men draped around the snooker table. The old men told their stories, and the young men posed with their cues and talked of going up to Dublin to find a job.

There was a bond, a kinship there — a warm refuge from the wet and the dark that made us all a family. As the Guinness flowed, the kinship grew to include even me. The old men, especially, were quick to ask my name and swap tales that might have remotely involved the family tree. It was warm and embracing, all I'd ever needed by way of community. I wondered that great (etc.) grandad's son had ever left. It was all I could do not to cry, so deep was the ache and the joy of finding this missing piece of home.

I wish I could end the story there, slobbering in a pint of Guinness over the symmetry of life, where the pieces of human tide can be reassembled like some jigsaw theory of continental drift. But that would be less than honest. The truth is, I made the mistake of staying another night, and another, doggedly trying to reclaim the emotional climax that had come too soon. On my third night in the pub, as on the second, the crowd reassembled like the well-rehearsed cast of a play. The old men told their stories, and the young men talked of going up to Dublin to look for work. The butcher had blood on his cuffs. The same lines drew the very same laughter, and the warmth of the scene dissolved itself in pathos. If the snooker table had transformed itself into a Camaro or a '52 Ford with flames on the fenders, the restless young men with the tension in their eyes could not have been any more familiar. And knowing what would become of them, the ones who would leave and the ones who would stay, made me want to weep for them all.

Waiting for the bus to take me away, I saw — for the first time — a boarded-over window, a thistle growing from a step, and the Gaelic letters on the sign at the end of the town reformed themselves into "Home of the Falcons . . . ."

Looking back at yourself from 20 or 120 years away puts the linear progress of man in a sobering perspective. Great (etc.) grandad could no more have stayed in Ireland than I could have stayed in Eden Falls. And now I'm sure that my own son, too, will someday leave our own new Eden to find a place of his own, where the tales the old men tell are not repeated.

Legal Spouse and I are here to stay, however. We know that it's as good a place as any other. Indeed, it gets better day by day. We're gradually fitting in. There are even some more new families moving into the district. The neighbour (the one who watched us raise Titanic from the mud) was just saying the other day that the new people who moved onto the old McAuley place have spent $30,000 fixing it up. He heard it from the reeve. Nice people I understand. Couple of kids. Moved out here from Toronto about two years ago. We wave when we drive past. We must stop in and meet them one of these days. Make them feel at home. One of these days. ∎

Frederick Doe is known to his eastern Ontario neighbours by another name.

Surviving the Dream-Come-True

"If we were doing what we wanted to do, where we wanted to do it, why were we so unhappy?"

By Anna Johnson

It was a particularly cold and bitter winter's day. We were completely snowed-in courtesy of a blizzard that had started during the night and that was still blowing snow at us spitefully, in the way that foreigners always imagine Canadian winters to behave all the time. Our son was three years old. He had developed a slight fever during the night and refused breakfast — an awe-inspiring first in his short but ravenous history. The austere northeasterly wind seemed to suck the heat right out of our log home and created spine-chilling draughts, so I brought the ailing child downstairs and made him a makeshift bed on the couch beside the fire. The open fireplace was the only inadequate means of heating the house at the time. As the day wore on, Grant's fever rose alarmingly. He became delirious. I was worried; he had a profound heart murmur, and I didn't know how it would react to an extremely high temperature. The nearest phone was three miles away. There were no close neighbours. There was no way to get the truck through the snowdrifts in the lane. When he started to go into violent convulsions, I knew that I had to act quickly to reduce the fever. I stripped him off, despite the cold room temperature, and bathed each of his limbs in cool water. He screamed and resisted until I felt like a wicked stepmother in some fairytale, but the treatment sufficed to lower his temperature and he slept peacefully. Sometimes you are forced to play God.

That is just part of the reality of winter under isolated conditions. But judging from the questions of friends, acquaintances and those suffering from over-gregariousness, it is anticipated as being the most onerous of problems facing the getting-away-from-it-all set. "Isn't it lonely in winter?" . . . . "What do you do when you are snowed in?"

But isolation is not something we fear or battle against most of the time; it is a commodity that we truly appreciate in the same way we relish a bottle of our best wild grape wine. If you can accept the responsibilities that go with it, it can be regarded as one of the many perks of living beneath the poverty line in rural Canada.

People who need people just won't make it in a homestead-style existence. Seclusion, particularly in winter, must be regarded as a positive rather than a negative condition by those choosing to dwell in the pastoral wastelands of Canada.

In fact, we contributed purposely to our sense of isolation by refusing to introduce the telephone. Our reasoning, as with most things, was multifaceted. To begin with, it was expensive; we would have had to pay for the line to be strung out to our property from our nearest neighbour. Then the service offered to us after that huge expense was, to put it generously, inadequate. We were faced with the expectation of sharing our line with 11 other subscribers — five of these phones would ring in our house whenever they got a call. There is, of course, not even a vestige of privacy on a multiparty line, and no guarantee that you can use the phone when you need it or when somebody else needs to contact you. But perhaps the biggest argument against the phone was a desire to ban unwanted interruptions.

So isolation to us was a personal choice. But just because isolation, loneliness and boredom (a triumvirate that is frequently and inexplicably melded together) did not prove to be our personal Armageddon does not mean that we have lived an idyllic life since we moved to the country just watching our dreams blossom into a glowing reality. To the contrary, we discovered a number of other difficulties inherent in the back-to-the-land game. We found our own set of problems.

Amazingly, one good friend came close to predicting our near nemesis, although he approached it unwittingly and from the wrong perspective. We had just spent a hot, lazy summer's day together surveying the new property and weaving bright plans for the future in the sunshine. As we attained the summit of Sumac Hill, Andy sprawled his portly frame flat upon his back in the sweet-smelling grass, legs and arms splayed out in all directions. He drank in the sunshine and the glorious lake view and sighed, "If I lived here, I wouldn't do anything but this all day long." This should have been our first clue to the ensuing riddle.

You see, our biggest troublemaker was Time or, more appropriately, the lack of it. We had avidly read the Nearings' book *Living the Good Life* and basked in their marvellous philosophy of working 50 percent of the day and spending the other 50 percent in leisure activities. We totally ignored three important facts:

1) the Nearings had a house to live in while they built their new one
2) they had no children
3) they had no animals

We were, we thought, being realistic when we accepted the fact that we would have to forgo the leisure time right at the beginning, until we were established. I wonder if anyone has a definition for "established?"

When we originally bought our place in the country, it consisted of an old log house, barns (some good, some hopeless) and 100 acres of sylvan rockscape — in other words, an agronomist's nightmare. The house was rotting on its earthen foundation, which housed a dug-out root cellar inhabited by groundhogs. The downstairs seemed sound enough despite the charred beams above the rusted-out cookstove, but the upstairs was a lost cause. The roof had started to leak 40 years before, we were informed, at which time the occupants had abandoned it to the elements, after moving their sleeping arrangements downstairs. The upstairs with its unforgettable stench was now occupied by a multitude of bats, whose droppings had coated the forsaken furniture with a solid crust of excrement. There was plenty to do, we realized, to raise our dream home, phoenixlike, from this wreckage, but it was only a matter of time. How true this proved to be.

Before we cashed the last paycheque and finally resigned from urban life, we had dismantled the log house, numbering the logs as we went, built a foundation in a neighbouring field with fewer groundhog holes and farther from the road, moved the numbered logs (some of which lost their arithmetical adjuncts in the process) and resurrected our new home. It was chinked, there was a roof, a chimney and some loose

Graham Pilsworth

boards across the beams between upstairs and down. That was all — it could well have been portrayed in the local classified ads as a handyman's special. There was an untrustworthy ladder instead of stairs, no insulation or inside walls, and water had to be hauled in from the hand pump outside the back door. Likewise, the dirty water had to be lugged out again and dumped. (We had a baby in cloth diapers.) The toilet facilities consisted of a portable plastic chemical toilet, minus the chemicals, which had to be carried out very regularly and with utmost care to guard against spills, before being buried (no mean feat in a land of rocks, tree roots and frozen snow — thank goodness for groundhog holes!). Our children at this time were aged three and one.

This was when Time first raised his ugly head. We had intended being further along in the renovations before moving in with our naïve little family. We attributed the lack of progress to the inconvenience and time wasted in commuting back and forth to the work site. We were confident that we would compensate for lost time when we actually occupied the premises. However, it wasn't all quite as simple as we had expected.

The workshop was also the living room, kitchen, dining room and children's playroom. It is not easy to work in a confined space with two small children always underfoot or carrying off tools to play with and then abandon in some obscure corner. Diapers always had to be changed at the least opportune moments, the table which was moonlighting as a workbench had to be cleared for meals. The most mundane of household chores took an exaggerated amount of time without running water on tap. Nap times had to be observed with the cessation of hammering. The garden had to be established on a plot of old pasture which necessitated a continuous and infeasible battle against the omnipresent twitchgrass. Later the vegetable patch had to be harvested and processed for winter consumption. There was so much to do and so little room in which to do it that we hardly knew where to start.

FALLING BEHIND

Time had once been my ally, malleable, adaptable and in constant supply. As I look back and remember "auld lang syne," I was always a person with tidy work habits. At the office, I would try to clear up the paperwork and leave my desktop naked and unashamed at the close of day. If a balance sheet was urgently needed or a budget had to be completed, I would work into the evening to accomplish it. Unfortunately, these work habits did not translate well into our new environment. To begin with, we had no cupboards or closets in which to put neatly away such items as tools and utensils. No job ever seemed to be completed before some crisis arose which had to be tended to. The time schedules that we had drawn up in our minds had been revised repeatedly, but we still seemed to be constantly falling behind. We worked seven days per week, often 16 hours per day and still ran out of that infuriating commodity — Time. We were exhausted and quarrelsome. There was no time left for the children, despite our rationale that the move to the country was for their benefit too, allowing them the input from two full-time parents.

Life became more difficult as winter approached. We dashed to complete the inside walls as the frigid weather blew down from the North. At night, we shivered in the tin bathtub in front of the open fire, surrounded by eddies of Arctic air. We comforted ourselves with the assurance that we had known in advance what we were undertaking and that we were now duty bound to prove to all the cynics that it really could be done. After all, it was only for one winter. Had we only known then what we know now, I wonder if we would still be here. Our plans were to build a stone addition onto the house the next summer and install plumbing and heating in this annex.

But Time played tricks with us like the distorted mirrors in a fairground booth. In our minds we could always see, in glorious technicolour, the finished product — the completed house as we had dreamed it would be, the workshop and the farm actually in production. We were so far from completion and so blinded by this vision, it was small wonder that we could hardly notice any progress in what we had actually accomplished. When we did manage to finish any small project, we would be filled with a rush of protective pride. It would look so unblemished and vulnerable in our weather-beaten surroundings, we were terrified that it would get scratched, mashed or crayoned upon before we had had ample time to bask in its new handmade glory.

I can well remember laying the pine floors down-stairs over the rough subfloor. Having just one room downstairs, we decided to build the floor one-third at a time, so we could still use the kitchen equipment and have a work space. Thus we would laboriously move all the furniture off one-third of the floor space, lay the new floor, apply two coats of urethane and leave until completely dry — then shift our attention to the next third. We had just finished the centre third and applied the first protective layer of urethane before retiring to bed. Since the night was cold, and the house unheated, the varnish had not dried completely by the next morning, so my husband built a bridge across it by balancing a narrow plank between two urethane cans. He lined up the family at the bottom of the stairs and solemnly lectured them about not stepping on the newest stretch of floor because it was still tacky. He demonstrated how to use the bridge to cross from the staircase end of the room to the breakfast-table end. Our three-and-a-half-year-old daughter, Gretchen, was first. She thought it was a great game and had no trouble negotiating the walkway. We then held our breath as Grant, 18 months old, who never walked but always ran and who can trip over the pattern on a polished marble floor, took to the bridge. Walking very slowly on the slender board while balancing himself with the aid of his tongue, he actually made it safely to the far side. We cheered in unison. In an explosion of pride, he ran back across the new, sticky floor to the beginning of the bridge to show us again.

TRICKLES OF SPRING

The arrival of spring acted both as a catharsis on our spirits, so long beset with cabin fever, and as a catalyst as we burst outside with renewed vigour to start on the addition. We were desperate for more living space and storage room. But first, Time dictated that we must harvest the maple syrup, then the garden had to be planted and expanded, necessitating a renewed offensive against the everpresent couchgrass and weeds. It wasn't quite as early as we had expected when we actually got down to marking out the foundation. Funny how Time always seemed to turn to liquid in our hands and end up trickling through our weary fingers.

Our plan was to build in stone. After all, in this area it is the cheapest and most aesthetically pleasing building material, just lying around waiting to be used. We had drawn up a time schedule (as usual) that could only have emanated from the heads of people who, like us, had never actually laid one stone on top of another with a neat layer of mortar between. Stonebuilding, we discovered, is not something that you can do in a hurry — unless you can summon the aid of hundreds of thousands of serfs, as did the Incas when they built their mighty cities and fortifications perched high amongst the lofty Andes. There were just the two of us to haul the stone, mix the mortar and lay up the walls. Often city-weary relatives came to stay — we had never realized until that summer how many of our relatives suffered from back problems that precluded lifting anything heavier than a sandwich. Friends would visit and cheer us along, but it was awfully dirty work for city folks in their neatly pressed leisure clothes. It became painfully obvious that we would never finish the project before the snow flew once again. In desperation, we worked faster and more furiously against the mental picture of another winter without water and heat. The simmering frustrations from the first winter that had been pushed aside when spring had brought us freedom from the confines of the house began to seethe once more, but closer to the surface now, like the rumbling of an active volcano. We were working ourselves up into physical and emotional exhaustion, always trying to live up to the impossible time schedules, constantly feeling like failures as Time moved along relentlessly on a faster cog than we. Eventually something had to give, and of course it did.

After a bitter argument full of disappointment and disillusion, we sat down to review our situation, the alternatives available to us, and most important of all, we vented our personal feelings. There was a tremendous feeling of alienation, as though we were working against one another instead of together. My husband felt pressured by all the work involved and felt that I was blaming him for the lack of facilities and the difficulties in our daily lives. This was a misconception, but it goaded him into working harder and faster, thus increasing the pressure he already felt. He still sustained the traditional outlook that he must shoulder the burden of providing the necessities of life for his family. I was feeling totally frustrated at never having enough time to complete a task or to do it properly. I was trying to toilet train a toddler in the midst of a construction site — a job that requires both time and patience, two staples that seemed to be perpetually in short supply. I felt guilty about not giving more positive time and attention to the children, but also thwarted by them for distracting me constantly from my contribution to the construction. I tended to blame my husband for the pressure to work longer hours on the stonework than my small frame could cope with. This was another misconception, but it caused me to feel guilty if I quit from physical exhaustion before he did. Of course when the building stopped at the end of the day, there were still the household chores and cooking to fit into the picture. Neither of us had had time for any recreational pursuits in such a long duration that we were as spent and jaded as an ashtray full of yesterday's cigarette butts.

ENSLAVING THE MASTER

First, we established that we still loved each other and that this beautiful place in the woods was where we most wanted to live. We were in fact doing what we wanted to do and doing it where we wanted to do it, so why were we so miserable? Time had become our master instead of our humble servant. We realized that because we couldn't leave the work at the office at the end of the day, we were constantly confronted with the unfinished projects, unable to close a door and walk away for a few hours. This was what constituted the pressure to keep working 16 hours per day. We decided that we must block it out mentally, since we couldn't

physically. Just ignore it during a newly enforced lunch hour and, in the evenings, instigate a quiet reading session or some purely recreational activity.

We also realized that woodworking and related tasks that my husband used to consider enjoyable hobbies had become his full-time work and could no longer be classified as a therapeutic diversion. We decided that one day per week should be put aside for relaxation and family fun (who were we to argue with the six-day Creation?) such as taking the children swimming or visiting friends.

Our working days were shortened to more manageable hours. If work pressure began to mount again, it was time to take a lunchtime walk through the woods to unwind. In winter, when we were working inside again, we would take turns (someone always had to stay and babysit) skiing or snowshoeing through the bush, until we would return feeling delightfully renewed and once more considering ourselves the luckiest people we knew.

One night per week, we observed an evening for the adults. The children would be fed, bathed and tucked into bed with books before we sat down to a romantic dinner with candlelight, soft music and wine. We finally realized that we could work together, helping each other to build the life we both wanted, and at the same time, we could strengthen our marriage (instead of destroying it). Our close-knit family could enjoy life for what it was really worth, and Time was relegated to his rightful role of serf.

It was after this that "the office" began to appear regularly in our conversation. When one of us would complain about working conditions, the other would sympathize and reply, "Well, you're right. Why don't you complain at the office?" When we were short of money, we would threaten to "go to the office and demand a pay increase." The office was, of course, nonexistent, but as the Czars discovered when they introduced their pogroms, it's easier to unite people and divert their attention from daily wrongs if you can blame somebody else for their vicissitudes. And so we joined together against the impossible working conditions — we even formed our own union, and on hot afternoons, caked in cement dust and stone chips, we would call for a union beer break, in clear defiance of "office procedure."

It is now six years since we moved out to the farm, and although circumstances have changed significantly since the early days, we still have more work to do than is humanly possible, but with Time now safely under control, we are no longer pressured to do it immediately. We spent four winters without heat and water before finally moving into our beautiful stone addition with its arched windows. The house is still not finished, inside or out, as we come up with bright, innovative ideas to add a greenhouse here and a workshop there. However, we no longer have time schedules, we are enjoying our lives and can live with unfinished projects without demanding that everything should happen at once. We have other priorities now that the house is basically habitable. Our children are, at present, in school full-time — they appear to be unscarred by their early years of pioneer life and, in fact, have developed into individuals with many skills and character traits that will stand them in good stead in the years to come. The time that was once devoted to child care is now used for animal husbandry.

The livestock, of course, come with their own built-in system of time schedules — feeding, watering, milking, etc. These are chores that we all share and can be executed in short order to accommodate time for other activities. One is, of course, tied down to the farm on a daily basis, unless you have neighbours who are willing to trade off chores with you on an equal exchange every so often to allow you a weekend off or a vacation. This is an important consideration for anyone undertaking the care of animals and who does not wish to become the slave of Time. It is advisable to have some contingency plans before purchasing the first dependent. We still have no close neighbours but are blessed with several good friends who don't suffer from hay fever and who are willing to trade a few days in the city for a few days in the country, even with chores. Some friends will barter goods and services (i.e. the milk, eggs and fresh produce, plus help on one of their projects) in return for farm-sitting. Anyway, it is essential to have someone who can take over sometimes to enable you to get completely away from the work place occasionally for a change of pace, sneak a symphony break in the city or fill whatever void you feel exists in your life.

Once you have mastered the art of Time manipulation, people are quick to query the problems of boredom creeping into this new leisure gap. One of the reasons that boredom never seems to raise its head in this household is that our daily work tends to be a variety of so many skills, most of which we have had to learn on the job, that there is always a challenge. We can't afford to go out and buy the usual answer to a problem — we improvise. Our hard-earned spare time is full of the crafts and ideas that our heads were bulging with when we left the city. We are always trying something new; in fact, my favourite quotation goes as follows: "A human being should be able to change a diaper, plan an invasion, butcher a hog, conn a ship, design a building, write a sonnet, balance accounts, build a wall, set a bone, comfort the dying, take orders, give orders, cooperate, act alone, solve equations, analyze a new problem, pitch manure, program a computer, cook a tasty meal, fight efficiently, die gallantly. Specialization is for the insects." (Robert A. Heinlein, *Time Enough for Love: The Lives of Lazarus Long*.)

The need to make some money has also provided us with an opportunity to be creative and ward off stagnation. We both make time to write for pleasure and profit. We soon discovered that our newly acquired skills were in great demand: build a fireplace here, teach evening classes there, in all those skills and crafts we had slowly mastered by trial and error over the years. It was a way to get out, keep our minds alert and earn some necessary cash.

Our life has not always been easy, but I don't think we ever wanted it to be. We made our own decision to choose the more difficult course, and it has provided us with the challenge and satisfaction that we would never have experienced on the easier path of urban living, even with its large paycheques. So what does it take to make it succeed? Patience, determination, flexibility, ingenuity and self-confidence for sure; but for us, it was taking the time to enjoy what we were achieving. It should also be a shared commitment (there are so many little jobs that take two pairs of hands). Both parties must share equally in the planning, the execution and in the desire to make it succeed. And finally, each person must accept responsibility, not only for his own life and decisions, but also for his own happiness, or lack of it — the realization that you, yourself, are in fact "the office." ■

Anna Johnson (not her real name) homesteads with her family somewhere east of the Rockies.

Breaking Up For Breakup

Malaise nothing. This man has Cabin Fever.

By Lamont Bassett

Traditionally, much attention has been given to the wonders of winter and the rites of spring, but little is said about the transition period from one to the other, which is for the North a season unto itself: breakup. Sandwiched between winter and spring, breakup is the time when hardpan frozen rivers suddenly rupture, sending shock waves up the mountain sides, setting avalanches thundering back. And for northern folk, it is the season when sanity, like the cornice, kisses off the granite face of reason and pitches headlong into chasms of madness.

In Nature, breakup is simply the change of a few degrees Celsius liberating the Earth's surface of her icebound mantle. It is the season of the switch: the between-the-acts costume change when the Earth is caught without her snowy cloak or spring pansy panties, exposing to all a battle-bruised body. It is time to dispense with last year's corpses, to wash the debris from winter's inactivity out to the great sea dumps and begin the cycle afresh. Fluidity is the norm, and everything not attached to the land by life flows in this annual *danse macabre*.

My first realization of the full force of breakup came at the age of eight while watching my grandfather in the centre of a mud bog on the road to his ranch. Grandpa, normally tall in stature with a stoic nature gained from 30 years as a guide/outfitter in the Rockies, was standing knee-deep in the quagmire facing an equally stuck Model "A" Ford pickup.

"Now Slim," warned my everwarning Mormon Grandmother, "there's no need to talk like that in front of the boy." She was inside the truck, dry and warm.

Grandpa stood motionless, and one might think his anger had been subdued were it not for a slight twitch jerking across his jaw line and a low muttering undertone of guttural insults seething from his tightly pursed lips. But suddenly, he could control his composure no longer, and he again exploded with unreserved rage, hitting the "A" with his Stetson, electrifying the air with clear, crisp curses. Mud and madness go well together.

Mud, it seems during breakup, is the prevalent paving material of all back-country roads. Rural ribbons of gumbo ooze lie between you and everywhere you wanted to go. Working the land is equally impossible. Fields in need of planting, for example, suck down tractors like quicksand, while feeding corrals, like brackish swamps, become living systems unto themselves. And though breakup does give the forest a brief stay of execution from the timber industry, for the logging truck driver, it always comes 10 loads and 2 truck payments too early.

With the vanishing snowcover, things once held suspended in three-dimensional frozen space become plastered upon a planar surface, and like a recurrent nightmare, a winter's worth of garbage returns to haunt you. (This fact is worth remembering when weighing the differences between a snowmobile and a dog team, for while the machine is noisy and depends upon fossil fuels, after the winter melt, there isn't a six-inch layer of "fly factory" under the machine.)

Mind you, thaw is not without some rewards. With

the receding snow, tools left out over the winter emerge once again — dressed in rust. Remember the thrill of finding the lost hammer which you dropped while getting the camera for a shot of the first snowfall? Or the joy of finding the camera which you misplaced while looking through the first snow for the lost hammer?

Another characteristic of the breakup season is the appearance of numerous vermin around the homestead. With the collapse of the snow, scraps of moose meat and rodent corpses rot pungently, enticing martin, mink, weasels and even the odd wolverine out of the bush. Coyotes and fox, fresh with pups and cubs, bring around the family to meet the chickens and check out the dog dishes to see what the rich kids got over the winter. Porcupines amble out of the foliage to forage on anything potentially salty: saddles, hydraulic lines and even wooden planks. But the worst wild panhandler is the yearling bear cub. An adolescent, abandoned by Mother, disoriented, famished, and too young to fear man, can do indescribable damage to an outside root cellar and expand your dump by a couple of acres.

SEASONAL ILLNESS

But nature in a state of flux is only one component of the breakup phenomenon. The second ingredient is the human condition after a winter of solitude. Ironically, breakup is not just a season, for the term also refers to the advanced, if not terminal, stage of cabin fever. Given a small enough cabin and a sufficient distance from the nearest neighbour, boredom, like a fungus, seeps between even crystal-hard brain cells, turning them to the consistency of morning mush. The inevitable result: breaking up for breakup.

Unlike many diseases which require isolation to check their spread, cabin fever is *caused* by isolation and confinement. For without the stimulus of the novel, our imagination mixes reality and fantasy so often that soon they become inseparable. And if you figure that the meaning of our ideas is also supplied by the self — our personal stamp of importance — then both content and significance become variables which can be scrambled over the long winter nights.

Of course, there's no problem marrying fact and fiction until you're forced to compare your reality with everyone else's. Sanity, you see, is the social endeavour which takes at least two to play: a judge and a judgee, a measure and a measured, a standard and a standee. Without a human mirror, reality is what we think it is, and, likewise, we are who we think we are (the Solipsism of Solitude Syndrome).

On the other hand, having too good a grasp of reality and self can also be a problem. After a winter of living in the shadow of your self image, come breakup, the pressures are strong to go a little schizoid and try on a new identity. So common was this malady in a community where I once lived that a specialist evolved to treat the seasonal metamorphosis.

Though the weather sign outside his shop proclaimed merely the dwelling of a hairdresser, "Mr. Anthony," as many of his patients preferred to call him, was also the village psychiatrist. And though he'd never had training in the profession, Tony was one of those individuals gifted with patience, perception and an ego as well grounded as a spruce. The union of barbering and "shrinking" was natural for Tony; as he once confided, "My technique is to treat the entire head, not just the fur and fuzz." And his ad in the weekly paper pointed that out. "Put your best head forward! Treatment of Mane and Mind $3.50, Shampoo Extra." Or, "This Week's Special: Flip and Freud, Half Price."

Under normal conditions, Tony's duties were no light load, and on more than one occasion, his was the sole surviving sanity amidst a community of calamity. But it was during breakup that his talents were really put to the test. Bouffants of many colours were top-selling identities for usually conservative housewives, while the "Betty Crocker Look" was the rage among hard-line feminists. Pacifists *demanded* duck tails, while a D-9 Cat skinner abandoned his mountain masher, preferring, instead, bangs, spit curls, eyeliner and leotards.

Unfortunately, no one is immune to the final fit of cabin fever, not even the doctor. Last breakup, Mr. Anthony fell in love, and as a gesture of his strong emotions, he took the clippers to his own black curly locks, sculpting them into the shape of a valentine. His beloved terminated their relationship soon after, and in a moment of remorse, Tony shaved the slate as clean as the head of a Hare Krishna recruit.

SHUFFLING THE DECK

When the call for change comes, even our ethical convictions take note. After a winter labouring beneath the weight of wholesome natural virtues, like breathing clean fresh air, getting lots of sleep, etc., many constitutions revolt — demanding some decadence and depravity to offset all that powder-snow purity. During breakup, it is not uncommon for marriages to be shuffled and reshuffled like playing cards. Hands of monogamy are played as polygamy, while polygamists play celibate solitaire. Even the time-tested unions are called into question.

"I'm thinking of trading my one 40," mused a rancher/friend about the merits of wife swapping, "and getting myself two 20s."

"Shoot!" snorted his wife from the kitchen, "you're hardly wired for 140; 220 would fry your circuits!"

I find in myself during breakup a bottomless cache of intolerance, especially toward doing winter chores well after winter has gone to Argentina. My threshold for splitting wood, for example, is usually reached one and a half cords too early. And though the snow has melted and there is a sea of water flowing around the cabin, I know I'll have a few more weeks of carrying the damn stuff because the pipes which froze five feet down are still locked in ice. Trivial hassles become significant sources of anxiety and anger, like scraping a molasses mixture of Klister ski wax and fireweed from the bottoms of my cross-country skis. Even saunas, once mellow meeting places where friends and neigh-

Graham Pilsworth

bours gather to collectively sweat away their cares and woes, lose their appeal during breakup. Imagine yourself roaring out of a sauna — baked to well-done, neurons tingling, pores wide open. You lower your head, dive, not looking, for the snow bank . . . but the bank has gone to the ocean leaving only a puddle glazed with mosquito larvae.

Having considered at some length the breakup phenomenon, I've come to the unhappy conclusion that there is no cure . . . except, of course, moving to sunnier climes for the winter. To some degree, we all break up a little during breakup. The actual direction of one's "bonkerness" is purely subjective; for only you can plot the course of your flight pattern. You can, however, calculate how long you will stay aloft by the amount of "fuel" accumulated over the winter.

The following formula is not an absolute, but it should give you an indication of your mental stability or at least the factors which eat away at it. The first thing to consider is your degree of isolation. This can be quantified as the number of miles to your nearest neighbour plus the distance to the nearest tavern, pub or bar. (If, perchance, you're not a drinker, substitute church or synagogue.) Obviously, the greater the distance to these oases of sanity, the longer you'll be gripped by the "crazies" come breakup.

The next factor to take into account is your wintering area, which is, in most cases, the floor area of your

cabin. (Your breakup potential will be inversely proportional to the size of your living space, such that the smaller the cabin, the greater the potential.) Multiply this figure by what might be called your "hassle coefficient," which is simply the total number of children, pets, relatives and livestock that are sharing your winter quarters. For every child between the ages of six months and three years, double the sum. For every in-law relative, regardless of age, triple the figure.

Some attention should also be given to the amount of amusements and diversions available to you. Things like a working radio and a well-stocked library are definite assets provided the former can give you at least a few hours of static-free sound, and the latter is not composed of old university texts like Quantum Physics or Biochemistry. These are more conducive to madness than sanity. The merits of having a television are also questionable, since it can make you crazy in even the best seasons.

Finally, multiply the total of all previous calculations by your past performance during breakup. This figure is determined by adding all of the breakup seasons you have survived — vacationing in Mexico or on the Mediterranean does not count as a survived season — and then subtracting the number which you have failed to survive. That is, subtract the breakups during which you were committed to an institution, or you have attempted either suicide or homicide, or you have conversed with God in King James English, or during which you have discovered "The Truth" with a capital "T," which only you can understand.

If the resultant sum of all these computations is positive, then chances are there will be only a few hairline cracks in your ego this year. If, however, your results are negative, then the passage of the seasons may not be as orderly. If your calculations indicate that hard times loom on your horizon, don't panic, because there are precautions you can take to lessen the impact of your affliction. First, scatter the stock and ship off the family. Hide the bullets and razor blades. And finally, tether one leg to a bed post and wait. Eventually spring must come. ∎

Lamont Bassett is a writer, rancher and seasonal rodeo clown living near Smithers, B.C., who recently spent a winter nursing a broken leg.

James Tughan

The Saga of Roscoe & Lulu

Sometimes survival is not enough

This is the true story of Roscoe and Lulu, an overweight couple in their early forties. Both had enjoyed a taste of life's more flamboyant pleasures, both had suffered the headaches, late hours, smoke-filled rooms and madness of aggressive careers, one in academia, the other in newspapering, before they decided to scrap their past lives and go into the backwoods to pursue a *modus vivendi* based on fishing, hunting, gathering and gardening — all pursuits in which they had considerable weekend experience. They would build a house in the wilderness, establish a homestead by the sweat of their brows and the labour of their hands, and set their lives to the cycle of the seasons. Writing an occasional magazine article would, they thought, supply them with enough cash for nails, dentistry, bottles of rum, flour, spices, coffee and typewriter ribbons.

They put a few pieces of furniture and 2,000 books into storage, sold the rest of their civilized belongings, paid off their debts and started on their woodland adventure with $28 in cash, a decrepit '49 Ford pickup called Wonderful Feller, and an overweening belief in their ability to make caviar out of cow poop. They kept a journal for the three years of this experience, and several of the hundreds of entries punctuate this narrative. The names of people and places have been changed to protect the anonymity of the idiots and half-wits mentioned here. Reader, consider long before you leap into the wilderness.

Lulu and Roscoe find a landowner — Dr. X — who is willing to lease them land on which they may build a cabin, put in a garden and keep chickens and pigs, but no cats or sheep, for Dr. X mistrusts both these animals for secret reasons. Dr. X spends his summers on the land in a small bachelor cabin. As time goes by, he is revealed as a peculiar person given to drawing cabalistic symbols in the dust of the road and chanting sutras from the interior of a huge, rotted-out yellow birch. Finally he becomes an absentee landlord, spending most of his time in retreat in the Bahamas.

The land is a high, tilted chunk of boreal forest half a mile from the Canadian border, lying so it catches the full force of the violent northwest weather. The soil is cold, wet clay, and so acid the county agent says that in all his years he's never seen anything like it outside a test tube. There is water, water everywhere, brooks, springs, seeps, bogs, swamps, rivers, lakes and ponds; a lot of this wetness is on Lulu and Roscoe's spruce-rimmed acres.

Eight miles away, across the Cornucopia River, lies the town of Coleslaw — five or six bright lights and a three-store shopping mecca where Lulu and Roscoe rarely go because they have no money, and because Wonderful Feller lacks a legal inspection sticker. Every six months, Roscoe gets out his coloured pencils and India ink and laboriously fashions his own sticker, but in mortal fear it will be detected. When they travel, they do so at night, after slinging either mud or snow, according to the season, on the sensitive area of the windshield.

The two pioneers set up their big green canvas tent on this land at the end of May sometime in the mid-'70s. They live in this tent for five months while building a tiny shack they call "the literature hut," cutting, twitching and spudding the logs for the main cabin and working on the cabin's foundation. Water is hauled in a bucket from the brook, and all cooking is done on an outdoor fireplace — fun on a two-week camping trip, but awful after months and months. The cook's teeth are always black with smoke.

Thirty days hath June, and for 28 of them, it poured on Roscoe and Lulu, one of the rainiest, coldest summers any old-timers could remember; no good for building, no good for gardening, no good for homesteading.

June 10. Rain started falling again at 1 A.M. Lulu makes the first drip coffee in two weeks — it tastes papery after a diet of campfire-boiled Java. She makes bacon and eggs and toast which she shares with me in the tent — luxury. Cleared up a little later. Put up half the gable on the literature hut, and dinner was cooking when huge sheets of rain fell, soaking everything thoroughly. Dinner soggy *avec* H_2O. Beautiful sunset with rainbow anchored in northeast during downpour. Go to bed soaking wet, disgusted. Blackbird sings. Tobacco paper wet and no good. Bah!

June 11. Roscoe woke up in a vile mood to the all-too-familiar sound of rain on the tent. Snatched radio with evil weather report from my hand and, hearing of more

rain on the way, stomped off into the drizzle to brood over a sullen fire made with wet wood — what else? Around 5, the rain came pouring down again. Tent smells musty.

June 12. Raining again. Started at 7 A.M. We awoke in dank tent, rain dripping in through loose-fitting flap, making a big puddle in the corner. Radio plays a hymn, "There's a Balm in Gilead" — captures Lulu's Gilead-touched soul. Dr. X is away for the weekend; said we could use his cabin to get out of the rain for a while. We have NO SHELTER. Now we know why the Chinese water torture works. Lulu blacks Dr. X's stove and tidies up. Roscoe spies a woodchuck and boosts it with the shotgun. Between working on the gable, writing and taking a bath, the chuck is cleaned, salted and made ready for supper. Good thing, too, since there was nothing for the evening meal. Providence? We take our first bath in three weeks. Sheer delight. Share one bottle of beer to wash down the "Italian chuck" done standard pasta sauce way. Our garden looks like a floodplain.

June 14. Trip over to Coleslaw. Worried about sticker all the way. On the rough road, Wonderful Feller's wooden brace gave out, and he limped home with one wing flapping. Cursed the raccoons for tearing up our camp again. Cornstarch in the typewriters, flour all over the damp books and paper. They've got to go. Got some good recipes.

Went fishing. Lulu caught a 16" rainbow which we have for supper with a few catfish. Saw a fisher cat cross the road on the way home. Timber doodle led us all the way up the hill. Owls really talkative tonight — wonder if they're the ones who left the head, wing tip and fluff remains of cock robin in front of the literature hut? We desperately need some siding for that structure. No money. Got to stop smoking.

June 15. Writing by the dying campfire after a dinner of "Sweet and Hot Woodchuck" done Chinese-style. Roscoe popped the chuck off for supper. His left eye — Roscoe, not the woodchuck — very inflamed today — hope it's only from smoke. Wind blew like hell today, but it was sunny. The woodcock flew over the garden at twilight, as he does every evening, before he begins his twittering rise and descent of courtship flight. Cold tonight. The tomato plants look frightened. Night hawk crying now, and insects in the fading light flash silvery like minnows in dark water.

June 16. Roscoe awoke feeling like Job this morning. His eyes are swollen shut. Coffee very good and the day is gorgeous. Cut roof overhangs even on the lit. hut and started stapling on the felt paper — hope it's waterproof! Worked in the garden. Lulu made salad of thinned radishes and Chinese cabbage and weeds. Went fishing in the afternoon. A black bear waved at Lulu on the highway. Got some catfish and a bunch of frogs which we had for supper. Tried to make tea, but the wood was wet, and finally the pot tipped over and extinguished the smoldering fire altogether.

Graham Pilsworth

June 17. Began the day in the rain again. Roscoe muttered "resinous pine, acrid oak" which Lulu thought was sarcastic spleenishness, so she slapped his hand. Crossness. Rain getting to us. Today saw the end of the coffee and the last of the store-bought cigarettes. Low on food supplies except olive oil and soy sauce. We need an endless succession of woodchucks.

June 18. Nervous discussion about when is a raindrop a drop and when is it mist . . . when is a "slap" (of yesterday morning) a slap and not a punch? All meaning that we're going ziggy because all the coffee is gone and it keeps on raining. Running really low on food — rice porridge for breakfast, bread and greens for lunch, tea, cocoa and conversation for dinner. Hope a chuck ambles by . . . gnarl!

June 19. Rain and raccoons in the night. Discussion about killing one with a sharpened hoe or a splitting maul, but Roscoe says the maul would be overkill — better for a 5¾-year-old bear. Much daydreaming about lobster, chicken cacciatore, lima beans, Caesar salads, etc., as we eat our rice. Garden begging for attention.

Hut is *finito* except for the door, floor, roofing and some interior shelves. We put our crockery, books and clothes in place, and Roscoe cleaned up outside with the broken rake. Lulu busted it raking the hut floor. Just plain dirt — nothing fancy like boards until we get some money. Celebrated hut completion with a spaghetti dinner — Roscoe's famous sauce enhanced by another woodchuck. What progress! We actually ate at the table *in the hut* by candlelight as it RAINED outside. Our first meal under shelter. Spent our last $2 on beer and a pack of cigs — blowing our minds completely, wild, mad abandonment. It rained four or five showers — heavy, torrential, savage French rainstorms over from Quebec. Tomorrow, we begin a schedule — Lulu writes and Roscoe will start cutting poles for the main cabin.

June 21. Summer solstice. Rain all night and raining now. Won't it ever stop? The ground is saturated with water. The success of the garden is doubtful, and we need it badly. In towns and cities, it's easy to lose sight of the fact that our human existence is very much at the mercy of nature. In earlier times, a summer like this would have meant death and starvation for an isolated group. Writing today — damp typewriter keys — ugh! And not even a drop of coffee to lighten the gloom.

A lousy day. Rained almost steadily. Uncomfortable, damp and cold. Lunch was exciting — popcorn balls. Went fishing at 6 — Roscoe caught nine perch, Lulu nothing. Blackflies fierce. Home in the rain too tired and low to eat any supper. Roscoe said he saw a snowflake.

June 25. THE WORST RAIN YET! HOURS OF IT! Garden a lake, brook a torrent. We are being pushed close to failure on this project with every rainy day. Impossible to work on slippery peeled logs in the rain, or in the garden or on the roof. Like Shackleton at the Pole, they'll find us in our tent, writing down our last thoughts . . . .

June 26. Sunday. Torrential downpour all night long. Roof of the hut gives in under the battering and springs leaks stem to stern — guns, books, typewriters, clothes, all soaking wet. In the night, raccoons managed to steal the last of the bacon. Both grumpy at bedtime without any supper, but fire won't burn under water, y'know? Quavery voice coming out of the heavy mists, singing, "There's a balm in Gilead . . . ." Loaded the rifle and went to bed hoping the raccoons would visit again.

By late July, things had improved a little. Some money had trickled in and out again, editors unaware that sparkling prose was coming out of a rusty, wet typewriter and that those strange marks on the pages were the footprints of bold raccoons. The work was going along steadily, and the two pioneers were having a wonderful time exploring the backwoods on foot and doing plenty of trout fishing, often on all-day expeditions. Lulu spent hours each day gathering edible wild plants and fungi to supplement the diet of woodchuck and trout. Roscoe and Lulu have each lost 30 pounds at this point and are back at the size they were in their early twenties. The garden is close to a total loss.

July 4. Damp and grey. No-see-ums pouring through the tent mesh like the incoming tide. Today log-peeling again, the dry ones slow going. One dreadful one had a bark disease that smelled like old lemons. Roscoe says, of course, it is the infamous "Lemon Bark Disease." After lunch, we both fell asleep. Is it hunger, fatigue, poor diet or advancing old age that's making us so tired? Set off for the trout streams at 4:30.

Light rain. We got 17 trout, and standing on the beaver dam watching the line disappear into the black water while a thrush close by sang the most incredibly beautiful harp-like series of scales, and old Roscoe there under the shadow of a spruce, Lulu had a rush of great happiness, one of those isolated waves of intense feeling that come only a few times in one's life. The beavers cruised back and forth impatiently waiting for the interlopers to leave, so we did.

July 6. More beaver ponds, after a four-hour ramble over the ridges and down some newly discovered streams. If we do this several times a week, we'll be powerful and agile by bird season — or dead. Got 20 trout, making 60 this week. Sat down to a delicious dinner at 10 P.M., the sky still tinted orange in the west. Long days up here. Tablecloth, candlelight, cocktail-lounge music on the little radio before the batteries faded out. After dinner, went up to bed in the tent under a sky brilliant with stars. Fabulous place for star watching, but too cold this night to linger gazing at the Milky Way. Roscoe dreamed in the night that some man was trying to kill him in a restaurant while he hid under the tablecloth. Fortunately, another man came in with a frog gig and did in the first fellow. Those cheap restaurants are all the same!

By autumn the literature shed was finished, the pitiful garden harvest reaped (the pea crop was substantially less than the amount of seed that had been planted), homemade wines and wild berry jams made, most of the logs for the big cabin cut, hauled and peeled, and ready to go the next summer. The two pioneers look forward to the hunting season with keen anticipation.

September 4. UGH! Weeks ago, Roscoe fixed up a nasty mixture of fish guts and elderly eggs to lure raccoons. It has been sitting in the sun for many weeks "ripening." Guess who just scored a direct hit on it with the lawn mower right in front of the tent? Gawd!

Graham Pilsworth

September 14. Rain, wind and cold increased in the afternoon. Roscoe strained chokecherry wine through an old T-shirt. Cherry pits and juice everywhere. He tried to light the supper fire in the driving rain and wind with ferocious gusts, using damp wood and wet newspaper. Fire goes out 738 times. Crowning outrage of the day comes when Roscoe, demonstrating how to light the tricky new barn lantern his folks sent, shoots the wick irretrievably down into the oil reservoir and dances around the hut with red face and rolling eyes, screeching. Tomorrow, the sun had better shine, or two disillusioned and cold old homesteaders are hijacking a tangerine truck and heading south. Tent floor soaking wet, said tent leaking, yard a sea of mud, out of firewood, out of clean clothes, out of food, toothbrushes getting splayed, etc. Now wearing winter clothes.

September 24. Last night was our last night in that damn cold, wet tent. We have moved into the tiny loft of the hut — just room enough for both of us to lie there — can't even sit up. Today was a red-letter day. It was the opening of the Bird Season and the day we got the stove together in the hut — HEAT AT LAST. Roscoe got a bird near the big spruce on the edge of the field, but Lulu got none. Legs felt like mushroom stalks at the end of the afternoon and shotgun like a cast-iron cannon.

In October, the rains gave way to snow, but Roscoe and Lulu were eating well, for supplementing the occasional woodchuck and the mainstay of trout and panfish, there were now grouse, varying hare and ducks. Their time is divided equally between hunting, fishing, getting up firewood and writing. They both know it is impossible to spend this winter in the uninsulated 10' x 16' literature hut with only an inefficient Franklin stove to keep them warm, so they have been working up book proposals that will involve research downcountry. Finally there comes a visit to the publisher, 200 miles away, a hair-raising trip in Wonderful Feller whose false inspection sticker falls off midway through the trip. On the way home, after a successful meeting, they buy shotgun shells, pinto beans and raisins. With their pockets full of publisher's money, they visit old friends, only to discover that the experiences of their lives are so different from other people's that there's nothing to talk about.

October 29. Terrible evening. Bored, tired, full of beer and smoking too much. Same old conversation about bosses and overtime and office gossip, who's layin' up with whom. Headed for home before dawn. Nice to be back home again on this cold mountain. Grouse with cabbage *à la Escoffier*, not bad! Tomorrow, Roscoe will do *hassenpfeffer*. We lead enviable lives.

November 13. First snowstorm. Winter light reflected upward. We went out into the woods where the edges of the fallen leaves are still uncovered by snow, thousands, millions of fragile earth-coloured cups full of white crystals. A flattened clump of grass an icy spiral nebula. No animal tracks anywhere — all waiting out the storm. Dr. X and a lady friend visit after dinner, and Roscoe drinks many glasses of wine and pinches the lady's arm lasciviously. Lulu, alas, jealous, and it is a cold, sad night with the two homesteaders far apart. Early morning mends are made, but like all patches, that's what we've got — repairs on something neither thought could be torn.

At the end of November, Roscoe and Lulu realized they had been at their new way of life for six months and sit down to take stock. In their assets, they list 400-plus fish caught and eaten, many grouse, hare, woodchucks and raccoons simmered in memorable sauces, the literature hut built, a sturdy log outhouse put up, five articles sold and a book contract signed, all the logs for the main cabin cut, peeled and on the site, and, with some reservations that it *was* an asset,

they list Roscoe's luxurious new moustache. Their only problems they see as the poor cash flow and the disaster garden, and they blithely assume both were temporary conditions — an error, as the next two years showed.

On December 7th in the middle of a savage snowstorm, they pack their typewriters, winter clothes and a few saucepans onto the toboggan and drag it down the hill, heading for Montreal and a winter in the libraries. They live frugally in two tiny rooms just around the corner from the St. Lawrence Market, where they can hear the squawks of doomed chickens awaiting their fate and buy goat chops or fresh crab. Four months later to the day, they're back on the hill, struggling through six-foot drifts to drag the toboggan back again. This time, it is loaded with typewriters, a lot of exotic food and a new fishing rod for Lulu. They are wearing all their winter clothes.

April 7. Tomorrow is the opening of the fishing season. What a laugh! 12 degrees F and a howling blizzard adding to the five to six feet of snow already on the ground. Insane! Tried rapping the compost heap with a shovel — it rang like a bell, it is so frozen. Wood supply poor, and what we left is wet and frozen. Haven't we been through this before? Anyway, there's plenty of food in the cupboard — in fact, it's jammed full for the first time.

Yet spring was coming. Springtails leaped and the pioneers hung out their sap buckets, boiling down a few gallons of syrup on the old familiar outdoor fireplace, which lies at the bottom of a huge well of snow. The last quarts of syrup are almost black, with pyramids of nitre in the bottom of the jar — grade Z. The snows linger on and on, and it is tiresome slogging around on snowshoes or skis all the time, and very frustrating to eager cabin builders. The old-timers say that this is the latest they can remember such deep snow staying on the ground. Snowstorms keep on coming, leading to violent journal entries.

April 30. 6:20 P.M. 18 degrees F. SNOW. HEAVY SNOW.

By early June, the last of the snow is gone, the blackflies are a torment, and the fishing is terrific. Lulu and Roscoe fall back into the pattern of their now-familiar life. A friend, impressed, horrified and fascinated by their willingness to eat various critters, comes by early one morning and drapes a dead porcupine, with its tongue hanging out, over the fireplace in an artistic manner.

We tried to cook the porky liver with red wine and garlic, but alas, it proved dreadfully spruce flavoured, and we had to throw it out — the first inability to eat any wild food. Dinner of pasta and porcupine sauce was delicious, though. Takes a long time to skin those critters out. Used pliers, knives, vise-grips, forks, you name it, in the job.

In early June, the garden is planted after energetic applications of compost and manure and lime, and dotted all over with cold frames of varying designs. A major worry is whether the rainy season of last year will be repeated, but with horror, Lulu and Roscoe soon realize that the enemy is appearing in a new and more terrifying guise — frost.

June 16. FROST! And we were up too late to get the plants watered before the sun rose — up at 6 A.M., and the sun had been up for about 20 minutes. Will we lose squash, tomatoes, pepper? Probably.

July 2 and 3. Well, 31 degrees and 30 degrees F — two consecutive frosts in July. It is unpleasant to wear a parka and gloves in mid-summer. Up early in the A.M. watering plants. What a bloody cold place to live!

August 25. FROST. At 5 A.M., it was 24 degrees F. Watered down the survivors of earlier frosts. Garden better than last year, but suffering from low temps. every month. Beginning to doubt we can garden here, and gardening supposed to be our main source of food. After all, how many trout can we catch from October to April? Old-timers say they can't remember a summer with so many frosts.

There were few journal entries during this summer except for the frost watch notes. Both Lulu and Roscoe were busy building the cabin, every log sawn by chain-saw attachment by Roscoe, and all the joints and notches cut by Lulu with hand tools in the old regional *pièce-en-pièce* style. Grown-up children as well as other relatives and friends came in droves to see what was going on. They all had to be fed, whether with trout or bass or whatever came to hand. Journal entries were sparse. In mid-August Lulu wrote:

It has been a long time since we wrote in this journal — partly because we're terribly busy this summer, partly because our joy and sorrow at small events are less marked than a year ago. Weird dreams, the calling of night birds, ghastly weather are all rather common-place now. We are more sharp-tempered with each other this summer.

Major events: Dr. X has sold 600 back acres to a no-toriously wicked logger from over the border. Our fa-vourite fishing streams and beaver ponds lie in the mid-dle of this terrain. Our house walls are all up. Just wait-ing for money and time to put on the roof and do the floor. Dr. X is making a lot of bustle and noise with chain saws and work crews and trucks clearing land this summer. No reason for it, either. We're musing with magic thoughts of moving the cabin away to a quieter place. We are still hungry a lot, and the cash flow is as bad as ever. All those editors work by tele-phone, not letter. There is not a chance in a million years of ever getting telephone or electricity up here! Saw a new mag today called *Harrowsmith*. Canadian, and nothing like it here. Looks like our kind of mag.

On September 2, following a strange evening where Wonderful Feller seemed, all on his own, to drive into a ditch, despite a certain amount of Pernod Roscoe had

swigged, something odd happened. The truck was hauled out of the ditch ignominiously, and the home-steaders, after a vigorous fishing session on the lake that yielded a few decent bass and a nice German brown, went home with the clanking, damaged truck. Early the next morning, as Roscoe is making coffee over the campfire, something went to hell.

Awoke feeling fine, did odds 'n ends chores in the early A.M., then started getting bad, real BAD, chest pains. Thump. Thump. THUMP. Dropped a nitro — fair; got up to go to the door — vertigo, blackout, sit down and pop nitro number two. Then, Painsville.

Lulu drives Roscoe to the tiny Coleslaw Hospital with various bits of metal and parts pinging and clang-ing into the roadway as the old truck shakes his way along, and a grey-faced Roscoe fights the pain and fright of his second heart attack. There is a slow hos-pital recuperation for Roscoe and a crisis for Lulu faced with oncoming winter and no roof on the cabin and no wood in. At the low swing of the pendulum, two neighbours give up their own autumn plans to help Lulu put a roof on; in a week, the thing is done — crooked, but, by God, on! Roscoe comes out of the hospital and lies in the literature hut fretting as Lulu lays the cabin floor. As soon as Roscoe can hold a sta-ple gun, he is putting up insulation and willing health to return. But Roscoe has to go slow, and both pioneers stop smoking forever and vow to give up Pernod. (Both promises were kept.)

In October, despite Roscoe's heart attack, despite slow money, poor garden harvest and low larder, they begin the happiest period of their lives. Dr. X has gone south for six months. The cabin is big and beautiful, the winter wood is in, somehow, Roscoe is coming along well with doctor's advice to exercise, the pioneers have a new stove, and the grouse season is on! For weeks, the journal entries are full of pulse rates, de-tailed data on coverts, crop contents, birds put up, birds missed, birds brought down and grouse recipes.

Then the winter comes on, savagely cold, with tem-peratures of -30 degrees F for weeks at a time. Always, the stars are brilliant, the sky an arching ribbon of light, the snow like crushed crystal underfoot. Yet the wood-pile, which looked so substantial in October, begins to melt away, and the two pioneers find themselves on snowshoes in the woods with the chain saw and the worn toboggan looking for standing dead hardwood.

February 5. Montreal weather reports -35 F with high winds tonight again. Stovewood low, and the little that remains is sodden. That big dead yellow birch from be-hind the outhouse has a punky heart that takes in mois-ture like a sponge. Cursed with a bad creosote problem. The stovepipe runs some 20 feet to tie into a "Y" above the cookstove and acts like a giant still coil. Burning a wet piece of wood several days ago with the inside temperature at 32 degrees F caused condensation all along the pipe inside the cabin; drip, drip, drip, drip, black smelly slop all over the table, floor and stove. It stopped when the room got warm.

Very hard going in the woods with the chain saw slung over shoulder with Fat Indian's belt. (Fat Indian was the former tenant of our last winter Montreal "apartment," and he left his used Calcutta plane tickets, a *huge* leather belt and a white plastic purse in the closet. We kept the belt, and see how useful it is?)

February 7. This cold spell is raising hell with the waterhole. Have to break through three inches of thick ice every morning before we can dip out any water. A whole flight of stairs chopped in the ice to get down into the water hole. It all drifts over every night and has to be dug out anew in the A.M., then the long walk back up the hill to the cabin, slipping and sliding with the heavy buckets.

Severe winds and low temperatures make working outside hard. Roscoe cut his left snowshoe with the chain saw — lucky it wasn't his foot!

Cross words and bad feelings. Wood going fast in continued bitter cold which has a severely depressing effect on both of us. Tempers short. How do the Inuit do it?

Because of the long run of stovepipe in the cabin, Lulu and Roscoe make themselves take down the pipe entirely once every three weeks, carry the lengths outside and scrape, shake and claw out the creosote accumulations which are awesome. This is the most hated and most necessary chore they have, a cold, dirty job full of mechanical frustration because the ill-fitting, recalcitrant pipes never want to rejoin.

Their keenest pleasure comes from daily tracking expeditions. Every morning, they go off on skis to see what animals have been moving around and what they've been doing. They learn the patterned routes of foxes, the hare trails, notice the landing marks in the snow of the elusive flying squirrel, and spend one fine day tracing a pair of fisher cats back to their den in a hollow tree several miles from the cabin. They know two deer yards, the snow trampled down in the big bedding areas under the cedars.

But as the winter wears on, an ominous sound comes closer and closer — the sound of chain saws and skidders, the noise that wakes Lulu and Roscoe at first light and that stops only at darkness, an alien, cruel sound in the white silence of winter. By March, the beaver ponds are gone, the deer yards cut flat, the fisher cat den down, knocked over by a felled tree. A whole mountainside is being levelled, its unsightly shorn flanks visible 20 miles away. It's not a good clear-cut. Slash and tops lie in choking tangles, once-shaded forest streams are laid mercilessly bare to the sun, and the faint game trails are run deep by gouging skidder tracks that will erode to the bedrock in the spring melt.

Although Roscoe and Lulu will be here almost another year, their pleasure in this private place disappears with the cutting of the forest. Their habitat, as well as that of the region's animals, has been destroyed.

All through the next summer, the chain saws and skidders roar until Roscoe and Lulu sit on a small island surrounded by desolation. The old-timers say they've never known such continuous heavy cutting. The chain of beaver ponds where the thrush sang and the nameless trout-filled streams are gone, the terrain unrecognizable. Roscoe and Lulu know the game, if that's what it was, is over. The last entry in the journal is dated September. Although the wood is stacked in neat cords against the winter, although the garden is thriving as never before, Lulu and Roscoe leave on the following day for another mountainside 150 miles south, where there are no frosts in July and where skidders do not come. They never return to the briefly lived-in cabin.

September. A day of wind, of increasing clouds, the lake below us blocked by mist and flying fog. We walked down to the wild apple trees we released last year. They're doing well. Spent an hour in the late morning with a fish biologist doing a fish count in the Silvery Stream where there are some nice gravel spawning bars and a few deep pools. We've had some 18-inch rainbows out of those pools. This section of water is slated for gravel strip-mining next month. This last wild region of the state is vanishing under chain saw, skidder, dirty politics, closed eyes, shady legislation, greed, hunger and no alternative ways to make a living up here except by raping the land. The rain comes on softly, and we go home. As we walk up the road for the last time, two grouse run ahead, clucking confusedly. Young birds, who don't know the season opens in a few days. They're not in our dinner plans this year.

Everywhere we walk we know. We recognize the best mushroom places, particular bent saplings and even patches of weed, the trees that went down with groaning cries last winter in the great ice storm. The young grouse cluck at us in outrage at our use of their road, then they fly the familiar path of air into the wild apple meadow.

Home again, everything packed, and the storm breaks. Torrents of rain, thunder, the poplars' leaves smashed off the branches into pulp. Mozart is playing on the radio we bought after two years of saving. Our only link — except for the mailbox — with civilization, such as it is. Feeling of loss and regret. Roscoe stands in the doorway watching the poplars bend in sheets of winding rain until he is soaked to the skin. This close rapport with the natural world that we've enjoyed here is a rare thing in our day. We cannot live or work happily elsewhere, but cannot stay here. The sky is slate, dull slate, spruce fading away now from a silhouette to black night. The last night. ■

"Lulu" and "Roscoe" are the temporary pseudonyms of a couple now living in Vermont. They write frequently about country matters for a number of publications, including Harrowsmith *and* The New York Times.

The Trapped Homesteader Syndrome

Life among the rustic pitfalls

By Kit Gifford

It would be akin to collaring the starry-eyed bride and groom at the wedding feast and detailing to them the problems and pitfalls that lie in wait for them in the future. Clearly the time to learn about potential boredom, mental and emotional stagnation, social and cultural sterility, is before the big step is taken, whether that step be choosing a marriage partner or choosing a "homestead" life style. But no one would listen: The belief is firm that these problems only afflict Someone Else.

Then, gradually, the honeymoon is over. The marvellously desirable Peace and Quiet degenerates into lack of communication and nothing to do on Saturday night. The picturesque farmhouse on the picturesque country lane, the isolated and equally picturesque cabin in the isolated and picturesque valley become dismally dark and uncomfortably chilly after the first adventurous winter of cutting your own firewood. The thrill of baking fragrant brown bread in a wood stove turns into an encounter with a werewolf, consuming more time and effort than you thought possible. Everything from washing dishes to washing your hair takes three times as long as it used to. The bucolic pleasure of watching your own hens scratching in their yard clucking to greedy chicks turns into the drudgery of hauling feed and water, shovelling manure and dealing with more roosters than you thought existed. Livestock, garden, woodpile become far more confining than any routine job in office or factory; and there is no going off and leaving the problems at the end of an eight-hour shift. There is no holiday pay . . . and no holiday. No one appreciates your endless efforts because they don't show. No one but you seems to realize that you will have to face the same wretched stove, water bucket, woodpile, chain saw, chickens, garden . . . again and again and again. All the creative and marvellous things you planned to do as part of this new, free, country life, the painting, writing, carving, inventing, even reading and thinking, become more remote as the demands on your time intensify. Chores become burdens; a partner becomes either a slave driver or an unappreciative freeloader; the sameness and inevitability of tomorrow's tasks become boring, then frustrating, then crushing; there seems no escape.

This scenario sounds much like the Trapped Housewife Syndrome that received so much publicity a few years back, and likely the causes and cures are similar. Some sufferers try to mask the problem with pills or alcohol. Some drive into bridge abutments or simply go missing. Some country newcomers retreat whence they came and take up their former lives on the theory that familiar devils are better than unfamiliar ones. The lucky individuals, couples or families pull up their socks and do something. From experience, I can understand the feeling of being trapped or bored, and I do believe it is possible to claw your way up from the depths of rural malaise. Or urban malaise, for that matter.

Personal creativity must, I believe, be the basis of the rescue, and that entails some soul searching and determination of priorities. The first and foremost task is to isolate the essentials for survival and arrange to get these done in minimum time and with as little stress as possible. Then decide what is the most important and satisfying outlet for your personality, whether it be volunteer work with handicapped children, Little Theatre, creating distinctive fabrics from the wool of your own sheep, writing the Great Canadian Novel, isolating the perfect strain of beans for your climate, reading Aeschylus in the original Greek, keeping a spotless house, educating your children yourself, collecting and preserving local history, contemplating the growth of an oak tree, designing a workable alternative power system, running your own successful small business, bucking the local economic system to save a unique wilderness spot from rape by industry, creating a productive and weed-free garden from a pile of sand and gravel, learning to play the harpsichord, doing original research into the social patterns of starlings . . . and then, get on with it!

The possibilities are as endless as the variations of persons and personalities. Each endeavour has its pitfalls and prizes, and each is surely a way out of the boredom and stultification that can and does wear thin so many lives. I offer as examples four personalities, four situations, four dreams, four ways of coping.

First is a writer/artist friend. She loves the country, the wildness and wilderness of the Coast, the sunshine of summer lakes and orchards, the wild beauty of rivers and mountains. She needs them; yet she has long since concluded that she could not live and do her chosen work from a rural location. She requires the references and materials available only in libraries and museums. She needs the groups with whom she studies and to whom she lectures. Still, she is intensely involved with a simple and "alternative" way of living and grows much of her own food in a tiny backyard urban garden. Rural and wilderness friendship, a commitment to waste as little as possible of the finite resources of the earth, and the determination to leave the world a little richer than she found it have given her a contentment and serenity she would never have found in rural living.

Then, there is a young woman I know only through several years of correspondence. Seeking a more basic life, she left a suburban home in the East and tried, in succession, life as a farm labourer, as a member of a commune, a rather wistful relationship with an over-aged mystic type and, eventually, marriage with an equally unrealistic, very "talented" and sensitive young man of no appreciable abilities. Living in an uninsulated shack in the Oregon mountains produced one child and the itch to move on. The last I heard from her, she was stuck in a log cabin on a small island off the northwest coast, with no amenities, two babies and another on the way, no communication with the outside world and a husband off trying to make a tenuous living at fishing, an art about which he knew nothing at all. Bored to tears by the company of two infants and weeks of sodden grey skies, exhausted by carrying water and wet wood, often hungry and near the limits of desperation, she wrote a pitiable letter. That was a year ago. I've not heard from her since.

Third, I know a family who has lived a rural self-sufficient life for far longer than it has been in vogue. They live on the fringe of a tiny, isolated community in the cold North, raise their own food, work hard at productive crafts, teach their many skills to local people on request and in the local school, give aid in time of trouble and illness and do all in their power to help with community social problems. Yet, after nearly 20 years, they're not completely accepted by the community. There is still a feeling of "meddling newcomers" evident at times, and some resentment of the situation they have carved for themselves through their own intelligence and hard work. Even so, their lives are satisfying and rewarding to them, and their children are growing up with the ideals of hard work and service to others constantly before them. The warm family life is a talisman against the arrows of the world.

Last, I can talk of our family of three. I cannot now imagine being bored living where and as we do. Most of my creative inspiration stems from our life, our surroundings, our lovely little corner of the world. Our house is not as spotless and tidy as it might be, the garden is a long way from weedless, and my correspondence lags. I write instead of scrub; photograph instead of weed; weave instead of any number of other things. I know my husband feels more than I the stint of mental stimulation, but he left the intensity of a career in business and mathematics. Still, he has found immense satisfaction in designing and building our house, in the creation of a hydroelectric system that meets our limited power requirements with no environmental degradation of the stream, and he finds great pleasure in the wildlife and wilderness that share this spot with us. Our daughter has grown to adulthood here and could not, I think, ever be bored except if deprived of her beloved books, beaches and the birds that are her chosen field of study. We, certainly, have gone through our times of boredom, depression and frustration, and they still sometimes recur. But we also know that these times pass, and the satisfactions of our life here are lasting.

It is all too easy to sound smug from the altitude of personal experience and reasonable success, and to offer simplistic solutions. I do not mean any of this in a smug or preachy way. It is, after all is said and done, a matter of personal opinion and individual effort, and that is what makes the world turn. "Different strokes for different folks" is trite, but each of us must work out his own unique and personal pattern for dealing with the varied frustrations of life wherever we choose to live it. But surely it can be done. ■

Kit Gifford moved to the Queen Charlotte Islands with her family in 1969. She is a gardener, weaver, beachcomber and logger.

Well-Sheltered Spirits

The owner-builder philosophy: creating mortgage-free homes with heart

By Charles Long

Years ago, we tore apart an old log cabin, the one that is now the living room. Starting with a missionary zeal, we took crowbars to rip away the scum and rotten plaster, anxious to purge the decay so we could get on with making a real house. With each layer of rubbish stripped away, we went back another generation: past the 1950s' plasterboard, past the gaudy flowers of pre-Depression wallpaper, through a more affluent time of rich wooden panels and into an age when weekly newspapers covered the walls. By then, the crowbars had been set aside, and we worked with gentle fingers and a great deal more respect. Out of the whitewash came stories of heinous Boers, then another depression. Beneath that were the dastardly Fenian raids and a scandalized account of John A. Macdonald's habits. And finally, behind the unknighted John A's sins were the crudely axe-hewn logs . . . someone else's owner-built home.

Blessed with an amateur's ignorance of conventional techniques, author Long and his wife, Liz, discovered the joy of building with stone.

 Dan Maruska

Photos by Dan Maruska

The last bones bared were the ceiling beams. And there on a beam, above the spot where the bed had been, someone had carved a heart. No initials, no arrow, no later attempt to efface the sentiment. Just a lumpy, lopsided, amateur heart.

His walls were as lopsided as his heart. One end was seven inches higher than the other, and the sides were at least four inches out of square. An equal number of whiskey jugs and liniment tins were buried in the chinking. The walls showed scars of fire, and the floor in front of the cookstove was worn thin with five generations of weary feet. Like birds, wiggling our bottoms into the nest, we give our own shapes to the homes we make. That's why they are so very comfortable — despite the lopsided walls and amateur mistakes.

And to his mistakes we added ours. The new cellar unwittingly included a spring and a resident frog who still croaks happily behind the preserves. The marbles always roll to the same end of the hall, and the trap door only works in winter, when an icy draft blows in all around it. In summer, it seals itself shut again. We have fallen off ladders, zapped ourselves with the wiring, brushed the sawdust out of sandwiches and hammered our thumbs more than once. I even nailed my own foot to the floor in the rush to put a wall around the bathroom before mother-in-law arrived to visit.

FEAR OF FAILURE

The first — and biggest — mistake of all, however, was our initial fear that building a house was a job for professionals. All the mumbo jumbo of building codes was more than a little intimidating to two paper pushers who had never built anything bigger than a bricks-and-board bookshelf (and the baby dismantled that while eating the cover off a novel). What did we know of spans and corbels, headers and slaking? Lintels were things that collected in navels, and foundations were worn under matrons' dresses. In fact, we never would have had the nerve to start at all if that old log house had not been sitting there like a pioneer Pan-Abode kit. All we had to do was lift off the logs and reassemble them on a new foundation. All the tricky bits, the notching and measuring and fitting and . . . had already been done by the old-time craftsman who knew what he was doing. Right?

Wrong. That rash assumption was made before we found that the walls had been measured in jug lengths. The pioneers — this one at any rate — were just as much the novices as we were. But his crooked walls had absorbed Fenians and Boers, poverty and affluence, fire, babies, fatigue and love. It was a home, and judging by the whittlings over the bed, a happy one. If the whiskey and liniment man could do it, so could we.

We planned a smallish addition, a kitchen tacked onto the back of the "main" house. Ever so cautiously, full of all the doubts, all too aware of our technical naïveté ("don't craftsmen apprentice for years to learn this job?"), we spread a timorous bed of mortar and set a rugged fieldstone on it. And another, and another, and another. Damned if it didn't look like a *real* stone wall.

As the stone walls grew out of the earth, the plans and our confidence as builders grew with them. We added two more bedrooms, winding stairs, a study loft, toilets, pantry, flagstone floors, woodshed annex, et cetera. Now the workshop and a smokehouse are underway. In case the people buildings are ever finished, I've been doodling with plans for a fieldstone doghouse. Then there's the greenhouse, a garden wall, verandah, garage and guest house.

It's the stone. Some weekend dabblers get off on the smell of pine shavings curling out of the plane. Here, it is the texture of the stone. The process is so simple and satisfying, the stone so abundant and beautiful, that the walls have grown far beyond any thought of what is being built.

What begins to grow inside the builder is not some previously untapped talent or the spark of nascent expertise, but a new awareness that one doesn't really have to be a full-fledged expert in order to build an ordinary wall in an ordinary house or to slide a plane along a board and enjoy the results. Ancients and peasants have been doing just that for millennia, piling stone upon stone and calling the result a wall. It probably never occurred to them that they had to be trained, graded and officially licensed before attempting such a complex job. Our pioneer axeman sighted along his thumb, took another pull at the jug and whacked away at the logs. I doubt if he had ever heard of a scriber, level or calipers. His crooked walls are still standing, though. And our stone walls, our patently amateur piles of rock, suit us just fine, thank you very much.

The point is, there is a great deal besides skill that goes into the owner-built home. And the result is much more than a house. There's a joy in creating something real, something tangible, functional and sometimes even beautiful. It doesn't have to be perfect. Perfection would be a poor reflection of most builders anyway. Besides, the joy is not so much in the product as in the process of creating it. Any professional mason could build a carbon copy of our rambling walls, and there wouldn't be a lick of fun in it for us. As in "Ozymandias," the walls will eventually crumble away. It is the making of them that matters, not the end result.

That's why I feel a little sorry for those who take their shelter so seriously that they turn the actual building over to contractors so there won't be any mistakes. They're missing the best part. An owner-designed home is *not* the same as an owner-built home, not even when the owner does the landscaping and the rec room himself.

Even amongst the true owner-builts, there are vast differences in approach. At one extreme is the on-site assembly of factory components: pre-cut studs, plywood sheets, snap-on soffits and the ready-mix truck. At the other end are the purists who build from scratch — originals that no modular components would fit, that no mass-marketing architect could conceive.

Author Long: "From beginning to end, we have done things the simple way, using methods we could see and understand and perform with our own hands."

Dan Maruska

Somewhere in-between are those of us who started without any particular ideology. All we wanted was shelter. The only requirements were that it be cheap to build and cheap to operate. That's what brought us to processes that were basic and easily understood, not any early stirrings of planetary consciousness. Those rationalizations came later. In the beginning, there was no more noble motive than the need for an affordable home.

The stone was free and already littered the site. It was durable, beautiful and an integral part of the landscape, but most of all it was cheap. The bedrock just beneath the grass was a ready-made foundation. As owner-builders, we could control the process and accept these "shortcuts." Commercial builders, on the other hand, can rarely afford to be that flexible. For the commercial builder, "cheap" means sticking to the standard pattern, no matter what the site might offer. Even here in bedrock country, the standard practice is to bulldoze the fieldstone aside and stick imitation stone on the outside face of concrete blocks. Since the standard pattern includes a basement, the bedrock house is built up in the air, then half buried with trucked-in dirt to cover the foundation walls and the septic tank.

We, however, were free to decide that we would rather have a bedrock foundation than a basement. The pantry/cellar would simply be two steps down from the kitchen instead of the usual ten. The toilets would connect to a Clivus Multrum composter instead of the standard septic tank. Cellar, entrance and utility floors could be natural stone instead of the normal concrete variety.

Owner-built homes differ from the commercial models for reasons other than just plain cussedness. The economics of standard housing stop at the sale price. The owner-builder, however, is also concerned with operating and maintenance costs. For us, there is value in having a cellar that maintains its own mini-climate for food storage. The bedrock floor, insulation, vents, and waste heat from the freezer do it all, at no extra cost to us — ever. The composting toilets were less than half the cost of a bedrock septic system. They also freed us from plumbing and pump-out bills forever. The flagstone floors are not only free and indestructible, they are also insulated for passive heat storage. The list could go on, but the conclusion should be clear: Commercial housing does not offer features like that, not even as optional extras.

There is even more to it than stubbornness and conserver economics, however. I admire those builders who can consciously integrate the best of the new technology into their plans: double envelopes, triple glazing, solar collection, thermostatic vents and fans. Such systems would be the icing on the owner-built cake. But they aren't the essence of owner-built. The essence of it, the joy of it, is the very act of creation. Whether it is an uninsulated shack or a windmill-studded castle, there is more satisfaction in building the thing than in owning it. A factory-built solar system may meet conserver objectives, but it would do very little for the subjective pleasure of the owner-builder.

Building this place from what was available at the time, we ended up with a mulligan stew of store-bought materials, salvaged junk and wholly homemade components. Again, it was a mix with no other ideology than to use what was already here and to buy as little as possible. Some of the windows are factory-built, double-glazed and that sort of thing. Others were salvaged from the dump. My favourite, though, is made from the iron ring that held the top of an antique butter churn. We dug the iron out of the earth while gathering stones for the wall. With only a single pane of glass, it would be an abomination to dedicated energy conservers. The only reason it is there is because I like it — for purely subjective reasons — and that is what building your own house is all about.

If this place has a benign impact on the planet (a little wood smoke is about all that comes out of it), it is not the result of any sophisticated plan. It is not an end in itself. It is, however, a direct result of the *process*. From beginning to end, we have deliberately done things the simple way, using methods we could see and understand and perform with our own four hands. It just so happens that the simple means are also usually the cheapest means, the most environmentally harmless means, and certainly the most satisfying means for two amateur builders who didn't know their ash pits from their septa.

In the end, there really are no ends — only means. If the means are good, the ends take care of themselves. Harry pitches in to help with the house for a few days every year, despite the fact that he considers the whole thing madness. That is one of the things I like about him. He was standing on the ground, shaking his head in even greater dismay than ususal as I carried stones up into the peak, 17 feet above the ground. "Stone? Up there? Why?" he asked. "Why not just fill in the peak with wooden siding? You can't see this end of the house anyway, except by crawling through the brush."

I didn't tell him the truth — that I was actually enjoying myself immensely and that I would beat a path through the brush to look at the wall, even if the rest of the world ignored it. As usual, I couldn't think of the perfect riposte at the time and probably mumbled some excuse about the price of lumber and the stone being free. The one explanation he would have understood was means and ends. Harry, you see, is a hiker, a backpacker. I should have told him that he could get in and out of the woods with much less effort if he got himself one of those all-terrain vehicles or, better still, a helicopter. Harry, however, prefers to walk. And I prefer to build with stones. Getting there is more than half the fun.

"Amateur" is a word that applies to the same sort of people in French or in English. In English, of course, an amateur is a nonprofessional, an unskilled duffer. In French, however, the emphasis in on the pleasure rather than the lack of competence. An *amateur* is one who does something for the love of it. An *amateur* builds a gable end in stone, knowing no one else will ever see it. An *amateur* chops a crude log house out of the forest, then carves a heart on the beam . . . even though it will be buried under stories of Boers and Fenians, flowered paper, fancy panels and factory-made sheets of plasterboard. He knows it's there. I know it's there. *Vive l'amateur.* ∎

Charles Long is the author of The Stonebuilder's Primer, *a Camden House publication.*

Farmhouse Renewal

Wide-open architecture and energy efficiency combine to rejuvenate a creaky Maritime relic

By John Barber with photography by Eric Hayes

To the knowing eye, there is a defiance in this house, the way it faces north, straight into the path of winter gales peeling across the Bay of Fundy, fully exposed and refusing to hunker down with its back to the winds, drawing a heavy cape of fibreglass over its vulnerable shoulders. No structural trickery or excessive sacrifice of interior space is evident, and in fact none of its walls holds more insulation than the other new, conventional Maritime homes. Windows are new, but single-glazed and of old-fashioned double-hung design. A massive masonry chimney extends up the north side of the house, sucking heat up through an impressive open brick fireplace. Skylights and huge windows look north, and there is a noticeable absence of anything hinting at energy-efficient design or solar paraphernalia other than a small attached greenhouse. The site itself is an exact mirror image of what every book on autonomous house design considers desirable for a workable plan: A high, tree-topped hill rises immediately to the south of the house, reducing winter sunshine to a feeble, intermittent presence. Undeniably, the best view is down onto the waters of the bay, due north.

The owners of this house, one might suspect, are Gold Card-carrying patrons of the heating oil establishment. One would guess them to be people of taste — this is not an ostentatious house, but it presents a solid, distinguished exterior to the world — and people with the wherewithal to live oblivious to Maritime energy prices.

Rebuilt literally from the underground up, expanded and dramatically remodelled, the Mackay house nevertheless retains all the character it acquired over 140 years on the windswept Fundy shore.

What the knowing eye cannot see, however, is the annual fuel bills for this residence, and one might be tempted to assume that the owners had forsaken or ignored all conservation ethics in their plans. The facts are otherwise. No oil truck ever visits this isolated farmhouse; it is heated entirely with wood, a paltry four cords per winter. Its total yearly heating bill runs to $300.

HISTORICALLY FAITHFUL

This is the newly redone home of Jamie and Jackie Mackay, and it can be found near Donnellan's Brook, Nova Scotia, although would-be visitors must be cautioned that the name of this particular settlement is recorded on a local signpost but does not make its way onto maps. One reaches it by following a maze of dirt roads, and one wonders how the Donnellan family, who left the sheltered Annapolis Valley and crossed the North Mountain down to the weathered Fundy shore, came to choose this place to settle. One wonders, too, whether they would recognize the Mackay place as the post-and-beam home they erected in about 1840.

The Mackays would like to think so, and it is evident in the way they talk and in the subtle ways in which they display their attachment to this house that their concern for the historical integrity of the Donnellan farmhouse runs deep. Their decision to renovate, rather than build from scratch, was essentially an act of faith; with considerably less effort, they could easily have built the same house with all new materials for the same price.

In designing their retirement home, it would have been far easier, from a contractor's point of view, to demolish and rebuild — perhaps retaining some relics from the original structure as decorative details in the new. But the faith that animated the Mackays would have been no more satisfied with a pseudohistorical pastiche than with a modern bungalow decorated with foam-moulded false ceiling beams in the living room.

Having lived, worked and raised a family in Halifax, 90 miles to the east, the Mackays began casting about for accommodation more suited to their changing circumstances. Their children were now ensconced in university, Jamie Mackay, 57, was taking an early retirement from the insurance agency he had run, and they were looking for a rural alternative to the large Halifax home they had been heating.

"We had been prisoners of an oil furnace for too long," explains Jamie. "Our last house in Halifax had 3,000 square feet and no insulation. That old oil truck would pull up at our door at least once every 10 days during the winter. We were spending $3,000 a year on oil, and that was before the price went up."

It was not until Halifax architect Jon Murray saw their creaky summer home at Donnellan's Brook and became enthusiastic about its renovation potential that the Mackays began to think seriously about making it the object of their escape from the city and oil truck.

Their initial skepticism is understandable: the house was the oldest surviving structure in the neighbourhood, a tumbledown, draughty architectural artifact set on an uncemented rubble foundation. Every aspect of the house showed its utilitarian service to the Donnellan family over a period of six generations. Still, the original components of the home were heavy 8-inch posts clad with wood shingles over spruce boards almost 18 inches wide. With Murray's encouragement, the couple concluded that despite the handicaps, the structure could be converted into an exciting, easy-to-heat home without obsessive excursions into the world of untried renovation and conservation techniques. "We weren't conducting an experiment," says Jackie, 45. "We wanted a nice home."

Murray's plans called for a full basement to house an ample master bedroom where before there had been little more than an earth-floored crawlspace. The Mackays chose to position the house on a new foundation of preserved wood, partly for less-than-practical reasons. "I know you can't see it," explains Jackie, who served as the final arbiter of taste during the renovation, "but there was something about the thought of sleeping next to concrete blocks that didn't appeal to me at all." For contractor Roland Woodworth, a local man who previously had done minor work for the Mackays during their tenure as summer residents, installing the new foundation was the job's greatest challenge. The first step was rolling the house off its old foundation. "It could very easily have fallen apart, it was so frail," he recalls, although only a few sills in the basement were actually rotten and needed replacing before the house was winched onto its own front lawn — minus the enormous chimney, which remained, precariously, in place.

With some understatement, Woodworth describes the excavation, in the shadow of the unsupported chimney, as "quite scary and quite dangerous." The new foundation was studded with pressure-treated 2 x 8s on 12-inch centres and covered with two sheets of plywood sandwiching a treated six-mil polyethylene vapour barrier. "Then the house came back the same way it went out," says Woodworth. "We left slots in the foundation for the timbers, and as luck [or skill] would have it, it came right back in place."

Many of the walls Woodworth and his crew ripped out had been plastered with mud and straw. "We went through layers and layers of who knows what," according to architect Murray. The old cladding of spruce planks was left intact on the original post-and-beam skeleton, with new exterior studwalls fitted neatly between the 8-inch posts. New double-hung windows, patterned on the old, were custom made and installed after the incredibly skewed structure was straightened and the old windows no longer fit. Appearances dictated conventional single-glazed windows, fitted with external aluminum storms in the winter. All partition walls on the main level were removed

---

*Jackie Mackay prepares coffee in the kitchen area, **right**, separated by only a single half-partition from the main living area. Otherwise, the comfortably furnished main floor, **above right**, is left entirely open.*

and ceilings came out to expose the original timber beams.

So did large areas of flooring on both of the above-grade storeys. If the exterior of the house gives the impression of a crisp, traditional colonial home, stepping inside is a spectacular impression of open architecture: Gone are the old room divisions, and in their place are long, unimpeded views across the sun-splashed living spaces. If the plan spreads outward to the eye, it also soars, with open air spaces between the floors where conventional homes would have wood, tile or carpeted flooring.

First, two feet of the main floor were cut away along the entire length of the south wall, with only the original timber beams left running through the gap into their supporting posts in the wall. This connects with a large empty well also carved out of the first floor, separating the living and dining areas.

A third dramatic hole, slightly offset, breaks open the south half of the top floor. In effect, it divides the upper storey into two wings, each with a bedroom, connected by a "bridge" along the north wall. A compact spiral staircase runs up the north side of the lower well, reaching a landing on the upper floor to the east of the bridge. The design not only promotes the easy circulation of heat rising from the main airtight wood stove on the lower level, it creates a very modern, dramatic sense of spaciousness which is the outstanding characteristic of the finished interior.

Lost floor space was recovered by building a new entrance and an addition onto the east gable end of the house and wrapping it around the north side in a long L-shape. Unwilling to sacrifice their view of the bay, the Mackays fitted this addition with windows, heresy among solar purists who would prescribe an almost entirely blank north wall stuffed with insulation and made as airtight as possible.

In Murray's original drawings, this addition was

completely partitioned off from the main structure by glass, affording an airlock entrance as well as a thermal buffer zone that would negate the worst effects of the extensive north-facing glazing. As a conservation compromise, it made good sense.

"But design-wise it just didn't look good," says Jackie Mackay. "It would have closed off the entire new section of the house, and I didn't like the idea of something stuck on the side like that. It seemed like a lot of space that wasn't really going to be used." By dispensing with the glass partition, the Mackays were also forced to forgo some of the more desirable glass that overlooked the bay. Rather than a single panoramic view, the three narrow windows Murray fitted to the new north wall afford a series of what he calls "point views" of the bay. "There was no way we were going to sell the view for the sake of energy savings," he says.

The effect of the new addition proves the wisdom of Jackie Mackay's instincts. Both inside and out, it complements the style of the existing structure with clean lines reminiscent of a saltbox, steeply sloping roof and minimal obtrusiveness while yielding a surprising amount of useable space — for the entrance hall and living area above and the bathroom and workshop below. In fact, the addition and new lower level together pack an extraordinary amount of new floor area into what was a deceptively compact farmhouse, notwithstanding the holes in the floors and insulation-thickened walls. At 2,700 square feet, the new building is twice as large as the original 45' x 14' structure. An enormous preserved-wood deck runs 30 feet along and 15 feet out from the main living area, further extending outdoor living space.

Although located in the newly created basement, the Mackays' master bedroom enjoys ample natural light, both from the floor well above and the adjacent solar greenhouse.

In spite of all their space, the Mackays hardly rattle around in their house. With almost the entire basement level given over to a large master bedroom, most day-to-day activity takes place on the main floor above. Except when guests arrive, the two bedrooms on the top floor are empty during the winter, although they are used regularly in the summer when the two children arrive home from university. The top floor also houses Jackie Mackay's loom and studio, where she can spend a good part of each day uninterrupted by distractions. During summer, the Mackays claim to spend most of their time on the outside deck, all but abandoning the house itself.

COSMETIC FIREPLACE

In winter the Mackay house is heated exclusively by wood. The decision was as practical as it was ideological. "To have a furnace here wouldn't do you much good, because the oil truck couldn't get in most of the winter," Jamie says. "And electricity wouldn't help because the power goes off whenever the wind blows strong." There are two stoves in the house, not including the brick fireplace that burns up its share of cordwood for purposes that are "purely cosmetic," according to the Mackays. A new, medium-sized Lakewood stove on the lower level shares a brick-cased, free-standing flue with a small and rarely used Trolla on the main floor. The Mackays have found that together they are more than adequate to heat their house evenly. Like most wood heating systems, this one requires its share of attention, and it took some time for Jamie Mackay, as master of the hearth, to perfect his thermostatic expertise. Not that he resents the effort; with ample leisure time, he concentrates on keeping a fairly brisk, clean-burning fire going. "I'm just tending stoves all the time," he admits, "but I love it."

When he isn't tending fires, the house can coast for at least 12 hours without becoming uncomfortable. If they are away any longer, the Mackays use backup electric heaters.

What sets the Mackay's heating system apart is the evenness with which it heats the house. Tight, newly insulated walls help, but the huge openings between the upper floors are the obvious determining factors. Rather than blocking the flow of heat, the floors of the Mackay house act merely as baffles around which it flows easily. During design, Murray and the Mackays agonized endlessly over the location of both stoves and holes in order to optimize the efficient circulation of heat. But in the end it does not seem to have really mattered; given so much room to move, the internal convection currents hardly needed engineering. The one exception to that rule is the Casablanca-style

electric "thermo-cycler" fan located in the ceiling above the uppermost hole in order to prevent layering. It is controlled manually with a rheostat and left running on a constant low speed.

To Murray, that simple, low-tech fan is the key to the efficiency of his design. "The thermo-cycler is utterly essential and utterly freeing to you as a designer," he says. "I was afraid that the energy crisis was going to handcuff me into little boxes with little windows, but I found that with the thermo-cyclers and wood heat I was perfectly free to make use of the large, open volumes I prefer."

A young Halifax architect specializing in home renovations and additions, Murray is not by nature enchanted with technology — a bias that shows to advantage in the Mackay house. He would prefer to find a simple arrangement that works and then concentrate on design rather than tinker endlessly with an over-engineered "system" whose effect is more rhetorical than functional. "My practice is not a theoretical workshop," he says. "Everything I do comes down to one

---

Even bathroom walls on the top floor step aside to admit light and circulating heat from the upper well, **above left**. *Skylights in an upstairs room,* **left**, *provide natural light for a built-in sitting/sleeping area.* **Right**, *Jackie Mackay inside the greenhouse addition.*

fine line: Will the client accept it and how much does it cost?"

How much *did* it cost? The Mackays, feeling no particular sense of responsibility to the general public, are not saying. It was not cheap. On the other hand, the "incremental costs" of the energy-saving features were tiny. The essential decision to open up the interior, which made the unducted wood heating system possible, was taken as much for design as conservation reasons. And in the context of the total cost of renovation, the price of the lone piece of conservation hardware — the fan — was negligible.

Certainly the Mackays spent no more on insulation than most others. To Murray, the technical problems of super-insulating the house, not to mention the prospect of losing so much floor space, simply overpowered the anticipated benefits. "Three different experts I consulted told me I would be crazy for building beyond R20," he says, "and I saw no reason to disagree."

Both old and new walls were studded with 2 x 6s for R20 (using fibreglass) and sealed with a polyethylene vapour barrier. The roof got slightly heavier treatment — R28 — but only because Roland Woodworth felt it was structurally unsound and should be rebuilt. Murray's original plans called for only as much fibreglass batting as the existing roof cavity would allow. The end result is a layer of insulation standard in new Maritime construction today.

The architect did hedge his bets with a nominal electric baseboard backup heating system. "We installed the heating units in the basement and wired for them in the rest of the house in case they proved necessary," he says. In fact, none of them did. "We don't use them at all," says Jackie Mackay.

Both Murray and the Mackays were interested in installing a solar hot-water heating system in their house but were stymied by what they felt was a lack of accessible information available at the time of the

renovation. Certainly the technology would have been appropriate to their application, both in the general sense and also in the context of Maritime electrical rates, which are among the highest in Canada. In fact, the Maritimes is the first region in Canada where solar water heaters have become fully cost-effective. In the meantime, after observing the rather poor performance of their conventional water heater, the Mackays wrapped it in fibreglass and realized an immediate saving on their total utility bill of 15 percent.

The bright two-level greenhouse now attached to the west gable end of their house is one solar feature the Mackays did not hesitate to include in the renovation. Murray had originally planned for a sunspace/greenhouse attached to the south side of the house but was forced to abandon it due to local road clearance regulations. His solution was to dig the structure into a pit on the end of the house, with access directly from both the master bedroom below and the main-floor

living area. The main entrance on the upper level opens onto an L-shaped wooden landing running along the east and north walls of the greenhouse, with a small flight of steps leading down to the earth-floored lower level. The north half of its roof is insulated and follows the angle of the gable above, with the south face pitched steeply to make the most of Nova Scotia's marginal degree days.

The construction of the greenhouse is simple, with an outer layer of glass secured to wooden 2 x 2s with strapping over top and an inner glazing layer sandwiched behind identical wooden supports. "We got the glass second-hand from a dismantled commercial greenhouse for 50 cents a pane," says Jamie Mackay. "In total, we paid less than $200 for it." The same instincts motivated the Mackays' choice of thermal bar-

Cramped bedrooms in the top floor of the original house were expanded with 18 inches of headroom provided by a new roof.

rier to prevent nighttime heat loss. Rather than pay an enormous sum for a new quilted curtain, they rigged their own system using pieces of a laminated plastic swimming-pool cover. By day, they remain rolled neatly along the bottom of the glass; at night, they are unfurled with pulleys to curtain off the entire window area. The Mackays optimistically estimate their homemade curtains' insulation value to be R5. In all, the greenhouse cost less than $3,000.

The solar component of the Mackay greenhouse is again simple, consisting of eight 55-gallon drums filled with water and stacked against the insulated north wall as well as a small plastic thermo-cycler fan about as sophisticated as a department-store "ecologizer." Another fan automatically vents heat when the inside temperature rises above 90 degrees F, although there is no mechanism for driving heat into the house. "We talked a lot about having one, but in the end decided just to rely on the open doors," says Murray.

DORMANT DRUMS

It appears to have been a wise decision, because as a winter heat source the Mackays' solar greenhouse is a less than balmy place best-suited to growing rhododendrons. One impediment to its performance is a lack of sufficient thermal mass, coupled with an uninsulated floor. While excavating the pit, Woodworth quickly ran into bedrock, which had to be left exposed and ate up a lot of space on the lower level. This in turn restricted the number of water drums that could be fitted to store heat. Murray was unwilling, for the sake of design, to expand the size of the greenhouse to provide the extra mass. "It would have looked very strange that big," he says. The number of drums currently installed provides the minimum heat storage capacity necessary for a fully self-sufficient greenhouse, according to calculations Murray based on James McCullagh's *The Solar Greenhouse Book*. "The water drums work to a degree but certainly not as much as they could," says Murray.

The tree-covered hill rising to the south of the house does not help things either. "We almost completely lose the sun in winter," says Jamie Mackay. "It only manages to filter through the tops of the trees." Even so, on a net basis the greenhouse does not actually lose heat; the door to the house can be left open all year without overtaxing the wood stoves. On cold but sunny winter days, it is capable of throwing off considerable warmth and has never frozen during the long overcast spells that characterize much of the Fundy

View from above, **bottom right,** *shows some of the original post-and-beam skeleton. Jackie Mackay's loom,* **top right,** *fills the bridge between top-floor bedrooms.*

winter.

It is mainly the light problem that restricts the Mackays' indoor growing season, even though the heat is sufficient for some winter vegetables. "For three months a year it's pretty dormant in there," says Jamie. "Nothing much is growing, but then nothing is dying either."

Typically, the Mackays are less than upset that their add-on does not quite live up to its solar billing. "It's a nice touch, a lovely thing to have," says Jackie. "And if it's going to give off a bit of heat, so much the better," adds her husband. Murray echoes the view. "In our grey climate, having a greenhouse is more of a psychological than an energy advantage," he says. "Basically, we don't have a spring here, and in those dismal two months at the end of winter, a greenhouse with something growing in it helps prevent you from committing suicide and other crimes." Considering the Mackays' contentment with their revamped farmhouse, the local constabulary is not likely to be called to Donnellan's Brook as a result of cabin fever that has got out of hand.

A large part of the Mackays' dream was a house that would accommodate their desire for a quiet, isolated life with all the comfort of their previous urban existence. They seem to have succeeded both architecturally and in the subtler aspects of home design. For Jackie, who left a hectic job in a Halifax art gallery for the new home, the main advantage of her surroundings is their conduciveness to her weaving, which has blossomed into a consuming pastime since the move. She works at the loom for as long as five hours a day, preparing pieces that are sold during the summer and fall at shops and galleries throughout the province. Jamie Mackay has taken advantage of his new leisure to reform his "tin thumb" as an amateur woodworker. Both are avid gardeners. Hardly socialites, the Mackays exist on good terms with their neighbours but obviously prefer the tranquillity and independence of their new life to the rush of its urban predecessor. More often than not, the outside world comes to them, in the form of friends and family members, and the Mackays appear to feel no great attraction for the city lights. "You always feel you're on holidays here," says Jackie. Going away only emphasizes to them how much they want to come back. ∎

John Barber is a writer living in Toronto and a former associate editor of Harrowsmith.

The 100% Solution

Saunders-Shrewsbury House: the compleat solar dwelling

By Annie Proulx with photography by Eric Hayes

It is the office of a madman or a genius, a bunker of scientific reports and papers stacked in the kind of fathomless clutter that takes years and a special sort of mind to create. He sits here alone, hunched over the keyboard of a microcomputer, his silver hair flying and his eyes gleaming in anticipation of the house-simulation model he is running. To some, this may appear to be the proverbial egghead inventor, and in fact, this is a man with a long history of creating

and patenting devices that have proved less than earth-shaking in their applications. Still, one cannot help but notice that he smiles often, a deep and genuine smile — the smile of a man who has done what his peers said was impossible.

Norman B. Saunders is not out of place in the ring of high-tech genius-powered corporations that surround Boston, but his fascination with solar energy places him close to the fringe.

Saunders was an admitted professional student for much of his younger life, studying chemical engineering at the University of Cincinnati, then going on to the University of Illinois, the Massachusetts Institute of Technology and Harvard to delve into electrical engineering, geology, real estate appraisal and other subjects. In 1954, he retired from a career as a government researcher and set up three successful businesses, including a firm called Stereotronics, which dealt with solid-state instrumentation controls.

"Then I got smart," says Saunders. "In 1968, I fired everybody. I said, 'Heck, it's time I did something new.' So when the oil crunch came, I went into solar full time."

Harvard physicist William Shurcliff calls Saunders a "lone wolf with a passion for devices that are simple, homely and durable and who turns his back instantly, and with no apology, on most types of conventional solar-heating equipment."

Shurcliff, once involved in editing the report of the Manhattan Project and now a solar expert of international note, says that Saunders' patents deserve better attention, but it is difficult to imagine him not remaining unknown and obscure were it not for the Saunders-Shrewsbury House.

Visiting this solar home for the first time, I came, almost literally, out of the woods, where a neighbour and I had been hauling beech logs and enduring the mud, shoulder-knotting work and general fatigue needed to get in our firewood. For me, keeping the house warm calls for topping up the wood box daily; going through the morning ritual of kneeling on a chilly floor and stuffing the stove with crumpled paper and kindling; and regularly withdrawing the brimming shovelfuls of fine, pale ash that sifts maddeningly onto the floor. If my fire burns out during the day while I am away, I come back to a cheerless, cold place; if creosote builds up, there is the worry about chimney fires. On bitter nights, I worry about water pipes. I can never go away from home in midwinter because the aspidistra will freeze. Yes, the glow and crackle of a fire when I come in from the cold and put my feet up on a warm fender greatly satisfies the soul, but the wood stove, for me, can also be a demanding, uncompromising tyrant.

Stepping into the Saunders-Shrewsbury House, so named for its designer and the location — a sparsely populated area 35 miles west of Boston — I am immediately met by silence, warmth and no telltale traces of odour to hint at the source of heat. This is a large house, 2,200 square feet of living area, with a year-round greenhouse and a heated garage that bring the total space to 2,860 square feet.

Designed for a Polaroid Corporation engineer, it has eight rooms and a stained clapboard saltbox exterior that is not out of place in this part of New England. It stands at about the same latitude as Windsor, Ontario, roughly 200 miles south of Halifax, and the winters here would not be considered mild by most Canadians. We tour the house, and it is readily apparent that there is no wood stove, almost *de rigueur* as backup heat in many solar homes. Nor is there a furnace. Close inspection fails to turn up a single baseboard heating unit or even a portable electric heater. This is, conventional skepticism to the contrary, a 100 percent solar home.

Despite early enthusiasm, solar architects have, for many years, accepted as a classic rule the impossibility of building a cost-effective completely solar home in the North. Some sort of backup, it is held, must be included for the very cold, cloudy days when nuclear-energy promoters love to cast their eyes skyward and wonder aloud about the feasibility of solar power.

Consequently, virtually every solar home built in Canada and in the northern United States in recent years has been designed to take only 50 to 70 percent of its heat requirements from the sun. In compromising, things have all too often become expensive. It is something of a bitter joke that only the rich can spend $100,000 to save a few hundred dollars each year with solar heating.

This may be dismissed as glib criticism, but other drawbacks to conventional solar architecture are not so easy to fend off. To many, the tall, glassy façades, chicken-house roofs and disfiguring overhangs make for awkward appearances. Living areas along the south wall are often dominated by bulky, heat-holding thermal masses, often drums, columns or tubes filled with water. And thick Trombe walls, often up to 12 inches of solid masonry or concrete thermal mass, can give a house a feeling of clumsy stodginess and do a poor job of heating the back rooms.

The great south walls of glass can drown a solar house interior with fierce glare on bright days — a pitiless, sharp light that fades furnishings and makes occupants reach for their sunglasses.

The same cascade of sunlight can make solar houses unbearably hot during the dog days of summer unless an array of shades, shutters, curtains, panels, awnings or creeping vines shadows the glass.

Floors often must be a dark material that will hold heat — slate, brick, stone or tile — and remain ungraced by rugs and carpets. Solar houses are generally smaller to keep the heat requirements low; some occupants find them cramped. Interiors are commonly of an open design, characterized by intrusive noises and by the loss of privacy that the old-fashioned door once gave.

Windows on the north, east and west sides of solar houses are often kept to a minimum to cut heat losses, but also lost are important views and diffuse, even lighting.

Heat levels are often uneven, with north-wall rooms chilly as well as dim. Condensation is very much a

At the leading edge of successful solar design, Norman Saunders, **previous page**, *has designed the Saunders-Shrewsbury House with no backup heat sources and an interior that does not sacrifice comfort to engineering,* **above**.

problem in solar homes, according to one 1981 survey of people who had lived in passive solar homes for at least two years.

Condensation occurs partly because the open solar house allows kitchen and house-plant humidity to spread throughout the building and partly because the tight construction of such houses means less ventilation. But one of the biggest headaches with solar houses is the homeowners' creeping disenchantment with the manually operated systems that make the house work: night shutters and thermal shades must be folded, slid, retracted, rolled, removed or drawn both morning and evening; ventilators must be checked, opened or reset according to changes in the weather as well as the season; and ducts have to be closed and opened or adjusted. Commented Amy E. Saras, market research analyst for the Northeast Solar Energy Center, in an interview in the *New York Times*: "At first, everyone was enthusiastic about the novelty of it all. Later, they seemed to tire. They found it was not practical to always be in the house at a certain time of day. So we may have to look more carefully into designs that do not require the participation of the homeowner."

Norman Saunders has changed all of that with the Saunders-Shrewsbury House. It has come through two Massachusetts winters with no backup heating whatsoever, cruising at an even 70 degrees F. Summer temperatures remain the same, never overheating. It is roomy and private, glare-free and humidity-controlled, and there are normal-sized windows on all sides of the house. It is, furthermore, almost entirely automatic in operation and has no shades, no shutters and no overhangs. It can remain at the optimum 70-degree level for a week of cloudy, freezing January weather with no one home and no appliances, hot showers or warm bodies to add what the designers call intrinsic heat.

There are no looming Trombe walls or thermal masses along the south wall of the living quarters, no auxiliary heating system of any kind, no chimney. The lighting is diffused and graceful, rugs and carpets can go anywhere and not fade. There is a beautiful working greenhouse along the south wall of the house where plants and trees may be grown in the earth, rather than in the usual hodgepodge of pots and containers, as in the "sunspace" of other solar houses. Air temperatures never dip to 32 degrees in the greenhouse, and soil temperatures stay close to below 50 degrees. It costs only about $100 a year for electricity to run the two fans that direct the total airflow of the house.

News of this sort of performance has left many solar

architects disbelieving, and even Shurcliff, who has studied solar design for 14 years and is one of Saunders' friends, was at first baffled by how the house actually worked. "Understanding came hard," he wrote in the introduction to a study of Saunders' house. Shurcliff believes that the house succeeds because it uses a variety of simple devices and because many perform dual functions.

Although each feature of the house seems logical and even simple when abstracted from the whole, the real beauty of this unique house emerges only when the layered effect of Saunders' many ideas work as part of an integrated system.

Clambering up into the attic, one is greeted by the sight of 18,000 pounds of water in glass carboys — just like the ones Uncle Giuseppe used for making wine. The heat is astonishing. On a bright winter day, these 400 carboys store as much as 500,000 Btus of collected energy, and the air temperature runs as high as 130 degrees F in winter and 140 in summer.

Heat is collected when sunlight enters the south-facing roof, which doubles as an enormous solar collector with 480 square feet of tempered glass. Saunders calls this attic window the Solar Staircase, a name he has trademarked, and it is perhaps the single most important new feature in the house. Saunders laughingly remarks that his other patents for the attic include fusible plugs that could be placed in the bottom of the carboys to release the water in case of a fire.

On a bright winter day, the sun beats in through the window, directly warming the carboys, which are distributed evenly throughout the attic. The space is prevented from becoming a broiler during the summer by the panels of special louvres built into the collector roof. From the front yard, they look like a giant glittering shutter, but they have been fixed in position to act as a permanent year-round control feature. The louvres are 4-inch-wide pieces of mirrored glass, spaced and precisely tailored to the roof pitch and the latitude of the building site.

The Solar Staircase takes advantage of the fact that the sun is low in the sky during the winter heating months, and the louvres allow its rays to pass almost unimpeded at midday in January. The efficiency of the window is greatly increased by the interaction of the louvres: sunlight reflected upward from one mirror is not lost but, rather, it is intercepted by the louvre above and reflected into the attic. This effect boosts the transmittance from about 50 percent to an impressive 70 percent.

The roof was built in sections, with the topmost layer of tempered glass consisting of standard patio-door

A solar house that shines even at night, **bottom right,** *Saunders' design avoids the inconvenience of night shutters and thermal draperies, as the airtight house's nighttime heating needs are minimal due to its superior insulation. One fan,* **bottom left,** *directs the airflow through 13 channels, pushing attic heat that enters through the roof's Solar Staircase,* **top right,** *into the rock bin and through to the greenhouse. To cool the house during hot summer weather, a four-foot-long screened concrete culvert,* **top left,** *is uncovered to draw cool nighttime air from the north side of the house into the rock mass.*

glazing, tempered for strength and to resist hail. Wooden frames hold the 4-foot-long strips of mirror in place; Saunders specified fir because of its ability to resist damage by sunlight and temperatures that sometimes reach 150 degrees F.

To prevent heat loss at night, five layers of Mylar transparent sheets are mounted under the louvres, each in a "junior" frame just three-quarters of an inch thick. Temperatures within the attic become stratified — very hot near the peak and much less so near the floor. A modest layer of 3-inch fibreglass insulates the attic from the rooms below, but little heat seems to seep down into the living quarters. Instead, hot air is drawn down to a rock bin under the house through a rectangular sheet-metal duct.

While the attic solar storage can fluctuate greatly in temperature, the massive rock bin under the main floor is the steadying influence. The house has no cellar but sits on a concrete slab over a 2½-foot-deep bin of washed stones varying from 1 to 2 inches in diameter. They constitute a cheap mass for heat storage, approximately 100 tons altogether, with additional capacity in the foundation walls, the slab and the earth beneath the rock bed. Although the rock storage works well, Saunders is using 2-to-4-inch-diameter stones in his updated designs.

Two-inch Styrofoam rigid insulation lines the outside of the foundation, and a 2-foot skirt of the same material slopes down and out from the house to increase the underground insulating effects. The rock bin is separated from the house slab by a vapour barrier and a thin layer of dense fibreglass. The stones themselves vary in depth, and they rest directly on the earth below with no insulation or vapour barrier.

Although closed in during the month of September in 1981, the house did not have the benefit of the completed attic until the end of November. The Saunders-Shrewsbury House thus went into its first winter with a cold heat-storage bin and uncooperative weather: the month of December was very cloudy. Nonetheless, things warmed up relatively quickly, and the house performed with only one dramatic excursion from the 70-degree-temperature level. The first fan installed was unable to meet the demands placed on it, and when it failed, temperatures dropped to below freezing in the narrow south-facing greenhouse that covers the front of the house. A heavy-duty fan was installed, and no further problems have occurred.

PLANT PARADISE

The greenhouse itself does not heat the living quarters directly but is separated from the house proper by a wall of glass. Sunlight flooding into the greenhouse strikes this two-storey-high glass interior wall and passes into the rooms beyond, much tempered, to heat them. The greenhouse has five feet of good loam right down to the subsoil, and the south wall is single-glazed tempered glass that admits nearly 90 percent of the available solar radiation. In winter, the air temperature in the greenhouse can be kept above freezing and the root-zone soil near a comfortable 50 degrees by pulling heat from beneath the house.

"The greenhouse was designed for plants, not for people," says Saunders. "It's single-glazed, so we keep the wind off yet give the plants as much sun as possible. And then we've got the glass wall behind it, which gives enough reflection so that the plants get normal north light. We don't have this horrible reaching-for-the-sun bit. The loam goes down to the subsoil. This means that through a large part of the year, you never have to water the plants; in summer, of course, you do. And in summer, people find the greenhouse too damn hot, but the plants don't mind. I was down in Rhode Island talking to some greenhouse people, and they said, 'Oh, plants can't take temperatures over so-and-so,' but I have living evidence that they really don't mind in the least if they've got enough water."

The greenhouse is heated by direct gain and by warm air from the rock bin below. Enough heat is available to the greenhouse to keep it warm through a week of cold, overcast winter weather. Plants do enormously well in this structure. "Last summer," says Saunders, "there were geraniums in there five feet tall. They were a sight to behold." When I visited the Saunders-Shrewsbury House on a rainy, cold October day, seven-foot-high tomato collossi and summer squash plants with stems like fire hoses dominated the greenhouse.

Several of the house's numerous air streams enter the greenhouse. One flows over the plants — cooling them in summer, warming them in winter. Air entering the greenhouse from the lower level of the rock bin is about 50 degrees and has high relative humidity and a somewhat richer supply of carbon dioxide than is usual, making a very pleasant environment for plants. No gardener can look at owner Robert Bushey's greenhouse without longing for one just like it.

Five 13-foot-high glass windows and three shorter ones make up the glass wall between the house interior and the greenhouse. Direct-gain solar energy through the back glass wall of the greenhouse heats these rooms. The windows themselves are sophisticated — six inches thick and triple-glazed. They open at the top into the attic. A sheet of grey plastic sandwiched between the glass plates absorbs 75 percent of the solar radiation that strikes it. When the sunlight is strong, the sheet warms up and so does the air immediately adjacent to it, and as the air heats, it rises upward in a process called thermosiphoning, enters the attic and is stored there. Some of the radiation is reflected back into the greenhouse, giving the plants their beneficial "north" light. Room temperature in the house remains an unperturbed 70 degrees, whether the greenhouse is 40 degrees or 85 degrees.

Inside the house, the eye is drawn first to the Eden in the greenhouse but then looks beyond, through the two glass walls, to the outdoor world sprawled in unobstructed view. The master bedroom, a few feet lower than ground level, has a gripping view of the tomato plants, but this could well have been exotic ferns, fruit trees, orchids, bonsai or wildflowers and vines.

"Perhaps now is the time to retire from trying to reform the world," says Saunders, who has worked exclusively on solar design for years, with few converts until now.

Above, 300 six-gallon carboys provide 18,000 pounds of heat storage in a form that absorbs the heat of the sun quickly and easily. Hot air from the attic is not blown directly into the house but is fed to the rock bin through a duct, **inset.**

Nearly all solar houses have an expanse of south window, a few peepholes on the east side, very little on the west and solid, unbroken wall on the north. In the Saunders-Shrewsbury House, there are 12 windows — and an abundance of diffuse light — on the other walls, including 6 on the north wall. There is no familiar solar glare, and the occupant has good views in all directions. These windows are another of Saunders' patented inventions, which he calls North Windows. They have an R value of 5 and are triple-glazed, two panes sandwiching a special gold-coated reflective film that transmits most visible light but reflects much of the infrared light to cut down on winter heat loss. All of these windows can be opened to admit fresh breezes.

They are so carefully designed, built and installed that heat loss from them is a fraction of that lost through conventional windows.

The Saunders-Shrewsbury House is superinsulated with fibreglass and Thermax, a rigid foam insulation coated in aluminum foil. The north roof and gables of the attic contain 12 inches of fibreglass and 1 inch of Thermax, for a whopping R45. The house walls are R30, and the foundation walls, except for the internal run between the greenhouse and the living quarters, are insulated with 2-inch Styrofoam. The south outer-foundation wall rises 18 inches above the exterior grade and is covered on the outside with transparent plastic insulation.

In such a superinsulated house, the heat of occupancy — heat that is released by the oven, frying chicken, hot water, refrigerator, lamps and human occupants — becomes appreciable. Old-fashioned houses are swept by a full change of air every hour. In

this house, it would take 16 hours for a full change of air through normal infiltration. The occupants, of course, would be stifling as though they were in a submarine were it not for Saunders' unique airflow systems.

A fan (unheard unless you are standing near it in the attic) is at the heart of the house's air-drive system with its 13 airflows. The ¼-horsepower fan is inside an attic duct that leads to the rock bin far below. This is the main air train, and it sets the others in motion. The fan, which can run at a variable rate according to the attic heat level, pushes hot air down to the rock bin and into three passages near the east and west footings and the house's internal south-foundation wall. This air drifts down through the rock to the lower 50-degree stratum and is eventually channelled upward into the greenhouse. It hangs low near the greenhouse floor if the greenhouse air is hotter (daytime) or rises upward if the greenhouse temperature is chillier (winter nights).

The stale air is pulled out and up by an exhaust duct on the lower south side of the greenhouse, and it eventually emerges outdoors above the roof through a chimney with a turbine cap.

Fresh air flows into the house from either east or west attic gable vents, which are connected by a long duct. Air can enter the duct even when the vent covers are in place. A rectangular duct carries the new air down to the southeast living room on the second floor, which is doorless. From here, the fresh air spreads through the other rooms and/or goes up into the attic through ceiling grilles. The stairwell carries the fresh air down to the lower rooms, but the chilling effect of this current is negligible, even in winter, except on very cold days when people stand immediately under the grille where the air comes into the living room.

There have been condensation problems in the Saunders-Shrewsbury House, not because of design errors but because the vapour barrier was incorrectly installed, a common event in a building industry that has not begun to catch up with the rigorous procedures vital to the new energy-efficient houses. An imperfect seal meant higher relative humidity in the rooms than had been expected and some cold-night condensation on the attic solar-collector glass. A small fan was installed in the west attic gable to draw outside low-humidity air into the east, west and north walls to absorb the lurking moisture there. This decreased the relative humidity in the house and ended the condensation problem.

Says Saunders, "What we're doing in the future is putting a sheet of poly under the rock or under the cool store so we can flood it if we want this humidified action or not flood it if we want lower humidity. I think we should be able, by using an automatic waterer, to control the humidity range from 20 to 50 percent, but this remains to be seen. This is just a gleam in the eye at the moment."

HEAT SANDWICH

This 100 percent solar house has been monitored, measured, recorded and watched. It works. It cost $90,000 to build, virtually the same as a conventional house of the same size in the same area. After finishing the work, the contractor said that he would do it again "for about the same price." Norman Saunders has considered calling the design a Heat Sandwich, inasmuch as the living areas are contained between two separate heat-storage systems whose total mass is 172 tons. "This metaphor is imperfect," says his friend William Shurcliff. "Sandwiches are named for the central part (e.g., the ham) not for the enveloping parts (the bread), and in the Saunders-Shrewsbury House, it is the living regions, not the solar regions, that are sandwiched. I like the name 'trans-sol-attic,' which suggests the attic is of paramount importance and transmits much solar radiation."

In the end, the attic-driven house still defies most solar conventions. Among the many flows of air, none comes directly from the storage into the living areas. The design works, apparently because the house is superinsulated, because it takes in direct solar radiation during the day and because the greenhouse works as a thermal buffer zone at night, preventing the south-facing window walls from chilling the interior space.

It is, in the minds of some, a work of genius. Yet Norman Saunders worries that the significance of this house will be lost because of his own notorious inability to communicate his ideas on paper. "I have often thought," he says, "that if I get time to write my autobiography, I will have to title it *The Autobiography of a Failure*, because there is so much I can't get across to people.

"We can build an energy-efficient house that won't cost more than $100 a year to run, but we're just not doing it. Maybe I should retire again. In '54, I retired as an employee. In '68, I retired as an employer, so now, perhaps, is the time to retire from trying to reform the world. You know, all the things around us are on a bell curve. Almost everything is mediocre, very little is good, and almost nothing is excellent." Leaving the Saunders-Shrewsbury House to return to the world of mediocrity, one is struck by the fact that a slight man with the reputation of an eccentric inventor has done something that can only be called excellent: a house that history may remember as a turning point in the growth of solar architecture. ∎

Annie Proulx lives on a Vermont cidery and is the author of several books on rural arts.

Sources

SUPER-SOLAR HOUSES, SAUNDERS' LOW-COST 100% SOLAR DESIGNS
By W.A. Shurcliff
Brick House Publishing
140 pages
406A — hardcover, $16.75
Available from Harrowsmith Books, Camden East, Ontario K0K 1J0. This is Shurcliff's effort at making Norman Saunders' theories and specific designs understandable; highly recommended to anyone wishing to learn more about this project.

NORMAN B. SAUNDERS
15 Ellis Road
Weston, Massachusetts 02193
Information regarding Saunders' patented inventions, including Solar Staircase, Heat Sandwich, Dynamic Insulation, North Window and others.

Living Lego

Rebuilding the functional elegance of old log buildings

By R.A.J. Phillips

When we first came upon the old log house, it was as if we had found the carcass of a once magnificent beast settling into the floor of the woods. Maple saplings grew thickly against its walls and wove branches through the gaping opening of the window casings. The once handsome doorway was beyond salvation, grass grew profusely up the stairway in what had been the main hallway, and most of the finely turned stair spindles had been spirited away to fuel some vandal's wood stove. The floors were heaved and rotting and, from even the most optimistic point of view, hazardous to negotiate.

Nonetheless, it was obvious that this had once been a house of some architectural merit. A striking pointed dormer was elegantly framed with decorative bargeboard, and the massive squared pine logs were neatly fitted at the corners with dovetail joints. Inside, wood lath and plaster covered the walls and ceilings, a rarity for a farmhouse built in 1867.

But a farmhouse it had been — although the farmer who lived there was probably well-to-do, not an unusual circumstance in this still rich logging area of the Gatineau Hills north of Ottawa. Overlooking the Lièvre River near Buckingham, Quebec, the once proud home had been abandoned for years and was now threatened with the final indignity of demolition to make way for a modern aluminum-sided bungalow. When, in May 1980, my wife, Mary Anne, and I were given an opportunity to pay $800 for the privilege of removing the building a scant four weeks before its destruction, we paused to give the matter some sober re-

flection. Six seconds later, we were committed to the task.

It was not the first time we had leapt into such an agreement. Our 16-acre lot of rock and bush, laid out along a quarter-mile stretch of Quebec's Gatineau River just nine miles from Ottawa's Parliament Buildings, was already home to five other log buildings reclaimed from various parts of the Ottawa Valley and restored to, or beyond, their original elegance. This one, which we now call Buck House (the Royal Family's nickname for Buckingham Palace), was intended, as were all the others, to be the last.

We saw our first building, the one we call simply the Log House, under the gathering storm clouds of a spring evening in 1964. Mary Anne and I were searching for a family centennial project to share with our three young daughters, and the restoration of a log home built in 1832 appealed to all of us. We bought the relic for $200 and, with a road-building crew's bulldozers already nudging its front wall, rushed in with hammers, crowbars, enthusiasm and little else. Carted 30 miles on a collection of trucks ranging from a diesel-powered flatbed to the family pickup, the cedar logs, boards, spacers and bits of framing from doors and windows made an intimidating pile at which we laboured for the rest of that summer to reassemble into the modest house it had been originally.

---

*Visitors to the Phillips' Gatineau bush lot are directed to half a dozen restored log buildings, while Buck House, **right**, awaits the passing of its 117th winter.*

We had intended the Log House to be a museum piece, furnished and equipped as much as possible as it might have been on Confederation Day, July 1, 1867. And yet the standard of simple frontier comfort when Queen Victoria was young was far lower than the most modest requirements of today. Although we admired the pioneer's solid surroundings, we did not want to spend our days as he had — carrying buckets of water through the woods, reading by the flickering light of a homemade candle and breaking ice out of the dishpan on frosty mornings. We were anxious to combine the best of the past (the magic artistry of old wood) with the best of the present (the marvels of a flush toilet). Maintaining that careful balance was a fascinating

"I cannot completely explain my fascination with log buildings," says the author, "except that I love the feel of old wood."

problem for us, the focus of many family discussions and much pencilling on the backs of envelopes.

The guiding principle we established was to introduce any technology that would make for happier living without spoiling the visual mood. That meant concrete foundations below grade, so that in the next century and a half, the sill logs would not rot away again. A tight plywood floor was laid below the broad, knotty boards of old red pine, and in the crawl space below, we installed R20 fibreglass insulation held in place with chicken wire. In the loft, where faded scraps of wallpaper clung to the end walls, we rebuilt with a heavier frame, insulation, vapour barrier and plywood — and then hung wallpaper like the old.

Working during the hot summer weather of the pre-energy-crisis Sixties, we simply nailed pine boards and asphalt shingles to the old cedar-pole rafters of the uninsulated roof. Eighteen years later, when the shingles needed replacing, we rebuilt the roof, adding a vapour barrier and a new frame of 2 x 6s filled with R20 fibreglass batts, then plywood to which cedar shingles were nailed. The thicker roof is a small compromise with authenticity but an undeniable comfort in all seasons. At a demolition yard, we found double-hung casement windows of a style similar to the originals, and now we reinforce the single-pane units with standard storm windows during the cold weather.

We have encountered some pretty slick new formulas for chinking between the logs, but the fact is that ordinary mortar is simple, and even without the traditional horsehair (which is in short supply around our place), it lasts with an acceptable level of maintenance. The chinking on the Log House, which was done from both sides and entailed sandwiching scraps of Styrofoam in the middle, lasted for 15 years before it was necessary to pry out some of the loose pieces and to patch with fresh material. Inside, the walls remain unpanelled, their comforting 8-inch thickness offering a meagre insulation value of R10. The Log House was, and is, primarily a summer home, first for ourselves and now for friends.

For the discreet repose of culinary anachronisms, we built a long waist-high pine kitchen cupboard and installed an antique hand pump connected to a rain barrel outside. But lift a panel beside the pump and its crockery washbowl, and a stainless steel sink with hot- and cold-water taps is revealed; or slip off another panel and open two doors to cook on a modern electric range. Behind another door is a small refrigerator. But just as easily, the 20th century can be made to disappear, except for the primitive hand-crank wall telephone, a modern dial hidden behind its hinged front.

For safety as well as comfort, we chose electricity for supplementary heating and lighting. The electrified old lamps and lanterns can be set aside for an evening in the past with oil and candle wax. Inside, the wiring runs out of sight along the undersides of logs, and wall sockets are tucked in dim corners; outside, service cables are laid underground.

Then there was the plumbing. Many an envelope was covered with designs for adding a utility room, but all were scrapped — the integrity of the lonely little log building would have been damaged beyond repair. The solution was a washhouse in the woods, conveniently close at hand but in the thick bush and bulging bare rock of our Gatineau hillside, primly out of sight. Some of our purist friends are sad to see that it contains not only a flush toilet, sink and shower but a washer, dryer and freezer as well. If you recognize the invention of the wheel, where do you stop?

This, then, was our philosophy of compromise. The modern niceties were included but, like table legs in a Victorian parlour, hidden to protect the tender sensi-

bilities of polite company. Despite our inexperience, we felt that this first effort was a startling success, and it led us to rescue a modest one-room log shanty of the sort built at the edge of still unbroken land, when time and resources allowed for only the simplest shelter to be built before the dread of winter. Today, it is an isolated cliff-top guest house. Meanwhile, our struggle to furnish both of these buildings with authentic furniture and equipment resulted in a surplus of attic and farm-shed treasures for which we acquired a small log barn of about the same vintage as the Shanty.

BARN TO HOME

Then came the Grange, the biggest challenge of our lives — a project that stretched our physical abilities, finances and faith to the limit. Actually four separate structures, each built in 1819 — the year of Queen Victoria's birth — they were combined into one enormous, sprawling T-shaped barn with nearly 4,000 square feet of floor space. It took us the entire summer of 1973 just to dismantle it on its site near Carleton Place, Ontario, and transport the 700-odd pieces of nondescript lumber, ranging from 40-foot oak logs to small but precious spacers for doors and windows. The 35-mile trip from the fertile valley farmstead to our knobby Gatineau bush lot was made with a variety of rented and borrowed trucks. By fall, we faced a massive jumble of what seemed to be nothing more than low-grade pulpwood.

One wing of the original T, the old pig shed, now stands separate from the rest, and since finishing it in 1974, we have rented it to friends who call it the Piggery with affection. The remaining L-shape is our home. One room alone, which we call the Great Hall, is about 1,000 square feet, with the exposed ridge board some 30 feet above the floor. In the fall of 1977, five summers of hard work after first approaching the dilapidated barn with crowbars in hand, and after my early retirement from a career as a public servant, we took up permanent residence in the Grange.

By now, the balance we sought to achieve in the Log House had been set aside. Compromise turned to iconoclasm as we chose remodelling in favour of restoration. Of course, complete restoration would have required the rebuilding of cow stanchions, horse stalls and pigpens — hardly a model floor plan for our purposes. In this spirit, then, modern conveniences were not concealed in the Piggery but were mixed with venerable log walls, beams and antique furniture. In the Grange, we carried the process even further, with an unembarrassed array of modern gadgetry from bathrooms and wall-to-wall carpeting to central heating. The inside faces of exterior log walls were hidden behind studs, insulation, vapour barriers and panelling, for otherwise, the Grange would not have survived — who could afford to heat that vast and rambling barn without insulation packed into every wall and ceiling? Yet the Grange is like no other building. Even inside, there are generous reminders of its past — pine beams, exposed interior log walls, upstairs windows resting on the floor where hay was once forked out, the smell of

R.A.J. Phillips

R.A.J. Phillips

wood, the silences of solidity. We are happier and more comfortable here than those who tended our equine and bovine predecessors could have dreamed possible.

As it now stands, the Grange is no more or less energy efficient than the average suburban bungalow, and in the winter, we restrict ourselves to one wing and maintain the other just above the freezing mark. Our home is appointed with 19th-century furniture, but we enjoy the echoes of history at a cost somewhat less per square foot than it would have cost us to build in suburbia.

If the Grange was our biggest challenge, then Buck House was the greatest test of our accumulated knowledge and expertise. Unlike our other efforts, the elegant Buck House had been covered on the outside with siding, but damage to the front eave had allowed rain and snow to seep between the siding and the logs. The rot at the top of the front wall was far advanced and, from the outset, was a nagging worry. Of course, we had handled our share of decay before — sill logs always had to be written off, and we habitually raised the foundation wall to compensate for the missing bottom course of logs. Occasionally, upper logs were a hollow shell that we packed with concrete, leaving no one the wiser. But a quarter of a wall?

Still, we were by now, if not skilled craftsmen, at least practised labourers. First, we swept in with camera, spray paint and notebook. Every log got a spray-painted designation: a different colour for each wall and for beams, a letter to further distinguish each wall (N, S, E, W, according to future orientation of the building), number one on the sill log up to number nine at the top and an additional letter for each piece of log interrupted by a door or window, for example, W3c. We made detailed notes on forms of construction, the nature of joints, distinguishing marks and damage points. You think that you will remember everything, but the only safe working assumption is that all associated with the project will be struck with collective amnesia and that all markings will be obliterated in transit. The markings must be big and garish enough to withstand the bump and grind of transportation, as well as the ravages of weather if they are to be stored for any length of time. We never erase them — we mute them with steel wool but leave traces, for they are now part of the building's evocative history.

Four of us — myself, Piggery tenant John Jackson, Pierre Morrissette (from whom we bought the building) and a student helper — embarked on a hard week of demolition. The work is heavy, dirty, sometimes risky and also — except for the fact that one is buoyed by private dreams — tedious. It was the heat of June, a time for shorts and running shoes, but even in the choking dust of crumbling plaster walls and ceilings, we always wore hard hats, tough clothing, steel-capped boots and heavy leather gloves.

Brigid Phillips

R.A.J. Phillips

Buck House was rescued, in its ruinous state, from the encroaching bush, **upper left.** *After laboriously removing the lath and plaster from walls and ceilings,* **lower left,** *each log was meticulously coded and recorded,* **lower right,** *to ease the confusion, if not the hard work, of reconstruction,* **upper right.**

Barry Dursley, The Review, Imperial Oil Limited

The siding — unsalvageable — was easily pried off and, less easily, carried through the thick bush to an out-of-the-way pile. To the same spot went all the other junk, from rough shelving and broken furniture to the remains of a decaying back shed. Much later, the rotten floorboards were added to the pile.

Then came the roof. Viewed in a positive light, the removal of layers of old shingles creates respect for the staying power of the noble cedar — not much comfort when sliding down the roof with 100 rusted nails tearing into one's trousers and beyond.

We do not number the boards and framing lumber from interior walls unless their cut is unique, but we save as many as we can. If exploitable child labour is available, the neatest procedure is to remove nails before stacking the wood for transportation, but we never have enough time to do it all. The stairway came out in one piece, grass and all, and was carried home in our complaining pickup truck.

Everything came down except the walls and beams. The rafters were carefully removed by hand to avoid damage where they were mortised and pegged into the plate log. All salvageable parts, even broken window frames — which could never be restored but might be useful for measuring spaces — were kept in separate piles in the fond hope that they would stay that way until reaching their destination. Scraps of 2 x 4s were nailed along both sides of badly decayed logs for stability and protection, and as far as time permitted, which because of the tight schedule was not very far, we coated logs with pentachlorophenol, a colourless preservative, before they were moved — a good practice, even when the logs are to be reassembled promptly. Ours were not. That summer, another project forced us to postpone the building of Buck House for almost a year.

At 6 a.m. on the last Saturday of our allotted time, two huge trucks, their operators off duty from a regular five-day week of hauling logs, followed us to the Buckingham demolition site. One of the trucks was fitted with an invaluable hydraulic picker, which gently lifted each beam and wall log from the skeletal structure and placed it onto one of the two truck beds. By midmorning, the site was clear of all that was to be saved, and by noon, there was a large, melancholic new pile below the hilltop site we had chosen for the reconstruction of Buck House.

There it remained for 11 months. Early the following spring, while frost still anchored the thin turf and tangled tree roots to the bedrock, we began to clear the site with axe, pick and shovel and hand winch. As usual, our choice of siting (the highest point of land we own) had been dictated by future aesthetics, rather than by practical building considerations. The hilltop was only attainable by a construction road on one side and a narrow, hazardous path on the other, and the site itself was neither even nor flat. A week and $5,000 later, it was drilled and blasted into shape — sort of. We who call the Gatineau home claim not only the old-

est hills in the world but also the hardest rock. Unless the basement was to be inhabited by agile midgets, many ragged protrusions would have to be eliminated by the time-consuming application of chisel and sledgehammer. For us, it seems romantic (and inexpensive) to use the tools of Roman road makers or wilderness canal builders, but no pioneer would have chosen a site that needed that much preparation.

It was time to review the backs of those envelopes. Our umpteenth version called for Buck House to be reassembled exactly as it was (a 25' x 32' rectangle), but on concrete foundations set on bedrock. Nearly half the basement would be available for low-ceilinged storage directly on the Precambrian granite, and the rest would house utilities, laundry, shower room, sauna and maintenance area. Since it was not quite enough for the family of four (my daughter Margaret, her husband, David, and their two daughters) who would live there, we therefore planned a two-storey annex at the back, where the hillside slopes toward the river. On the basement level, well above grade, would be a guest bedroom and a large playroom; above them would be an open deck and equally large sunroom. Like our other new construction, it would be clad, in board-and-batten style, with stained, unplaned white pine, an ideal material to blend with the old without feigning imitation. The stain is our own simple half-and-half mixture of creosote and pentachlorophenol preservatives — the latter element gives a lighter, more pleasant colour than the creosote alone and reduces the gumminess of the finish.

Laying foundations at a Phillips' construction site starts with a ritual that keeps the whole neighbourhood in high spirits — we vacuum the great Canadian Shield. Using knives, teaspoons, trowels, whisks and a powerful shop vac, we clean every groove and cranny until it shines. Only then do we let the cement come in. This is done in the hope of having a perfect bond that will eliminate seepage. It never works entirely, but if you live on a rock, it is worth the effort.

After the poured concrete footing and cement-block foundation were in place, we laid down a conventional floor of 2 x 10 joists on 16-inch centres topped with plywood sheeting. Then came the dreaded search for the logs with the lowest numbers hidden somewhere in that jumbled pile. The east-facing front wall and the north end were accessible by truck, so those logs were balanced in the back of our three-quarter-ton truck and backed up the hill. Three workers with strong backs guided the free end, while the one with the quickest mind sat on the end in the truck. With no room to manoeuvre around the foundation on our small cliff top, four of us used two pairs of log lifters — one an antique, the other made by a local blacksmith using the first as a pattern — to carry the 400-to-500-pound logs up the awkward path for the other two sides.

Of course, when all goes well, it is like Lego or Tinkertoy. As the walls went higher, we fitted jury-rigged scaffolding and log cranes with pulleys and heavy ropes, for there was no ground space to make the traditional ramps that were used by the pioneers to roll their upper logs into place.

*Bought for $200 in 1964 to be a family centennial project, the Log House, **left**, was restored as a museum piece, but with carefully hidden modern niceties.*

Barry Dursley, The Review, Imperial Oil Limited

Barry Dursley, The Review, Imperial Oil Limited

The main problem was the rotted front wall. Despite more than usual care in marking, identifying the punky scraps was difficult. Since we would be installing an interior stud wall to recreate the original plaster walls, we simply reversed procedures. Once the first layer of logs was in place, we built the interior framing: 2 x 6s replaced the 2 x 3s on the long front and back walls, and 2 x 4s sufficed for the ends. The weight and thrust of the roof could then be taken equally on the inside frame and on the logs, except on the front wall, where the well-braced frame took the whole load. The stud wall also served as a temporary support for the walls during construction, and then, when the walls were complete, the logs, particularly those in front, were permanently wired or bolted to the frame.

That sounds straightforward, and, in fact, it worked superbly, but to pass so quickly over the agony of fitting those injured pieces — with occasional collapses — is to omit some of the most colourful artistry, as well as language, in the whole project. A few places on the front wall had to be patched with pieces salvaged from a opening cut in the south-end wall to install a modern heat-circulating fireplace. Their age was right, and dim-sighted visitors approaching on a misty evening cannot see the difference.

Lest it seem that the logs are simply serving, like rolls of 10-inch-thick insulbrick, as a decorative façade for a rather conventional house, let me point out that our primary purpose was to save a log home. We are well aware that gluing a bunch of logs to another structure would not make it a log building (for one thing, it would probably be full of right angles, and we log-house restorers have nothing to do with those), but if the only alternative to writing off both the building and the pleasure it gives us is to use a special technique for 10 percent of the walls, there is no doubt as to our choice. In short, we are not striving for uncompromising perfection in recreating the past but for a sound decision on how best to let the past serve the future. That is the art of our craft.

Along the way, we keep on making mistakes, no matter how much experience has been accumulated. We always try to supplement the original pole rafters, for without the Canada Mortgage and Housing Corporation's fatherly eye, the pioneers underbuilt their roof supports (they also underbuilt their floor supports but wonderfully overbuilt their walls). In Buck House, some rafter ends were too decayed to carry weight safely, although we persisted in using them, bolstered with nailed-on supports, to reproduce the angles and sags of the original. Matching old and new while carefully ensuring their correct positioning across the old walls and new inner frame was a horrendous task, and since they will never be seen, I am now convinced that

The Grange, built in 1819 as an enormous T-shaped barn, was transported 35 miles and reconstructed to a degree of comfort undreamed of by its original owners. Exposed beams and logs lend an atmosphere of solidity, while authentic Victorian furniture and double-pane windows where livestock once entered fill the Great Hall with light and elegance. No less energy efficient than the average bungalow, the Grange renovation cost somewhat less per square foot than a building in suburbia.

we should have scrapped all the poles and built a conventional roof frame.

The original house plan featured a simple but finely crafted stairway leading upstairs from a small vestibule just inside the front door. On one side of it was a large living room running the full width of the house; on the other, the dining area and traditional large kitchen. Aside from turning the staircase 180 degrees to make it more accessible from the back annex, we retained that arrangement. Upstairs, however, four equal-sized bedrooms were reorganized into a large master bedroom, two smaller bedrooms and a bathroom.

Since the original builders seemed to have lost their yardstick the day they installed the beams supporting the second floor, we changed their spacing to make them even, and happily, this allowed us to place two of them over the new stud walls flanking the staircase. Although framing the interior partitions was straightforward, placing the stairs was a major challenge. Mathematics beyond the ken of computers was needed to fit the upper set, with the sod now removed, into its reversed configuration. With the lower set, the barrier was the granite of the Canadian Shield, which, as always, yielded reluctantly.

The walls of the Annex, our 16-foot-wide addition running the 32-foot length of the main building, are modern and energy efficient. From the outside in, there is 1-inch board-and-batten, ½-inch aspenite sheeting, 2 x 6 studs with fibreglass batts and 6-mil vapour barrier, then 2 x 3 studs with more insulation covered with tongue-and-groove white pine. This system allows wiring and plumbing to hide behind the panelling without compromising the vapour barrier, and the R28 insulation in the walls and ceiling is appreciated both by those who sit and those who carry the firewood.

After thoroughly coating the logs with pentachlorophenol, we stuffed the cracks between them with Styrofoam and then, because the interior log faces would be covered with insulated stud walls, carefully chinked the walls from the outside only. One of the great advantages of building on solid rock is a lack of movement of house and foundation — a bonus that has helped keep our chinking in place and has prevented it from cracking.

The drywall, fireplace and chimney brickwork, wiring and plumbing were left to more skilled hands, but with student help, I installed double-hung double-glazed reproductions of the original windows and a fine Queen Anne door from the early 19th century found in an architectural warehouse.

Interior doors were made from a time-proven pattern used in our other buildings. Between layers of 1-inch pine planks, vertical on one side and diagonal on the other, is a plywood core that adds strength and takes the worry out of knotholes; the whole is framed in more 1-inch pine. They are handsomely massive and quite sound absorbent — also cheap, if you place on my labour the value most people think it deserves. On outer doors a 1-inch layer of Styrofoam is added to the sandwich and, in some cases, a factory-sealed double-pane window. These outer doors are great, except for the recurring problem of adapting hardware to the 3-inch thickness. On inner doors, we use latches instead of knobs — they are more tolerant of seasonal expansion and contraction.

The hardwood floors are wide-cut local maple milled to tongue-and-groove — far more pleasing to us than the narrow boards of suburbia. Our home-made kitchen cupboards of tongue-and-groove pine are more appropriate than factory plastic and just as convenient. We ran pine through a router for baseboards at a fraction of lumber-store cost, and to restore the vandalized stairway railing, we matched parts from the remains of six other demolished structures.

Anyone who restores log buildings with exacting blueprints has my deepest admiration. My own method involves lighting a pipe, sitting lost in divine meditation and finally exclaiming: "Right there!" That is how the basement sauna came to be built around bedrock, where, on rainy days, a natural stream trickles down its centre. Our pièce de résistance is the tiled basement shower room, with two shower heads sprouting from a wall of solid granite.

What has emerged from our efforts is not your average house. As well as the original large living room, dining room and kitchen, there are four bedrooms, sunroom, playroom, laundry, storage, work area, sauna and three bathrooms where none existed before. It is heated by an airtight wood stove on each floor, supplemented by electric heat, and we like to think that the fireplace, with heat chamber and fans, at least holds its own. Still, it is essentially a log house given its character by old pine beams, 16-inch-deep window wells and glimpses of log wall.

Why do we go to all that trouble just to sit in a chair in an old log house, when instead, we could afford, say, a holiday in Grenada? A log house is wonderfully unconventional shelter, and, financially, it is a sound investment. At $80,000 for materials and paid labour, Buck House cost somewhat more than a conventional house, but my realtor says it is worth half again what we put into it.

In the end, however, I cannot completely explain my fascination with log buildings. You would have to walk with me through the woods at dusk, past ghostly shapes with lights now glowing in the windows. You have to climb the hill and come into Buck House to stare past the river through the trees to Ottawa's flickering skyline where people dwell in their modern homes. We live in log houses.

Here, one can sit and stare at the never tiring patterns of old logs hewed and sawn and chiselled by forgotten people who left indelible marks. There are places to smell the pine and cedar, to touch old wood, to hear the elusive echoes of sounds long gone, to sense our roots, to know that this is not simply a dwelling but a small masterpiece created by nature and man — a treasure worth saving for our common history. ■

R.A.J. Phillips is a writer who lives in the Gatineau Hills. He is the founding executive director of Heritage Canada.

Barry Dursley, The Review, Imperial Oil Limited

Alternative Light Styles

Illumination beyond the power lines: enlightenment in the world of gas and kerosene lamps

By Tim Matson

I cut my electric habit with a vengeance: cold turkey when I was lucky, but mostly pork and beans warmed over a campfire or candle. By day, I built my cabin in the light of the summer sun, working with a chain saw, bucksaw and all the hand tools I could pack into my carpenter's harness. Twilight stretched from five to nine, and I made the most of it. At dusk, I would kindle a fire near my tent, laid in a stone nook that looked toward the flap. With the blaze set downwind, orange flames yielded enough illumination for me to scratch out a few letters and sharpen my McCulloch before I fell asleep and the fire died. Sometimes hard rain sizzled the fire, and I burrowed into the tent. The mix of canvas, chain saw and candle scared me, but I forgave myself a single, burning taper cradled in a candle pot that shielded the flame, caught melting wax and released little spokes of light through holes in the bowl.

Consider the alternative, my fuzzy mind mused, struggling logically against the onrushing currents of sleep: In the main, Vermont electricity is produced in the little town of Vernon, on the Connecticut River, by nuclear fission. There the rich river water is tapped to appease a searing hot reactor, while around the state, the dams that once produced 68 percent of our power now generate no more than pretty postcard views. Pictures of the Yankee reactor at Vernon, in contrast, illustrate newspaper accounts of radioactive leakage in the river, breeding problems on local dairy farms and rising rates of thyroid cancer and stress-related maladies.

Bedded down in my sleeping bag, I watched the flashing rays of firelight gyrate on the canvas and reflected on Plato's Cave — an image he used to compare reality and illusion — not knowing how ironic the reverie would prove, nor dreaming what rude substances would eventually intrude upon my drowsy assumptions.

By Hallowe'en I had the cabin sheathed in rough softwood, so I struck the tent and moved indoors. In one rough opening framed through the northwest wall, I set three 12-pane windows, yielding 30 square feet of skylight. I set a table at a right angle to the windows, flush with the sill, to work with a flow of milk-white light over my shoulder. For a brighter night life, after five months of campfires and candles, I bought a trio of cheap 19th-century kerosene lamps, orphans of the electric storm Ben Franklin had tapped. The first and simplest was a glass bowl and chimney lamp. A green glass shade tinted the second, spilling chlorophyll tones that I grew to like more and more as winter drifted along. The third lamp overshadowed the others, tall and elegant with a silver-plated fuel pot. Embossed in elegant figures at the lip of the pedestal was the maker's proud mark: Miller's Vestal.

With only its glass chimney liable to shatter, the Vestal made a safer light than the all-glass lamps. Set high in the lofty cabin, it flashed like the beacon in a backwoods lighthouse. At wick-trimming time, however, it made up for its extra light in extra maintenance. It was difficult to level off an even-burning wick, and

---

The forerunner of modern propane lighting systems, this Victorian gas lamp glows elegantly from a vanished age.

the fabric jammed in its tight casing during regular upward adjustments. One night, I discovered that the old wick would rise no more.

With a neighbourly flair, Mike St. John offered me a cannibalized Aladdin lamp from his stash of spare parts for outmoded models. He fashioned a rumpled lantern topped with a beige paper shade. I added a new chimney and some kerosene, and with one match stroke brought up the light on the brightest act of my illuminating career. The glow of the Aladdin's luminous mantle seemed magical indeed. Wick-burning candles and kerosene lamps illuminate by flame; the Aladdin glows. Like a tiny butterfly net set over a burning circular wick, the mantle caught the fire and released a brilliant ray: a 100-watt firefly.

For a couple of years, the Aladdin was my main beam, with the two vintage burners providing fill. I ritualized my lighting chores. Roughly every other day, I topped up the lamp bowls with kerosene. Sundays were for cleaning chimneys and trimming down the wicks to a sharp fresh edge. The Aladdin enjoyed special preening. The chimney had to be carefully twisted loose, lifted off and set aside. Not only was the glass fragile, but suspended in its throat hung the brittle mantle, a web of chemical ash easy to break and dear to replace. The Aladdin's circular wick, like the Vestal's, needed tending. Given the right twist, a black plastic scraper provided by the lamp maker turned out a fine edge. I learned that the Aladdin demanded a chary ignition ceremony. Carefully, I would uncouple the chimney mantle from the pedestal, light the wick and replace the unit. As the mantle began to glow, I kept an eye on the lamp. The Aladdin liked a leisurely warmup. Otherwise, overheated, my lighthouse would erupt like a volcano, spewing smoke and fire from the chimney and laying a crust of carbon over the mantle.

Gradually, I developed a sixth sense about my Aladdin. Easy as it was to move the light around without trailing an electric cord and searching dusty baseboards for an outlet, I knew I had to set the lamp down as carefully as I would cradle a baby. Unlike electric light, the flaming Aladdin requires overhead clearance of about three feet to keep the rig from overheating, not to mention torching the house. Lamp locations must be elbow-and-critter proof, besides. A wall bracket makes the safest lamp site, I found, as well as an efficient light shed. My knowledge was not acquired overnight. The lightkeeper's craft is won with a sacrifice of broken chimneys, cracked mantles and kerosene stains.

Reflecting one day on the development of my backwoods illuminating system, I saw that I had passed through a condensed evolution of artificial lighting, going from campfires to candles to kerosene lamps and halting about halfway through the 19th century. This occurred to me while lugging a five-gallon jug of kerosene up the hill to the cabin through snowdrifts up to my hips.

It might be time to move into the 20th century, I thought. Not to the point of electricity. Visions of my own windmill spinning a golden thread on the westward hillside had long ago faded in view of the costs. But partway into the *nouveau siècle*, say the twilight

Ernie Sparks

Propane fuelled lamp of fairly recent vintage lights a cottage residence located in an area not served by electrical power. Substantial amounts of heat are released during the operation of these lamps.

of the gaslight era around 1910, was a natural step.

I felt at home in places where I had seen gaslight burning, remote places with lamps like ghosts of a vanished age. Three thousand years of human history have been illuminated with the burning bloods of earth: tallow, whale oil and beeswax; bayberry, olive and coconut oil; coal oil, natural and distilled gas. Like torches passed through history, spirit lamps connect us with our origins, when we first dared to kindle our own suns and diverge from the path of animals content with sky light.

I remember the spring morning Dad made his first assault on the hill, his rusty red pickup spitting rubber and mud. Dad drove for Perry's Gas and didn't mind getting stuck. "After all, that's normal where people want gaslight," he said. He laughed and a fan of wrinkles spread out. "Yessir, more and more want gas today." We slid around under the truck linking up a pair of chains, and he made the hill. Then we dollied a couple of hundred-pound tanks around the back of the cabin and set them on a plank against the wall. Dad coupled the tanks with a regulator and covered them with a steel cowling. They looked like giant diver's tanks. "When that signal goes red, you know you're on reserve," he said, pointing to an offset glass gauge. He unloaded a coil of ⅜" copper pipe, I fetched a brace and bit, and we crawled under the cabin to lay the veins to feed two gaslights.

We tunnelled through the crawl space unrolling a coil of flexible pipe long enough to reach the lampsite furthest from the tanks, tacking it to the subfloor joists and feeding the end up through a fresh hole in the floor. Beneath the other post, Dad spliced a T-joint into the copper pipe and coupled on a length to poke into the kitchen. Throughout, we softened twists and turns to smooth the fuel flow. Inside, we mounted the two Humphrey Opalites. Then very, very tenderly, Dad slipped preformed mantles onto their ceramic hangers. Pinching together a spring in the pendant, I opened up a noose to hang the glass shade that completed the lamp.

"Looks like one of them flying saucers, don't you think?" Dad said.

I laughed. "I'll tell you when it takes off."

The Opalite suggests a traditional gaslight with one remarkable twist: It's upside down. Thus, since the liquid propane gas (LPG) travels to the mantle under pressure, upon ignition, the flame leaps *down*. This inverted burn is a positive turn in combustible light design. Gaslight shadows darken the rafters, not the middle of the table. And because the delicate mantle hangs down, it lives longer than standing Aladdin mantles, which collapse regularly despite support stays. "Light comparable at minimum to a 50-watt bulb," reads the Humphrey guarantee.

Dad struck a match and touched off each mantle's chemical glazing — dipped on to sturdy the frail netting during shipping and then burned off to reveal an ash "wick." Orange fire spread slowly over the conical webs, and out of the silty smoke emerged the metamorphosed mantles. Now the Opalites were primed and ready. Dad packed his tools into the back of his pickup, wished me luck and jounced down the hill.

I don't recall the sunset, but I know I waited until the sky turned dead black before I lit the first lamp. I struck a match and, sliding it under the mantle, pushed and twisted the black-tipped knob from *off* to *on*. I heard the gas breeze through the glass shade, and then, with a sound like a cork popping from a champagne bottle, there was light. A strong subaqueous tint bathed the cabin, like the yellow-green beams seen under water in a pond on a bright summer day. The spruce and hemlock cabin boards glowed warmly. The pale balsam lamppost took on a soft patina around the lamp, reflecting the golden mantle.

I carried the piano stool to the kitchen counter, opened a beer and sat basking in the bright new wavelengths. Close to the lamp, I heard the soughing of the flame, soft as the ocean inside a seashell. The rock-maple butcher block glowed, and the spritzy brew threw a froth that sparkled. And for the first time, no oily Aladdin squatted on the table. I was delighted to see how much more illumination fell on the cabin floor, where usually firewood or a stray boot waited in shadows to trip me up. Yes, the kitchen was glowing terrifically and, indeed, so was I.

As out in the big world, backwoods life intensified under brighter artificial lights. At last, I could read the fine print, if not between the lines. I wrote more letters at night. I found I could contemplate stereoscopic photographs through viewing goggles close to the light, with antique sepia tones cast on the 3-D images. Colour transparencies screened through a magnifier raised to the light glowed vividly. On the lamppost below each light, I opened a gallery to pin graphics. I even designed a book of photographs during long winter nights under the flaming lamps.

It wasn't until last winter that trouble flared — not the ultimate irony, but a hint of what was to come.

On the main deck, first one light and then the other began to leak. I smelled gas. Actually, LPG is odourless; what I picked up was the strong scent blended in the gas to betray leakage. It smells like a dead mouse wrapped in stale cabbage. For a while I let it pass. The supply tank was low, the warning perfume had settled to the bottom. Even the slightest seepage would seem magnified. Folks who burn gas learn to recognize the fragrance of a short tank.

I expected the odour to dissipate when the regulator kicked in the reserve tank. It didn't. Working at my desk during the day, I caught a spell of headaches, uncommon for me. I tried to sniff out the leaks, but it was impossible to determine whether the gas was venting from the coupling at the base of the pendant or within the lights. I spread a wet seal of liquid dishsoap around the couplings and looked for the telltale bubbles. Nothing. I removed the pendant from each lamp, tightened the connections and reassembled the units. Once again, the scent trailed out. I felt furious and sad. I hadn't anticipated poisoning myself in the search for a brighter vision.

I summoned Dad. He couldn't pinpoint the leaks either. In fact, he wondered if there were any leaks. "Must be my nose is out of joint, but I don't smell nothin'." I thought of *Gaslight*, the film where Ingrid Bergman slowly goes mad watching her gas lamps flicker and fade, while her husband assures her that nothing is amiss. Behind her back, the evil dude fiddles with the gas valves and schemes to have her committed and run off with the jewels. I wondered if Dad thought I was nuts. He sure seemed peeved as he tightened up the couplings to the suspect lamps. I was irked too, anticipating the bill for his 50-mile round trip from Bradford.

For a couple of days, I tried to pretend everything was fine. Then a neighbour dropped by. "I smell gas," was her greeting. Saved! I rushed out back and closed down both valves. "Leak now, stinker," I muttered. The reeking ceased. I began a new routine. Each evening, I paid two visits to the tanks, once to open up the supply tank for the evening's lights and once again at bedtime to shut it off. During burning, it seems, pressure on the flaws drops, and gas speeds straight to the flame. No more dead mouse. By controlling the supply at the source, I cut my worries about leakage and my dependence on Dad for maintenance.

I should have been pleased and left well enough alone. But the leaks piqued my curiosity about the safety of gaslights in general. Doubts from the Age of Paranoia.

Not that I'm looking for riskless existence and immortality. I quite enjoy a bit of danger. For years, I bailed out of small Cessnas and flew strapped to boat-drawn kites for kicks. I even lived in New York City, and that was more frightening than skydiving. Now, as a logger, I understand that I fill a high-risk notch in the hierarchy of human occupations.

These hazards are clear-cut. It's the chemical invasion of privacy I abhor, the invisible perils in high-tech air, water and food. Rather than quickening the spirit, fear of these imperceptible venoms renders us spineless and cynical. We live dangerously without doing a thing.

Consider the warning enclosed with each Humphrey Opalite: "Use in well-ventilated areas only. This product must be used with propane LP gas only. Such fuel has inherently dangerous properties. It is volatile, poisonous, flammable, explosive and produces carbon monoxide when burning. Such conditions present hazards to property and persons, including injury and death. Do not operate except in accordance with instructions and only after carefully reading the limited warranty enclosed. Gas leaks may develop in tubing, fittings, valves or other parts whether or not the light is on or off. Qualified LP gas personnel only should check the unit periodically for gas leaks with a leak detector. Never attempt this yourself."

I discovered this crimson-lettered tag tucked into the box containing my third Opalite. It promised a lot of jeopardy for merely sitting around reading a book. I remember scanning the warning, folding it up neatly and stuffing it down deep in a remote drawer. I refused to think about the questions this caveat posed.

When the system began to leak, I decided it was time to confront the troubling possibilities raised by the note. What is a "well-ventilated" area? Just how "dangerous" is LPG? And what about the light itself? Actually I wasn't terribly worried about the cabin growing too stuffy. Having followed the American Afterthought building plan, I had cooked up a draught-style home with a laughably lavish air-exchange rate. (Laughable, that is, until reports began circulating that superinsulated homes proved more polluted than city skies.)

Besides, hadn't LPG stoves and heaters burned long enough by now to constitute an endorsement of gas safety? Why the warning? Were those rumours that mantles might be toxic true?

Toxic in what way?

"We're trying to steer away from camper caps and ice shanties," Herb Rosenhagen, president of Humphrey Products, told me. "We do a large business with travel trailers, and we want to avoid asphyxiation in small airtight places. The light uses less fuel than a stove pilot light, but anytime you're burning anything, you have to have oxygen."

"In other words, the gaslights present no more of an asphyxiation threat than other gas appliances?" I asked.

"Right."

"Then what about the rumours I've heard that mantles may be toxic?"

Rosenhagen explained that several years ago a newspaper story appeared, warning of the dangers of mantle burn-off. "There may have been a problem, but not with our mantles," he explained.

A couple of weeks after our conversation, he sent me a letter detailing the mantle scare. It seems that a college student in California wrote his master's thesis on mantles and stated that the burn-off was harmful.

His report was picked up by a newspaper and created some alarm. Rosenhagen decided to get a full analysis of the Humphrey mantles, which are manufactured by the Falk Company in England. The report was prepared by Wilmar Associates of Houston, Texas, and dated December 12, 1973.

The gist of the study is that beryllium was the constituent in question: "When incinerated, there is no question that beryllium could be toxic. However, tests have been run on old mantles that did contain some beryllium in the hardening solution, and it was found that its content in the burned mantles was less than 50 ppm. Under no circumstances could the same concentration be toxic.

"Falk's mantles do not have beryllium. Basically a mantle is made with thorium and cerium hydroxide impregnated in a viscose rayon fabric, but on soft mantles, a hardening solution containing aluminum and magnesium is applied to the top of the mantle, and the area of this application is indicated by the dyed section of the mantle. A spectrograph analysis of the ash on a burned mantle shows about 99.26 percent thorium oxide. The balance of material in the mantle is listed as follows: cerium, 1,000 ppm; aluminum, 3,000 ppm; magnesium, 3,000 ppm; sodium, 50 ppm; calcium, 200 ppm; titanium, 10 ppm; iron, 20 ppm; copper, 7 ppm; zinc, 5 ppm; silicon, 50 ppm; lead, 10 ppm; sulphur, 70 ppm; traces of zirconium, yttrium, gallium and boron. You can see from the above that there is absolutely nothing toxic in the burned or unburned mantles."

Finishing the report, I glanced up at the mantle. That's what it came down to: Welsbach's brilliant notion to cap a Bunsen burner with a cotton fabric saturated in a chemical solution from which all organic matter could be burned off, leaving an incandescent metal ash. Others had soaked mantles in heat-resistant beryllium, but the stuff proved toxic. Welsbach had used thorium, and thorium it was still.

Ninety-nine percent *radioactive* thorium.

Oh yes. Oh ironic radioactive yes. The shadows indeed dance strangely on the walls of the philosopher's cave.

Let me tell you about thorium. In 1828, a fellow named Berzelius gave the name to the oxide he extracted from the rare mineral "organite" in Lovon, Norway. It is named after Thor, the Norse god of thunder. Potent! When heated, thorium ignites easily, burning with a bright white flame. It refuses to melt below 1,750 degrees C. Thorium is used in tungsten filaments for light bulbs and electronic tubes, but for the past 100 years, it has been used chiefly as an oxide in gaslight mantles. It is strongly radioactive. These days, thorium's natural radioactivity and its status as one of the most stable radioactive isotopes make it a

Strictly functional in design, the standard Humphrey Opalite gas fixture currently retails for approximately $40, with necessary installation hardware adding roughly $35 more to the price.

candidate for use in radiotherapy and conversion into fissionable fuel uranium-233 for nuclear breeder reactors. I understand that vast deposits of raw thorium lurk on the far side of the river in New Hampshire and across the border in Canada.

What was a backwoods lamplighter to do with this news? Was it possible that in my quest for alternatives to nuclear power, I inadvertently planted three radioactive devices smack dab in the middle of the cabin?

It used to be said that 90 percent of human knowledge is gained by vision. Could that be true still? So much that sets the circuits of modern life firing is invisible to the optic nerves. Delitescent waves of radio and radar and radiation ebb and flow all around us. Old-fashioned man can eyeball a cord of wood or a gallon of gas, a book or a balance sheet. But today's batteries, data books, utility lines and tape cassettes, as well as acid rain and fallout, lack visual content.

Without inhuman apparatus to measure and translate, these forces are incomprehensible. So, too, the measure of gaslight cannot be taken optically. To get a handle on lantern safety, I slipped into the invisible realm of radioactivity, carbon monoxide and LPG vapours.

"People are too damn worried!" was the judgment that first rebounded from W.S. Saese when I asked him about the potential for trouble from thorium mantles.

"You should see the amount of material that gets sent in here to be tested." I called him at Wilmar Associates, where the Humphrey gaslight mantles had been analyzed. "The activity is so low, you'd have to swallow 10 mantles to get an effect," he continued. "The mantle is about as radioactive as TV."

"Black-and-white or colour?" I asked.

"Either."

I could have accepted his assurance, but I wanted to balance my bias against his. He was a chemist with a business relationship with Humphrey gaslights. He didn't burn gaslight. I did.

Next, I contacted Consumers Union, the publishers of *Consumer Reports* magazine. "We've never done a thing about gas lighting," I was informed. At Underwriter's Laboratory I drew another blank.

I tried the Vermont Health Department. Tom Neiman, liaison officer for various department offices, seemed surprised by my query. "It's the first question we've had about gaslight. We have no regulations regarding gaslight, and we have no authority in private homes. The regs cover only rental and public buildings. In the rental housing code, gas heaters must be vented to the outside. Proper ventilation is the main concern. In fact, I've got part share in a cabin in the woods, and we use gaslights and they work fine."

Marty Johansen of the Vermont Occupational Safety and Health Agency told me that his outfit had no pertinent data. "Back in the 1800s, every house on the street had a gaslight," he mused. "For many years, gaslights have been going out of style. Now because of the energy situation, they're coming back, I suppose. I think a fire hazard might be a worry. I'd be concerned about pounding a hole in the wall and puncturing the pipe and getting a leak. As far as thorium goes, the amount is so small, it's no problem."

I learned from the state Fire Prevention office that any gas appliance must be approved by either Underwriter's Laboratory or the American Gas Association and that gas dealers are supposed to install appliances in accordance with the National Fire Prevention Association code. But in fact, the state office has no jurisdiction over private homes.

My gas dealer confirmed that he goes by the NFPA code book specifications when installing appliances. Trouble is, he couldn't find gaslights mentioned in either the book or AGA publications. However, the latest Humphrey light is brightened with the stamp of approval of the Canadian Gas Association, the one and only official imprimatur attached to their units. *Model 9T is CGA certified; installation must be in accordance with 10-Can 1-B 149.2 installation code for propane burning appliances and equipment, and local codes.* I asked John Doran of the CGA just what that meant.

"In general, gas appliances must be installed with an 18-inch clearance above and 5 to the side, according to the code. Also, there are specifications for making sure installation is secure." CGA specs also allow for gaslight valve leakage of no more than 20 cc an hour. "And that's very little," Doran emphasized.

I asked him about the mantle. "All I can say is that in 100 or so years, there's not sufficient evidence of trouble. It's less radiation than you'd normally get," he concluded.

A triple dose of what I'd normally get, these days especially, seemed less than reassuring. I turned my questions about thorium on the science department of Dartmouth College.

"I don't think you have anything to worry about," was the response I got from Roger Sodaberg, professor of chemistry. "Maybe from particles, but the pressure is so low and decay is extraordinarily slow. The half-life of thorium is extremely long. Gaslight is innocuous. It's been around 100 years and there have been no alarms." I refreshed his memory about the past problems with beryllium, and he recalled hearing about it. Then, much like chemist W.S. Saese, he jumped to the defence of electricity. "Gaslight is 10 times as wasteful as electric light. Gaslight disappeared for a good reason. It's grossly inefficient!"

Charles Drake, dean of Dartmouth's geology department, agreed that thorium presented little threat. "The reason it's used is that it doesn't burn away, so nothing gets distributed. It's no more trouble than a rock sitting in a display cabinet."

I discovered also that thorium is what physicists call a "beta emitter," as opposed to an emitter of radioactive alpha particles or gamma rays. A gamma ray, fierce and sudden, can penetrate three feet of concrete and still do damage to living tissue on the other side. But beta particles, radiating outward from their atomic nuclei, can be stopped by mere clothing, halted in their tracks before they can damage anything. Only if ingested — swallowed as Saese had put it — would thorium particles find the opportunity to enter the body, where they could concentrate in bone marrow.

Still, I was not entirely satisfied.

Some of the brightest gas mantle lamps I've seen are made by the Wetmore-Ceres Company. Although the lamps are fuelled by white gas or kerosene pressurized by hand-pump, not liquid propane gas, I knew that the mantles were of the incandescent Welsbach type. And because Wetmore-Ceres distributes thousands of lamps among the Amish community, I figured this might be a reliable source of first-hand information.

Jeffrey Wetmore seemed to think that the mantle posed no threat to lamplighters. He did, however, caution me about burning off the mantle to start operation. "I believe that initial burning off of the mantles releases a toxic gas. We do it outside."

The Wetmore-Ceres "Parlor Lamp" is an Amish variation of the Coleman lantern, modelled after Coleman's old Quick Light, which went out of production in the '60s. Since the Amish communities are growing rapidly, they decided to remanufacture the old lamp.

"The lamps do not flare up as pressure drops," Wetmore explained, "and carbon monoxide continues about the same all during operation. We have forgotten them at night and found them still running in the morning. But of course, that is starting off at good pressure. The basic rule of thumb is do not leave the lamps unattended. We do sell Aladdin lamps, but we can't sell any to the Amish. They say the Aladdin is too

Tim Matson

One of the author's three Humphrey Opalite LPG lamps being lit: "The kitchen was glowing terrifically, and so, indeed, was I."

dangerous around children. They cannot go out to the barn to milk and leave the children alone in the house with the Aladdin. However, we all leave the Parlor Lamp or even a Coleman lantern burning in the house with the children without any worry. Lamps that burn various fuels, Parlor, Aladdin or even plain old kerosene wick lamps, are all dangerous if left unattended. And of course, none of these can be used in a closed room without ventilation."

Wetmore's account of the Amish communities' experiences with gas mantle lighting squared with my own feelings, and I might finally have wrapped up my inquiry then, if I hadn't received a disturbing letter from the United States Consumer Product Safety Commission (CPSC). In response to my written query about the safety of LP gaslights, I was informed by one Abigail Fritz that "LP gas lighting is *not* recommended for indoor use." (Her emphasis.) "The principle hazards with using LP gas are the possibility of fire and explosion," she wrote. "Suspected cases of toxicity are more likely due to carbon monoxide. If used in a confined space, the safety would depend on the amount of carbon monoxide or other combustion by-product produced by it, and the amount of ventilation in the room."

Yet I knew that a gaslight consumes oxygen and produces carbon monoxide at about the same rate as a pilot light on a kitchen range. And the CPSC had no proscription against gas stoves. The gaslight taboo seemed absurd.

I contacted John Roba, proprietor of a recreational-supply outfit with a coast-to-coast trade in gas mantles. I keep a pack of his "Bright" brand soft tie-ons to replace broken mantles. I wondered how he would react to formal disapproval of indoor gas lighting by the CPSC.

"Most gas associations won't approve gaslights because the burn gives off carbon monoxide. If you accumulate enough lights in an airtight space, you will have trouble. I've never heard of anyone killing himself in a cabin, where there is sure to be enough air coming in. But I have heard of it in a recreational vehicle."

He cautioned me to be sure to have enough ventilation in winter, when the cabin is closed up, to feed both lights and wood stoves. He also assured me that the mantles were safe, though he was reluctant to identify his product source.

There is one American manufacturer producing mantles at a price competitive with Roba's imports: Coleman. Virtually synonymous with the gas mantle lantern, Coleman markets lights in such volume through secure sales territory that they can afford to sell soft mantles for less than a dollar apiece. Since their market is recreational, the turnover in mantles is greater than in the fixed indoor lighting trade. Mantles last a long time in a house or cabin but not so long in a recreational vehicle or portable light. I asked Wilbur Townsend, technical research engineer for Coleman, what ventilation requirements were necessary for gaslights.

"We recommend 'adequate ventilation' and that's it. There is no way to specify exactly what is right for each individual situation. Put too many people in a tight room, and they'll use up the available oxygen too."

Townsend told me that Coleman mantles posed no health threat. Composed of 99 percent thorium oxide and one percent cerium, like the Humphrey mantles, they are coated with a protective lacquer seal. "Burning off the lacquer poses no problem to health. As far as the thorium is concerned, we have people in the mantle shop continuously exposed, some of them for 40 years. They undergo periodic whole-body checkups in Denver. And they come out clean as a hound's tooth."

I felt I had taken the incandescent burner over sufficient hurdles to settle the question of gaslight fallout.

Besides, I was sick of the whole thing.

I decided that the real hazards of firelight — gaslight included — are as ancient as the original indoor flambeaux: oxygen depletion and fire. Carbon monoxide too, perhaps, but only if an adequate air supply is absent.

I will continue burning gas, perhaps taking the time to sharpen an old chisel and scratch over the hearth: God Ventilate Our Happy Home. It seems as safe as any other means of carrying the sun indoors.

And yet, Plato's dancing shadows have a strange power over the mind. My beta-emitting lamp seems safe, but one eye still looks askance, and a question mark remains. ∎

Tim Matson is the author of Alternative Light Styles, The Lamp Keeper's Guide to Illumination Beyond the Power Lines *published by the Countryman Press.*

Sources

WETMORE-CERES CO.
998 30th Street
Richmond, California 94804

ICG CANADIAN PROPANE LTD.
9765-63rd Avenue
Edmonton, Alberta T2G 4A4
(403) 435-3727
Humphrey, Falk and Primus propane lighting fixtures, parts, accessories and service. Outlets in all provinces and territories except the Maritimes. In Quebec, ICG is called Gasbec and can be contacted at Gasbec Ltd., 2253 Boulevard Taschereau, Longueuil, Quebec J4K 2Y3, (418) 656-9172. Write for complete catalogue, price list and address of nearest distributor.

PHILLIPS LAMP SHADES LTD.
172 Main Street
Toronto, Ontario M4E 2W1
(416) 691-7372
Aladdin kerosene lamps. Write for brochure on all products and prices. Send self-addressed stamped envelope for a reprint of a 1930 leaflet distributed by the original Mantle Lamp Company of Canada: "Correctional Operating Procedures." Service and parts for all Aladdin products.

A.B. OPTIMUS CANADA LTD.
2538 Speers Road
Unit 3
Oakville, Ontario L6L 5K9
(416) 827-6014
Write for information on the full line of Optimus products.

CANADIAN COLEMAN COMPANY LTD.
700 Kipling Avenue
Toronto, Ontario N8Z 5V6
(416) 252-6161
Three sizes of mantle.

THE MANTLE LAMP SUPPLY COMPANY
Box 959
Sutton West, Ontario L0E 1R0
(416) 722-6466
Aladdin lamps in all styles. Parts, service, accessories. Write for complete information and prices.

B.D. WAIT COMPANY
430 Wyecroft Road
Oakville, Ontario L6K 2G9
(416) 844-3224
Canadian distributor of Humphrey and Falk products.

Micro-Hydro

The personal utility: a spreading phenomenon for those of independent mind — and means

By Gordon Flagler

Tucked away on a high plateau on the southern fringes of Algonquin Park, the Beeler farm is reached only by a rutted driveway that climbs a long, wooded slope, cutting through thick stands of poplar and paper birch near the base which give way to sugar maple and beech at the summit. Emerging from the trees, a visitor abruptly finds a panorama of wide fields which drop gently toward a compact cluster of buildings and, beyond, a placid, hundred-acre lake.

Despite the size of the farm — 900 acres — the house is small and unassuming. The kitchen, the obvious hub of all activity, is dominated by a long harvest table and a Renfrew Acorn woodburning range which remains stoked even on a simmering late spring afternoon. There is a party-line telephone and a simple white tabletop radio, but relatively few modern appliances are in evidence. The scene would be little different from that in countless other North American farmsteads but for the fact that Alvin and Emily Beeler have achieved a state of energy autonomy only dreamed about by most: their farm is entirely powered by hydroelectricity they generate themselves.

The hydro arrives from the southwest, carried along two strands of wire strung on thick cedar poles cut and erected by Beeler. A Jeep trail runs near the line, traversing a field beside the house and disappearing into the woods. Followed, it grows rougher, eventually descends an escarpment and stops at the first pole, which rises

John Bianchi

above a flat-roofed, windowless, concrete bunker.

Providing a tour of his personal utility, Beeler unlocks an outer door then pushes open a second, sporting a red DANGER — HIGH VOLTAGE sign to reveal, beneath a constantly burning light bulb, the heart of the hydroelectric system he designed. Tall and narrow of frame, Beeler stoops over the generator and raises his voice over the steady, efficient hum of the machinery to explain that the project took four years to build and will soon provide electrical power to 10 additional homes in a nearby settlement.

"They will have *basic* electrical services," says Beeler. "They won't be able to heat with it, but they will have lighting and enough for a vacuum cleaner and refrigeration."

That this home-built system, purring effortlessly and unmanned, requiring virtually no maintenance, can free 11 families from the utility grid seems almost too simple, somehow magical. The powerhouse itself is unspectacular; the penstock pipe which carries water from the reservoir lake to the turbine is buried, offering little indication of the actual source of power. Indeed, because the head — the vertical drop between lake and turbine — is a sizable 100 feet, a relatively small flow of water is sufficient to turn the Pelton wheel. The millrace carrying the spent flow of water away from the powerhouse is but a foot deep and easily leapt across: Niagara this is not — in fact, there is no waterfall, and with the vegetative wounds caused by construction mostly healed, this certainly falls within the definition of soft-tech — benign, controllable, even lovable.

RAW DETERMINATION

Having caught trout from a millrace that ran past his childhood home in Lequille, Nova Scotia, Alvin Beeler has carried an affection for rushing water and whirring turbines through to this, his 71st year. But unlike many amateurs now being drawn to the technology of small hydroelectric systems, Beeler was not ignorant of the hard facts when he set about creating his mini-utility. He fully comprehended what it would take to tame a raw site and produce usable, reliable power.

He owned two bulldozers, a pair of loaders, a backhoe and two dump trucks. He had read the bibles of the field, books such as E.B. Kurtz's *The Lineman's and Cableman's Handbook* and R.L. Daugherty's *Hydraulic Turbines* until the key passages were ingrained in his thinking. He drew on a lifetime of experience as a Class A mechanic and amateur engineer but, even so, admitted his own limitations and called in outside consultants when necessary.

Beeler's system, while much larger than most owner-built utilities, falls within the so-called micro-scale hydroelectric classification. Commercial hydro technology is long-established and is without doubt the most economic, least problematic major power source available to the public utilities, but the equipment and installation expertise necessary for home generating systems remain in an embryonic stage in Canada.

Used almost exclusively in remote locations beyond the edges of the power grid, there are but 50 known micro-scale installations in British Columbia, fewer than half a dozen in Alberta, 5 to 10 in Ontario and 8 in Nova Scotia. The actual numbers are certainly higher, as some system owners have shied away from publicity or official scrutiny, either out of fear of being overrun by the curious or confronted with government regulations they have ignored. Even assuming that the unsanctioned systems outnumber the known installations, the figures remain small; what is encouraging is the rapid acceleration in micro-scale development — the majority of Canadian installations were brought on-line during the past five years, and the technology is advancing rapidly.

Generating one's own electricity is neither the simplest nor the least expensive of the alternative technologies: current turbine prices are in the $3,000 to $5,000 range for the smallest units, and most household-sized plants require an expenditure of $10,000 to $20,000. Furthermore, unless the turbine is carefully matched to the site, the money may be wasted. Any hydroelectric project requires detailed planning and meticulous installation.

Site assessment is the first and perhaps most important step in any would-be hydroelectric project, simple enough if one lives near a miniature Niagara with a constant, boundless supply of water but complex in most instances. The key figures needed to ascertain any site's power potential are *head* and *flow*.

The former is relatively easy to determine with simple surveyor's tools — a levelling rod and transit — used to establish the vertical drop between water level at its highest point and the location where the water will enter the turbine. Other methods for measuring the head are described in all basic hydro-power guidebooks.

Water flow through the system is much more difficult to evaluate, as it is rarely constant — unless a dam is present — rising and falling from season to season and year to year.

The nonprofessional who sets out to measure flow may be greatly aided by a series of documents available, except in Quebec, through the federal government's Environment Canada Water Resources Branch. Quebec residents may obtain this information from their own provincial government (see Sources for address). The first volume, published every two years, is the *Surface Water Data Reference Index*, which contains descriptions of the 2,000 river water gauges in place across Canada, an alphabetical listing of all rivers tested, the size of each drainage area and the period for which data exists. The second is the *Historical Stream Flow Summary*, a series of books also printed every two years, which gives monthly data for all sites within each of the eight regions into which these documents divide the country. The last series is *Surface Water Data*, published yearly, which gives daily information on flow at the 2,000 sites. Harry Rosenberg of Environment Canada says that "taken together, these give a global picture at any site."

If the considered location is not among these 2,000, there are other ways of gleaning already computed data. Keith Hypel, an associate professor with the De-

Erection of this 3½-foot poured-concrete dam allowed Neal Livingston to feed a 5-kilowatt micro-system from a relatively small Nova Scotia brook.

partment of Systems Engineering at the University of Waterloo, explains that statistics may be available from former owners — if the site was previously used by a mill or factory; conservation authorities can also be of assistance. When records exist for a few previous years, a skilled person can use "statistical extension" to arrive at a reasonably accurate estimate. "If there are records for upstream, the downstream flow would be just as great unless water is being taken away for irrigation or another purpose. If you have a down-stream figure, the upstream location will have less flow. If the two sites are only a short distance apart, there will be little difference unless a creek comes in between them."

Flow can also be measured with the weir, bucket and area-velocity methods. These relatively simple techniques are laid out within the aforementioned manuals. *Micro-Hydro Power*, an out-of-print Ontario Hydro publication, cautions that "these measurements of flow are best taken during the dry season, since the flow during this season may limit the capacity of the proposed hydroelectric installation."

Craig Murphy, a micro-turbine importer from Silverton, British Columbia, adds, "Theoretically, telling how much power you have can be a minor concern for someone who has a major river and wants only a bit of hydro, but it is highly important if you have only

a small site. With micro, it is often best to do this work yourself for economic reasons, but never go ahead until you have confidence in the numbers, and have your data inspected by a professional."

Once head and flow have been calculated, the amount of available energy can be determined as follows:

$$\frac{Q \times H \times e}{709}$$

Q = flow of cubic feet per minute
H = head
e = overall power plant efficiency per minute
709 = a defined constant

This gives the potential in kilowatts. To determine horsepower, another output measurement used by manufacturers, divide by 529 instead of 709. Overall efficiency ranges from 70 to 90 percent. Charts showing the efficiency rating of the most common turbines and other components are widely available. To ensure that the site's real potential is known, this equation should be calculated using both the minimum annual and mean annual flows.

All of this can prove intimidating to the newcomer, but expert advice is not difficult to obtain. Lawrence Ball, an engineering project supervisor in the Conservation and Water Management Department of Totten, Sims and Hubicki, a large Canadian engineering firm with headquarters in Cobourg, Ontario, says that an expert site and cost analysis is money well spent.

"I'm prejudiced, I guess, but I would hire someone to do the evaluation. For $500 to $1,000, a professional will be able to get a handle on the power potential and give a reasonable estimate on the costs of developing. I think you need experience in the field before you can accurately say what these costs will be."

Vic Enns, co-owner of Vancouver's Solace Energy Centres, which has consulted on or sold at least half of the 50 units in British Columbia, puts forward a slightly less rigid approach. "We are professionals, but we are not supporting a staff of 20 engineers. We have low overhead and appreciate the economies of scale. We never sell a turbine without having the customer fill out an inquiry sheet. We have to know as much about the site as the customer before anything is sold." If the buyer does not feel capable of following directions and garnering the needed data, Solace can provide both "a preliminary reconnaissance, which is a quick-and-dirty survey giving ballpark figures, and a formal feasibility survey — if the owner gives consent to proceed after the preliminary one is completed."

Some, but not all, of the firms selling micro-scale equipment in Canada also provide such services, but the buyer must constantly watch for the sales pitch creeping in to skew the evaluation or planning. The growing boom in this field, fortunately, is bringing forth a body of independent consultants, many with previous experience with large- or medium-scale commercial systems. Their expertise can prove invaluable in dealing not only with site and cost analysis, environmental impact evaluation and permit acquisitions, but also with power requirements of the household or business, equipment options and the long-term economics of various systems.

DAM CHOICES

The complexity of a project, as well as its performance, can be greatly increased by the erection of a dam, which can both raise the head and provide a steady flow of water. At the low-tech end of the scale, dams can be simple and unobtrusive. "Diversion dams for small mountain streams are easily built to a height of three or four feet," says Dermot McGuigan, author of *Harnessing Water Power for Home Energy.*

"Stones, logs or other materials at hand can be used. All that is required is a small pool that will accept an intake pipe with a protective mesh at the opening." This type of dam is thus used primarily for feeding water into the penstock.

"Dams and reservoirs on large rivers, designed to feed low-head installations, are another matter altogether," McGuigan cautions. "Even small on-stream reservoirs, when suddenly hit by flood waters, can cause considerable damage downstream.

"Apart from the safety problems with reservoirs, they do tend to be very expensive, the land they drown can be costly, they silt up, and, moreover, to make efficient use of stored water, an expensive hydraulic governor should be used to regulate flow to the turbine."

To raise his existing lake four feet in order to provide steady water flow to keep the turbine producing the 17 to 20 kilowatts it was designed to generate, Alvin Beeler constructed a quartet of dams which fall squarely within McGuigan's description of reservoir-type dams. Containing over 30,000 cubic yards of earth, the four dams, which when taken together run for about half a mile, were responsible for much of the project's paper work — "I've got over a bushel basket full" — which took him five years to complete.

These intricate negotiations with provincial officials were necessary in spite of the fact that he owns the entire watershed, thereby ensuring that raising the water level above the dam and reducing the flow below did not affect the traditional riparian rights of other landowners. These rights, which have stood for hundreds of years, guarantee every owner of river frontage equal access to water flow. Their existence often complicates the process of obtaining needed dam-building permits.

Many of the British Columbia sites with which Vic Enns is familiar incorporate dams, and it is his experience that a "modest structure" will encounter no opposition from B.C. government authorities. Neal Livingston, who built a five-kilowatt installation in Black River, Cape Breton, during 1980, used the experience in his 24-minute film *Water Power*. He says that his 3½-foot-high, poured-concrete dam was allowed because it was near the source of a very small brook, and Nova Scotia environmental officials determined that migrating fish never travelled that far upstream. In some instances, the construction of a fish ladder, which enables migrating species to climb past a reservoir dam, is mandatory. (For information on permits required in each province, contact the nearest office of the environment or natural resources department. To avoid costly delays or even cancellation of a project already begun, it is wise to ensure that all permits are obtained before purchasing equipment or breaking ground.)

Existing dams, on the other hand, are a micro-hydro builder's dream. "If a dam is still standing, as is the case on many southern Ontario rivers and creeks, there is not much that can go wrong," comments Lawrence Ball. "The concrete deteriorates and spalls or chips with time, but this is mostly a cosmetic fault that doesn't cause structural problems. One of the biggest hazards occurs when a dam is not used for power generation for some time. All the available energy is used to wash out the bed of the river downstream from the dam, causing a hole on that side of the structure. If it becomes large enough, the dam can fall in or water can go under it. It is common to have a small indentation; its size can be checked by standing on the dam and using a stick to probe underwater. It is an engineering matter to know if the hole is big enough to be a danger. The cure is to put huge rocks in it to absorb the energy and stop further erosion."

At the heart of every hydro-electric system lies the turbine, which, in being spun by the water, begins the process of producing electricity. There are two main types, *impulse* and *reaction*, each with different characteristics suited to specific locations.

The impulse turbine is primarily used in high-head situations common throughout British Columbia and the most rugged sections of eastern Canada. In *Harnessing Water Power for Home Energy*, McGuigan describes the principles behind the Pelton turbine — invented in 1889 by Lester Allen Pelton — which is by far the most common impulse unit.

"Water is taken from a high head through a pressure pipeline with a narrow nozzle at the bottom. The water is forced, under its own pressure, through the nozzle, to form a high-velocity free jet which is directed onto the buckets of the Pelton wheel. As a result of the near perfect streaming in the buckets, 80 to 90 percent of the energy in the jet is absorbed by the wheel. One to four jets can be used per wheel, though I have never seen more than two on small installations. As the Pelton is comparatively small for its output, it can attain high speed and thus reduce or eliminate the need for gears." Thus, with the Pelton and other impulse turbines, the velocity of the water is the key.

Less common impulse designs are the Turgo and cross-flow. Originally manufactured solely by Gilbert Gilkes and Gordon Ltd. of England and now copied by others, the Turgo is a modified Pelton in which water enters on one side and exits on the other; it is claimed to be an improvement over the Pelton, producing more energy from a smaller wheel. Most cross-flow turbines are made by one company, Ossberger Turbinenfabrik of Bayern, West Germany. According to the National Center of Appropriate Technology (NCAT) in Butte, Montana, the cross-flow is drum-shaped with the blades fixed radially along the outer edge. The unit, open in the centre, resembles a squirrel cage blower. Because of its design, the cross-flow is said to be largely self-cleaning and is well suited to low-head applications. This obviously sets it apart from other units.

According to the NCAT, reaction turbines "work on a different principle. The runner is placed directly in the water stream, and power is developed by water flowing over the blades rather than striking each individually. Reaction turbines use pressure rather than velocity."

The best known reaction turbine is the squat Francis, used in most mammoth hydroelectric projects. However, it is generally not as efficient as other reaction units in the very low-head situation common to many eastern micro-installations.

The propeller turbine, whose shape is described by its name, is usually better for a low head. When the blades are adjustable (to enable their configuration to change seasonally with the water flow), the unit is known as a Kaplan.

WATER-TO-WIRE

To convert the mechanical energy harnessed by the turbine into electricity, a generator is used. The power that emerges can be either alternating current (AC) or direct current (DC). Since the appliances most people own and can most easily purchase are AC, this type of electricity is the most practical to create. DC appliances are harder to locate, and DC powerhouses must be close to where the electricity will be used, as this type of current is easily dissipated in long power lines.

To produce AC current, the output of the turbine must be rated at a minimum of three kilowatts and have either an electronic or mechanical governor to regulate water flow and the turbine's velocity. Additionally, because AC cannot be stored for later use, the turbine must continually generate at the maximum level of power needed by the home. With a large system located on a significant river or equipped with a reservoir, this is not a problem, but with smaller units, especially those which have limited water flows at certain times of the year, an AC system will simply not be capable of generating the peak power required.

As a result, it is often best to produce DC and store it in batteries, then convert to the more universal AC using a solid state marine DC inverter. This is an expense of approximately $1,000, but going to DC at the source does away with a costly generator. While this entire topic can prove complicated, the majority of companies selling micro equipment in North America can provide what is known as a "water-to-wire" system, which includes all components. Says Neal Livingston, "this proves more expensive than if you gathered everything yourself, but if you are not a professional welder and don't have tools plus the time to run around and collect everything, the extra expense is worth it."

Would-be micro-hydro equipment purchasers are advised to exercise extreme caution in selecting sources of turbines and other components, as this is an industry with its share of ephemeral manufacturers and dealers. In the United States, where both micro- and small-scale technology has advanced more quickly than in Canada, there have been many instances of manufacturers appearing and disappearing almost overnight — a problem endemic in the field of emerging energy alternatives — leaving both dealers and customers seriously disaffected.

Ontario-based consultant William Trick warns that "the customer would be well-advised to spend the money necessary to visit the manufacturer and customers who have had systems made by the firm in service for two years or more, at sites similar to the one the prospective buyer possesses. The turbine must have decent electrical and hydraulic design, so you want to know: Do these people have the background? How many have they made? Do they have a warranty and are there trouble-shooters or field service representatives?"

Then, there are the Alvin Beelers, who search for a suitable, affordable turbine, come up empty and decide to make it themselves. William Trick cautions, "I've seen many balloons that have blown up; ones that work for several years are rare. To find information on turbine design is hard even if you work in the field, as most of the books are not in English, and you have to pore through technical papers and expensive magazines such as *Water Power and Dam Construction*, which costs $78 a year. Then, even if you find the data, you have to be persistent and apply it practically."

Once a decision on equipment has been finalized, it is time to decide if the hydro installation would be cost-effective. All costs must be projected; in addition to the generation and electrical equipment, this includes construction or rehabilitation of the dam, penstock and millrace, plus the erection of a powerhouse (if one is needed), electrical lines and poles.

Because some provincial utilities — namely those of British Columbia and Ontario — are considering buying electricity from private producers, this potential source of revenue should be investigated even though the rates now being contemplated are very low. Through the federal-provincial Conservation and Renewable Energy Demonstration Agreement, Nova Scotia has given grants to Neal Livingston and a number of other micro-system owners. According to Vaughn Monroe, Manager of the Pilot Projects Programme for the Nova Scotia Department of Mines and Energy, three to five more micro-installations will receive partial funding this year. Cam McNeil of the federal government's Energy, Mines and Resources Conservation and Renewable Energy Branch explains that this agreement exists with all provinces except Prince Edward Island, Quebec and Alberta. He suggests inquiring about receiving funding through this agreement by contacting the Ministry of Energy in the participating provinces. At present this is the only known grant programme that may provide funds for private micro-scale development.

Once total costs and potential revenue and grant sources have been calculated, the investment must be compared with what would be needed to install utility hydro lines or power from another source such as wind. It has been proved that when operating expenses are added in, micro is always cheaper than a diesel generator.

Other factors include whether or not money will have to be borrowed from a lending institution, how long the property on which the system may sit will be kept, whether future owners will consider it an asset or a liability and if the current landowner can help build the plant and then maintain it. During this decision-making process, nonfinancial arguments should be largely set aside — the investment must be carefully considered. An independent consultant can be a useful source of advice at this time.

As mentioned earlier, the dam must be rehabilitated or constructed with extreme care. Do not ignore the almost universal regulation requiring that an engineer handle the design. The intake pipe which gathers water at the dam must be covered by a high-quality trashrack to keep large pieces of debris and ice out, and, as well, screen mesh which has openings smaller than the diameter of the nozzle or pipe that leads into the turbine should be in place so that no foreign objects can slip through and cause serious damage to the turbine.

The penstock must contain few bends, never have turns of more than 45 degrees and always be on a downhill slope — except for siphon intakes that are sometimes used to carry water over the top of an existing dam that cannot be breached.

PVC pipe, which is commonly used with micro-installations, cannot withstand velocities of more than five feet per second and must be buried to avoid solar deterioration. Metal or rubber pipe that is not buried must have water flowing at more than five feet per second to avoid ice build-up. Any pipe used must be of the highest grade, be as large in diameter as possible to reduce friction and have a sufficient pressure rating. The turbine manufacturer can give advice on what diameter and type of pipe to use.

The turbine must be equipped with an emergency overspeed control so that the generator won't fly apart if the turbine begins to spin too quickly. For the same reason, the generator must be rated for the same runaway speed as the turbine. William Trick warns that equipment meant for automotive or agricultural uses will not be able to stand the strain and should not be employed. Micro plants that will run unattended should have an automatic shutdown switch or at least an alarm to warn of overheating bearings or other equipment malfunction. The absence of such a switch can result in severe damage or destruction of the system. Says Trick, "Every part that fails has the potential of causing a serious incident."

When Charles E. MacArthur purchased what is locally known as Brown's Mill, in Dover-Foxcroft, Maine, he had no experience with operating any hydro equipment, let alone the 600-kilowatt small-scale plant which provides the town of 4,000 with 85 percent of its electricity. "I learned by trial and error, I made mistakes, but, luckily, none of them were devastating." He saw, firsthand, one of the shortages in the micro- and small-scale fields — "a lack of experienced pilots." To spare others the same problems, MacArthur is providing the first known course in operating and maintaining micro- and small-scale equipment. The three students who have signed up for the eight-week course are working on a variety of turbines and older waterwheels, "getting the practicalities that are not otherwise available." In the future, MacArthur hopes to run a pair of two-week courses in summer and winter. "There are specific winter practices that have to be learned, for example, how to keep the trashrack and turbine chamber free of ice." For those who can't attend the school but wish access to experienced people, MacArthur suggests retired utility employees "who provide quite a resource and might enjoy coming in and offering suggestions or acting as part-time employees." Alvin Beeler, himself retired, is someone who has already done this. "I'm in cahoots with a number of old guys similar to me who like to play with it, to go right at it and see what they can do."

As should be obvious by now, hydro power is not for the individual seeking a fast, simple energy alternative. Those willing to read, research, investigate and spend both time and money may be rewarded by a long-term supply of energy, independent of world oil prices and utility rate increases. Falling water has the ability both to spur the imagination and to generate electricity, but harnessing even the smallest head is a challenge not to be underestimated. ∎

Gordon Flagler, a former associate editor of Harrowsmith, *is the author of* The North American Wood Heat Handbook.

Sources

Books and Pamphlets

**HARNESSING WATER POWER
FOR HOME ENERGY**
By Dermot McGuigan
Garden Way Publishing
101 pages
145A — paperback, $9.50
Available from Harrowsmith Books, Camden East, Ontario K0K 1J0.

DESIGN OF SMALL DAMS
Prepared by the U.S. Department of the Interior
Available from Superintendent of Documents, U.S. Government Printing Office, Washington, D.C. 20402. Stock Number 024-003-00155-4. $15.00 (U.S.).

**SURFACE WATER DATA REFERENCE INDEX,
HISTORICAL STREAM FLOW SUMMARY,
SURFACE WATER DATA**
Available from Environment Canada, Water Resources Branch, Attn: R.G. Boals, Ottawa, Ontario K1A 0E7, (819) 997-2078, or contact nearest regional office. All three are free but supplies are limited. Available to all provinces except Quebec (see below). Please specify the province for which information is required.

Environment Canada literature for Quebec available from Directeur Général Des Eaux, Ministère Des Richesses Naturelles du Québec, 1640 Boulevard de L'Entente, Québec City, Québec G1S 4N6, (418) 643-4553.

Manufacturers and Retailers

DEPENDABLE TURBINES LTD.
#7 3005 Murray Street
Port Moody, British Columbia V3H 1X3
(604) 461-3121
Pelton, Turgo, Francis, propeller turbines plus related equipment. Information brochures $2.00 to cover postage and handling. Turbine sizes range from 1 through 2,000 kilowatts.

SMALL HYDRO-ELECTRICS CANADA LTD.
Box 54
Silverton, British Columbia V0G 2B0
(604) 358-7761
Importer of Equipex turbines from People's Republic of China. Pelton, Turgo, Francis and propeller turbines plus related equipment. Turbine sizes range from 20 through 2,500 kilowatts. Project development, management and financing available.

SOLACE ENERGY CENTRES INC.
2425 Main Street
Vancouver, British Columbia V5T 3E1
(604) 879-5258
Market several brands of turbines including Dependable, Small Hydro-Electrics and Kenyon Industries. Have necessary accessories and can provide all levels of feasibility surveys.

CANYON INDUSTRIES
5346 Mosquito Lake Road
Deming, Washington 98244
(206) 592-5552
(206) 592-2235
Sells miniature Hydromite turbines from 50 to 750 watts, and Pelton and crossflow turbines from 300 watts to 1.5 megawatts.

PELTECH HYDRAULIC TURBINES
5141 Wickersham Street
Acme, Washington 98220
(206) 595-2312
Sells a range of Pelton turbines with outputs from 5 through 5,000 kilowatts. Also Turgo impulse turbines.

BARBER HYDRAULIC TURBINE
Division of Marsh Engineering Ltd.
Box 340
Port Colborne, Ontario L3K 5W1
(416) 834-9303

GALT ENERGY SYSTEMS
Box 1354
Cambridge, Ontario N1R 3B0
(519) 653-2531
Sells a range of turbines designed by the company's owner David de Montmorency. These include both Kaplan and propeller units.

MCKAY WATER POWER INC.
Box 221
West Lebanon, New Hampshire 03784
(603) 298-5122
Manufacturer of Hydropac low- and medium-head turbines.

POWERHOUSE PAUL'S PELTONS
Box 1557
Sussex, New Brunswick E0E 1P0
(506) 433-3151
Manufactures low-cost 5-inch epoxy Pelton wheel for high-head installations.

STAPENHORST TURBINES
283 Labrosse Avenue
Pointe Claire, Quebec H9R 1A3
(514) 695-8230
North American importer of the highly regarded Ossberger crossflow turbines made in Bayern, West Germany.

CHARLES E. MACARTHUR
16 Vaughn Street
Dover-Foxcroft, Maine 04426

Cast-Iron Phoenix

An airtight rises from the ashpan of an antique wood range

By Tom Daly

I t was like a two-dollar novel — love at first sight, and all I needed was money. It was about 50 years old, a little rusty, with its chrome peeling here and there, but it was a real honey — a big, old Peacock cookstove made right here in Nova Scotia — and now it was mine.

The lady to whom I wrote the cheque swore that it worked like a trooper, and she was only replacing it because it would not hold a fire overnight. She showed me her brand-new multi-thousand-dollar airtight cookstove ("made in Upper Canada, you know") with its gleaming nickel and enamel, but I was building my first house, and the kitchen-I-could-see-in-my-mind had a big, old Peacock right in the middle of it, so we both parted happy.

But, of course, she was right — the old stove would not hold a fire long enough to bake a pot of beans. Fortunately, a friend of mine stumbled upon a work crew repairing an industrial boiler and asked a few questions. As a result, the two of us worked out a technique that enables any inexperienced handyman to convert his antique wood stove into a highly efficient airtight. The process is straightforward and simple; no easily made mistakes lie in wait to ambush the inexperienced, and it involves no unusual tools or procedures. As well as conferring airtightness on stoves in good repair, this method can restore those relics with burned-out fireboxes or missing — and irreplaceable — grates or liners. All this for less than $50.

My old Peacock is now going into its sixth season as an airtight, and it still works like a champ. It easily holds a cheery blaze overnight, and I have cooked breakfast on it, banked the fire and returned 24 hours later to stir the coals to life for the next day's breakfast. Just like a real heat stove, it can be damped down tightly, with all the blessings (heat in the morning) and pitfalls (creosote) that this entails.

Basically, the conversion process involves stripping the stove's firebox of its liner, grates and ashpan, mixing some castable refractory cement (a process as easy as making cookie dough) and then pouring a one-piece liner for a new and enlarged firebox. Since doing my own, I have done two for friends and know of yet another that was made over this way. Each time, the result has been the same: vastly improved performance, with no troubles whatsoever.

To start the job, clean out the ashes (but do not bother to replace the ashpan), remove all the upper plates and vacuum the top of the oven. Then rig up a light so you can see what you are doing and start removing the pieces of the firebox. Usually, this consists of a number of cast-iron plates set around the firebox walls above some system of grates, plates or rollers. Take them all out, along with any ash deflectors or brackets — in general, if it is in there, take it out — then sweep up and vacuum again. My firebox, originally about 6 inches wide, 14 inches long and 7 inches deep, was opened up into a gaping 9" x 18" hole the full depth of the stove, about 14 inches — almost a fourfold increase in volume.

Because you are going to be pouring liquid cement against the walls of your newly enlarged firebox, you

Bob Suzuki

104   ENERGY

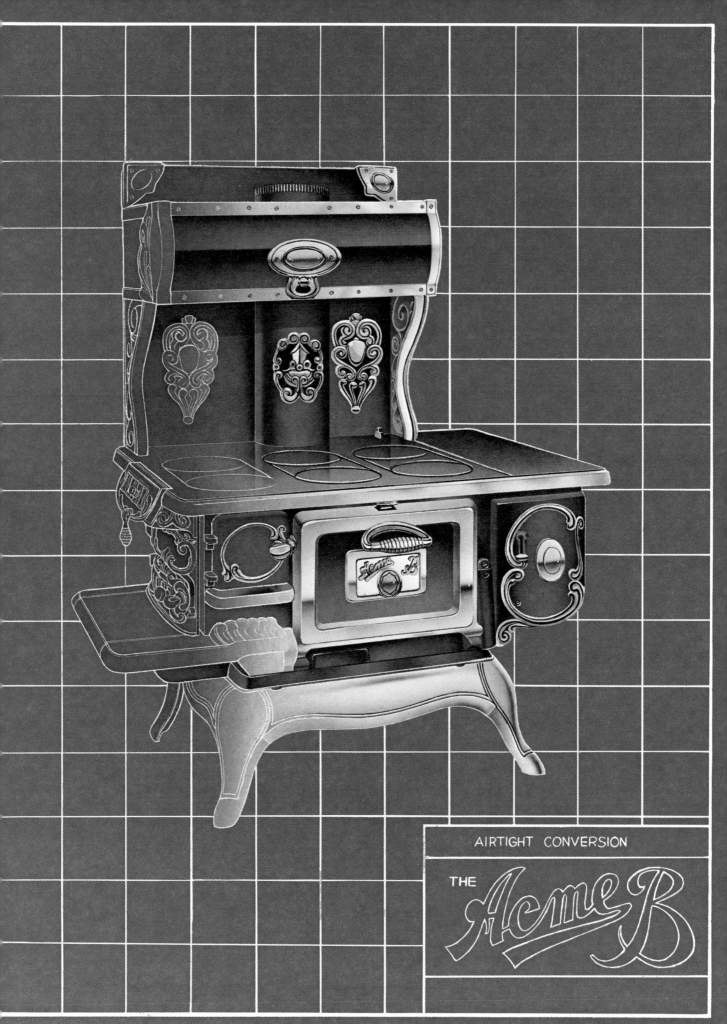

AIRTIGHT CONVERSION

THE

Acme B

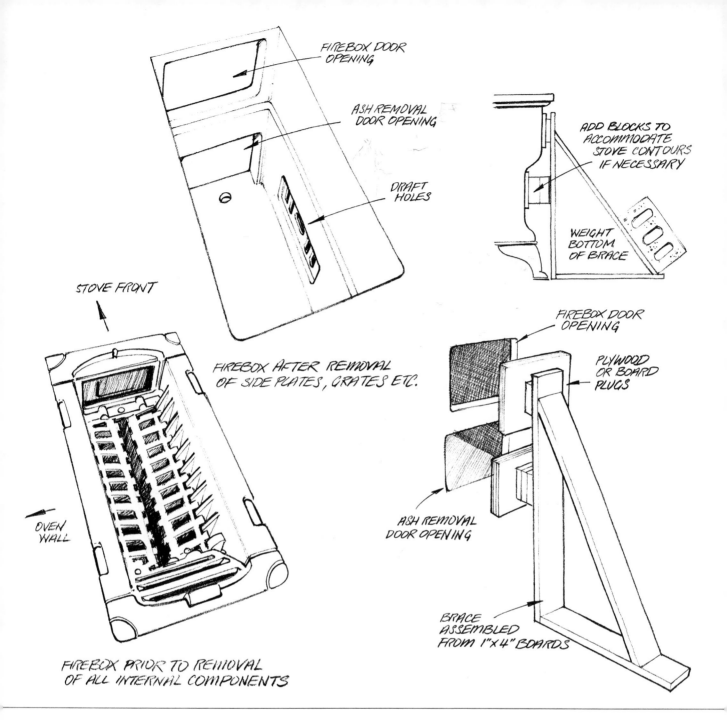

FIREBOX DOOR OPENING

ASH REMOVAL DOOR OPENING

DRAFT HOLES

STOVE FRONT

FIREBOX AFTER REMOVAL OF SIDE PLATES, GRATES ETC.

OVEN WALL

FIREBOX PRIOR TO REMOVAL OF ALL INTERNAL COMPONENTS

ADD BLOCKS TO ACCOMMODATE STOVE CONTOURS IF NECESSARY

WEIGHT BOTTOM OF BRACE

FIREBOX DOOR OPENING

PLYWOOD OR BOARD PLUGS

ASH REMOVAL DOOR OPENING

BRACE ASSEMBLED FROM 1"x4" BOARDS

Begin the process of converting an old-fashioned woodburning range to an airtight stove by gutting the existing firebox — removing liners, grates and ashpan. Plug each hole with coins glued in place or waterproofed boards braced from the outside. Pour a pad of castable refractory cement in the bottom of the stove, using chicken wire for reinforcement if desired, and build the first form with a bottom so that it will "float" on the wet pad. Ensure that the forms can be easily dismantled after the concrete has set.

will have to bung up all the holes, from the great big one where the ashpan used to slide out to the tiny ones where a bracket was bolted on. Small holes can easily be covered from the inside with a penny or a quarter (depending on the size of both the hole and your wallet) held in place with a dab of contact cement. Each larger hole will have to be covered from the outside with a board or a piece of plywood held in place either by propping something heavy against it or by shoring it

up with some Rube Goldberg arrangement of braces — it only has to hold up overnight. Any wooden pieces that will come in contact with the cement must be made waterproof by painting them with oil (used crankcase oil will do) or by wrapping them in old bread bags or some other scraps of plastic. As well as making it easier to remove the forms, waterproofing prevents the wood from soaking up moisture from the fresh cement, resulting in uneven curing.

The key to the whole conversion is the cement used: It must be a castable refractory cement. This material is designed for just this type of use, consisting of a high-temperature cement (calcium aluminate, instead of the calcium silicate used in Portland cement) impregnated with tiny pieces of crushed firebrick. There are several manufacturers across the country, with offices in all the major centres — try the Yellow Pages under "Refractories" — and most boiler-repair shops will sell a

Illustrations by Ian S.R. Grainge

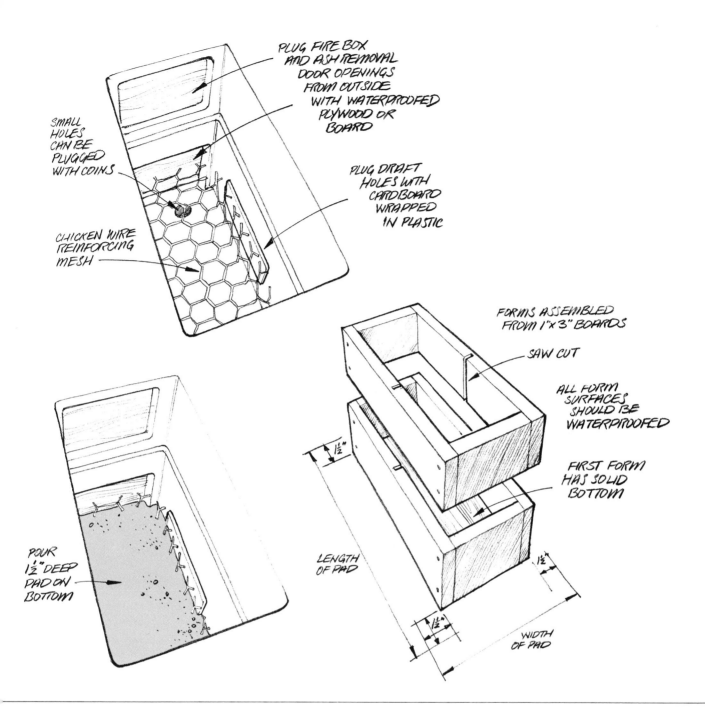

PLUG FIRE BOX
AND ASH REMOVAL
DOOR OPENINGS
FROM OUTSIDE
WITH WATERPROOFED
PLYWOOD OR
BOARD

SMALL
HOLES
CAN BE
PLUGGED
WITH COINS

PLUG DRAFT
HOLES WITH
CARDBOARD
WRAPPED
IN PLASTIC

CHICKEN WIRE
REINFORCING
MESH

FORMS ASSEMBLED
FROM 1" x 3" BOARDS

SAW CUT

ALL FORM
SURFACES
SHOULD BE
WATERPROOFED

FIRST FORM
HAS SOLID
BOTTOM

POUR
1½" DEEP
PAD ON
BOTTOM

1½"

LENGTH
OF PAD

1½"

1½"

WIDTH
OF PAD

bag or two. It comes in large and small bags and is made to different heat tolerances, depending on the application. I buy two 88-pound bags of 2,700-degree-F material for $35 each and end up using only one. I suggest that you do the same — if you just get one, you will run out and hate yourself. Although you may not need the second, it is highly likely that a neighbour will happen along and, inspired to convert his own stove, will want to buy your extra bag.

When you are ready to use the cement, *read the instructions*. It is as easy as mixing Kool-Aid, just add water and stir; these people make the stuff, they use it all the time, and they have no reason to wish you any harm, so follow the directions on the bag. I mix it on a board or in a pan or wheelbarrow, about 10 to 12 cups of dry material and enough water to make it look wet. Test for proper moisture content by lightly tossing an egg-sized lump an inch or so into the air about a dozen

times — it will break apart if it is too dry or will sag down through your spread fingers if it is too wet. Each batch must be well mixed, with no lumps or puddles.

Refractory cement is not supposed to need any sort of reinforcement, and indeed, any large pieces of metal will cause the cement to crack because of the different rates at which the materials expand when heated. I have always used some chicken wire, and the manufacturer says that this will not hurt, but because it is difficult to work with and because I have never seen the cement crack, I intend to stop using it. The choice is yours.

The first pour will be a simple pad on the bottom of the firebox, about an inch and a half deep. Sixteenths of an inch do not count here, so measure the depth by poking it with your finger — two knuckles' worth will do. If you opted for the chicken wire, lift it by the edges and jiggle it so it is more or less in the middle of the pour. Having a two-year-old assistant,

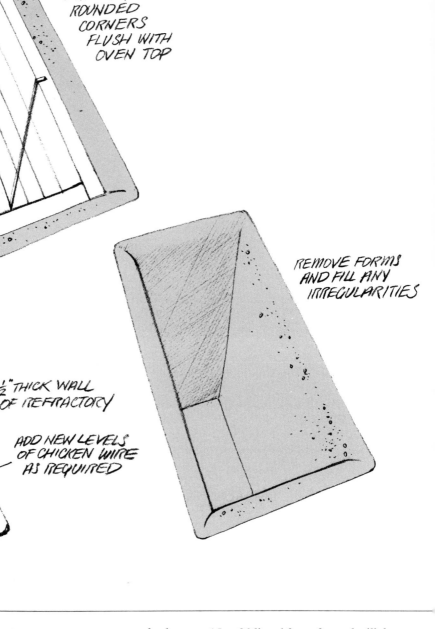

SHAPE INTO
ROUNDED
CORNERS
FLUSH WITH
OVEN TOP

FORM

1½" THICK WALL
OF REFRACTORY

ADD NEW LEVELS
OF CHICKEN WIRE
AS REQUIRED

REMOVE FORMS
AND FILL ANY
IRREGULARITIES

Building forms as they are needed, pour new firebox walls up to the top of the oven. Remove the forms the next day, and allow the concrete to dry thoroughly. Before using, temper the material with gentle heat from a low fire.

as I have, will avail you of plastic beach shovels, which make dandy trowels. If you must make a choice, you can get along better without the assistant than without the shovel.

With the bottom pad poured, you can start thinking about the walls. The idea here is to pour the refractory cement about an inch and a half thick all the way around the firebox, while leaving a void in the centre. You could just make one large form, plunk it down in the centre and pour around it, but I recommend using a series of shallow forms placed one on top of the other. They can each be made of four lengths of 1" x 3" or 1" x 4" lumber tacked together to form a

rectangular box — 15 to 20 lineal feet of wood will do the whole job. The advantage to this system is twofold: first, it allows you to poke through the wet concrete to eliminate any air pockets, especially important if you are using the chicken wire; and secondly, since the side walls of many gutted fireboxes are not even, you can make each form to order, thus keeping a more or less even thickness in the concrete walls. This produces a slightly cockeyed firebox, but the stove wood does not seem to notice.

To make the first form, measure the length and width of the bottom pad, subtract three inches from each measurement and make a small wooden frame of those dimensions. Although subsequent forms will not need it, this first one should have a bottom — also made of 1-inch boards. You are going to have to wait until the concrete has set to dismantle the forms, and it is imperative that they come apart readily. I build mine with the sideboards outside the ends and use 1-inch nails to hold ¾-inch boards — enough to hold but easy to pull apart. I also weaken the sideboards by cutting them about two-thirds of the way through so that they will break easily when I pull them.

As before, use oil or plastic to waterproof the form, and centre it on the pad. Shovel the mixed refractory cement around the form a little at a time, and use a screwdriver or a spike to eliminate air bubbles. Poke the material into corners and through the wire until you get to the top of the form. Repeat this process, adding new forms, mixing more cement and, if you want, twisting in new pieces of chicken wire as needed. When you get to the draught, cover it with the cardboard protector you made up beforehand, hold it in place with a handful of cement and double-check to make sure that the draught slides freely. Keep going until you reach the top of the oven, then give it a professional look by finishing with rounded corners.

Refractory cement dries three times as fast as Portland cement and will set up in about eight hours, so only wait overnight before removing the forms, a job that requires a delicate balance of enough violence to smash the forms and enough restraint to avoid damaging the still green cement. Pry out the lightly nailed ends first, allowing the sides, weakened by the saw cut, to be broken and removed. With the forms out, the concrete will cure more evenly, and you can have a look at your work. If there are any air bubbles or voids, this is a good time to patch with fresh cement, and any ledges caused by using different-sized forms can be rounded off now. In my experience, these patches stick very well — I have yet to see one fall out. After fixing your mistakes, give the whole thing 24 or, preferably, 48 hours to cure.

What you now have, or should have, is a rather large concrete hole in your stove, with walls and a floor about an inch and a half thick, probably no wider or longer but about twice as deep as the original firebox. To keep a fire going in it, you will have to reactivate the draught on the side of the stove. The best way to remove the cardboard form is simply to burn it by aiming a propane torch through the vent holes, although if you really enjoy an awkward, frustrating and unnecessary chore, it can be picked apart and pulled out with a pair of needle-nose pliers. The best tool to re-open the draught is a ⅜- to ¾-inch (depending on the size of your existing draught holes) carbide-tipped masonry bit — a cheap one will do — that can drill air passages through the poured side wall behind the draught-plate holes. You will have to use your own judgment about the angle at which to drill, but the idea is to get the air down close to the bottom of the firebox, but not so low that the holes will be plugged by ashes too quickly. The holes in my stove are four inches above the pad, and that seems about right. Fortunately, the hardened cement drills easily, and if you are not satisfied with the results, you can fill the holes and drill elsewhere.

With the concrete cured and the draught holes re-established, build a small fire in the bottom of the new firebox. By small, I mean a loose handful of Popsicle-stick-sized kindling, kept going for 30 minutes or so by adding a stick or two at a time. After this period of constant, gentle heat, you can slowly increase the size of the fire until it covers the bottom of the firebox. This slow, steady heat dries and tempers the cement, and you will notice it changing to a lighter colour. After an hour or two of controlled burning, when the whole pour is evenly coloured and hot throughout, the job is finished, and your stove is ready to use.

Be forewarned, however, that it will not behave the way it did before. You have lowered the fire, done away with the grates and added almost a hundred pounds of thermal mass. The stove will heat more slowly but more evenly and, like a new bicycle, will demand that you learn how to use it all over again.

You have also complicated the ash-removal process. As with the airtight in the living room, you will now have to wait for the fire to die before shovelling out the ashes. Of course, it is possible to continue removing ashes through the hole where the ashpan used to slide out, either by incorporating a chimney clean-out door directly into the pour or by using a block of wood to create a void behind the ashpan door and attaching a hinged door scavenged from another stove. I have done this successfully for other people, but it compromises the tightness of the design somewhat, and in our house, the priority is heat, not convenient ash removal, so we prefer the shovel-out-from-the-top model. As the philosopher says, "If you want your life to be a picnic, you have to deal with ants."

Lastly, your old cookstove is now a genuine airtight, and it must be treated as such — like fire itself, an airtight makes a good servant but a poor master. Use your stove's new-found capabilities wisely, burn small fires with lots of draught as often as possible and avoid large, smouldering fires with little draught to reduce creosote buildup and the danger of chimney fires. Clean both your stovepipes and the air chamber around the oven (usually emptied through a clean-out door located just under the oven) regularly.

But, of course, as well as the responsibilities that go with an airtight, there are the pleasures too. Pleasures like waking up to a fire in the kitchen stove and steaming hot water in the reservoir. Pleasures like propping your stockinged feet on the oven door after a day spent working in the woods. Like being able to fry and boil and stew and griddle and bake on the same stove that you use for around-the-clock warmth. Go ahead, fall in love with that charming old relic — be seduced by its antiquity, its ornate vulgarity, its affordability. Now you can make that delightful old cookstove into a versatile airtight. ∎

Tom Daly is a boatbuilder and cookstove enthusiast who lives near Bridgewater, Nova Scotia.

Mass Appeal

By Charmaine Gaudet and Michael Webster

> *In the Canadian country setting in which I was brought up 60 years ago, the kitchen was the only room where it was always warm. A kitchen stove well filled with split hemlock maintained a heat of anything from 100 degrees Fahrenheit to about 1,000 degrees Centigrade. You regulated the heat you wanted by the distance you sat from it. I am told that a kitchen of today can be regulated to an even 70 degrees by automatic stoking that is done in the cellar. On the other hand, we had the fun of moving our chairs backwards and forwards.*
>
> **— Stephen Leacock**

The sound of scraping chairs has returned to many a modern Canadian country kitchen, and with it comes the fun and frustration that Leacock knew in his 19th-century childhood. Now, as then, a wood stove comes to be loved and resented by owner-slaves caught up in the emotional tangle of its voracious appetite for labour-intensive split firewood and its money-saving warmth and self-sufficiency. Such was the case for Liz and Shorty Hearn, who never expected to be without their Vermont Castings Vigilant wood stove. But when they moved into a new 1½-storey partly earth-sheltered house tucked into one of the gentle slopes surrounding Wheatley River, Prince Edward Island, the beloved Vigilant was left behind, and the Hearns began a new love affair with a Finnish-style masonry stove.

The new heater lured them away from their more conventional stove with promises of a safe, clean burn and an even, more comfortable heat from less wood. And the massive red-brick heater, standing 7 feet tall on a base nearly 3 feet by 4½ feet, delivers. "We're extremely pleased with it," says Shorty Hearn. "You get a nice, even heat throughout the entire house. It's as warm in the back bedroom as it is standing next to the heater."

The 10,000-pound block of masonry that stands so solidly in the Hearns' living room is of a design that is a relative newcomer to North America but boasts a pedigree traceable through centuries of European wood burning. Indeed, when the apostle Paul wrote his *Letter to the Ephesians* in the middle of the first century, the addressees had been using an early form of masonry heater in their temple for some 400 years. An open fire in the basement was vented through flues set into the temple floor, whose warmth heated the entire building. This system, perfected in the Roman hypocaust (literally, underburning), was exported around Europe where, after the collapse of the Empire, it evolved into several similar but distinct designs.

Today, each style of masonry heater — whether it be the Finnish contraflow, the better-known Russian fireplace, the Swedish *Kakelugnar* or the German *Kachelofen* — features a twisting, convoluted smoke passage built into a massive construction of clay, stone, brick or other masonry material that soaks up the fire's heat like a sponge and then gives it off slowly and evenly over a long period of time. With a masonry stove, the fire does not heat the room; it heats the stonework, which, in turn, warms the room.

Wood-burning appliances of all kinds heat by a combination of radiation and convection. Radiant heat (or, more correctly, infrared electromagnetic energy) is thrown by a heater just as a light bulb emits light, casting "shadows" of cold behind walls and furniture. In practical terms, as anyone knows who has stood shivering in a cold room beside a freshly lit fire, a wood stove can heat your back or your front but not both at the same time. "Infrared radiation," explains Jay Shelton in his *Solid Fuels Encyclopedia*, "is not heat, since it has nothing to do with the motion of molecules. In fact, infrared radiation travels most easily in a vacuum. However, if some of it is absorbed on a surface, such as your skin, its energy becomes heat, which you can then feel." The almost imperceptible radiation of a masonry heater warms the walls and furniture of the house, which then radiate their own gentle heat. The front side, less intensely heated, does not make the backside feel cool by comparison.

Air in a room is heated not by radiation but by convection, the movement of air heated by direct contact with a hot surface. A metal stove is relatively small, offering little surface area to heat the air, and what air is contacted becomes intensely heated, causing the hot-at-the-ceiling, cold-at-the-floor stratification familiar to owners of wood stoves. With a masonry heater, air washes up the vast surfaces of warm brick in the heater's walls and sets up a natural, gentle circulation, resulting in an even, draught-free all-over heat that elicits

glowing testimonials from those, like Liz Hearn, who have experienced it. "It's more comfortable than any other kind of heat we've used," she says.

A masonry stove's warmth is more constant than the artificial fan-driven convection of a forced-air furnace, and at the same time, it is self-regulating. Without blowers or thermostats, a masonry heater depends on the temperature difference between itself and its surroundings to spread its warmth. In a cold room, the stonework distributes its heat rapidly, but as the room warms up, warmth is transferred less quickly. Ken Kern, author of several books on owner-builder construction, including one on masonry stoves, estimates that because of the constancy of its heat, a masonry stove can supply the same amount of comfort at an operating temperature 8 to 12 degrees lower than that of a forced-air furnace.

Since the living space is heated by the retained warmth of the stonework, a masonry heater continues to function long after the fire is out — for 18 hours after, or even more. And in fact, the heat output from a masonry stove does not peak until 6 to 8 hours after a fire is lit. In Prince Edward Island, the Hearns stoke their heater only once a day, letting the fire burn for about 2 hours at a time. In their earth-sheltered home, they find this adequate but admit that two smaller loads would give a steadier heat. While an obvious benefit in many situations, this time lag between stoking the fire and basking in its warmth has its disadvantages too.

Many people who depend on a masonry heater for their primary heat source without oil or electricity for a backup still use a cookstove or fireplace for the times when they want quick heat. A morning fire must always be laid with a mind to the evening's weather — and although the heaters are self-regulating to a point, there is no way to coax more heat from the stonework or to stop it from throwing heat if a major miscalculation is made. Jay Shelton recounts the tale of one New England man who built a colossal 45-ton Russian fireplace only to find he had to anticipate the weather by three days, a feat so difficult that he quit using the heater altogether.

A conventional wood stove, because it depends on an active fire for heat distribution, is controlled either by stoking a small fire frequently or, for long-term untended heat, by building a large fire but restricting the airflow to it. In the latter case, the result is wood smoke, a combination of tar, soot particles and unburned gases nearly as carcinogenic as that from other smouldering vegetable matter, such as tobacco leaves. Condensed on a chimney liner, smoke becomes creosote, that highly combustible scourge of the wood-burning movement. In contrast, masonry heaters eschew the long, slow burn in favour of a short, hot conflagration. Their design allows unlimited quantities of oxygen to mix with the fire so that combustion is virtually complete — most of what escapes up the chimney is water vapour and carbon dioxide.

Periodically, Al Baldwin clambers onto the roof of his 200-year-old farmhouse near Norridgewock, Maine, to peer down his chimney, but after four years

of heating with a Finnish masonry heater, he has yet to clean it. "It looks brand-new," he says. "The flue liner is still pink."

In the end, the effect of uncontrolled fires burning in a massive firebox is a rather astounding twofold efficiency. First, because unlimited oxygen gives complete combustion, more heat is extracted from each stick of wood, and second, the long, convoluted flue passage ensures that more of that heat stays in the room where it is needed, rather than disappearing up the chimney. "It's like you've got respect for the wood," says Ottawa Valley stove mason Norbert Senf. Both the Hearns and the Baldwins estimate that using a masonry heater has slashed their fuel consumption by more than half. With fire duration no longer a factor, long-burning hardwoods like oak and maple lose much of their appeal, and owners of masonry stoves tend to

"They work best with an open-concept floor plan, but generally, they can be built in any house," says Ulli Baumhard of his Kachelofens, or tile stoves.

pass over the valuable hardwoods in favour of slab-wood, slash, softwood or even lumber scraps. Baldwin, still in the midst of renovating his farmhouse, chuckles, "I like to tell people we burn a cord of house a year."

In addition to being more efficient, more comfortable, cleaner and more convenient, masonry heaters are safer — not only because of the vastly decreased chance of a chimney fire but also because the heater itself is never more than warm, a feature appreciated by couples, like the Hearns and the Baldwins, who have young children. According to Shorty Hearn, "We only have to watch our 2-year-old around the doors

The intense heat of an unregulated fire is tempered and retained by 4-inch-thick, glazed ceramic tiles set against a firebox and convoluted flue passage made of refractory cement.

and just for that two-hour firing period. After that, we don't worry." The Baldwins' youngest child, who had been taught not to touch black metal like that on their heater's door, burned his hands badly on a babysitter's white enamel cookstove. Baldwin says that only the cast-iron doors get too hot to touch.

Of the several designs of masonry heater that have survived the centuries, perhaps the best known on this continent is the Russian fireplace, a long, narrow mass of usually plain brickwork that can stretch as high as two storeys. The inner design features a ladder of horizontal masonry baffles set at intervals up to the top of the heater, resulting in a series of long, shallow cham-

bers joined at alternate ends. Smoke from a fire at the front of the bottom chamber enters the second chamber at the back of the stove, travels to the front, where it ascends to the third chamber, and so on, as long as the flue gases remain hot — at least in theory. A variation on this design uses a system of vertical baffles that force the flue gases through an up-and-down labyrinth of masonry passages.

In central Europe, the trend has been to make a masonry stove the focal point of the home design, with the result that the rather plain heater has been dressed up with glazed ceramic tiles. These Kachelofens (pronounced ka-ha-LOW-fens — if you clear your throat at the start of the second syllable), or tile ovens, can be dazzlingly beautiful and often feature a built-in bench (or even a sleeping shelf) that provides a cozy rest where family members can lean against the delicious warmth of the tiles. The normally chunky Kachelofens are located centrally in the house, offering heat in all directions, and their flue passages are often a combination of vertical and horizontal baffles.

Kachelofens are divided into two types. In the first, a cast-iron firebox is set in a mass of firebricks separated from the decorative tiles by an airspace. Grates set in the tiles allow a strong convective current that can be boosted by a fan. A more traditional design features a masonry firebox against which the tiles are set. Because ordinary mortar will not withstand the strong forces of expansion and contraction to which the tiles are subjected, they are normally wired in place, and the spaces between them are filled with flexible grout. Ulli Baumhard, a Toronto-area mason who learned to build Kachelofens in Austria, points out that the tiles which are used differ radically from normal wall or floor tiles. Kachelofen tiles are four inches thick, and Baumhard feels that only the very dense clays used in European-made tiles will stand up to the strain of long-term firing without cracking.

Finnish heaters are nearly square in shape and, at seven or eight feet high, are taller than a typical Kachelofen. This design permits a long, vertical flame path from near the bottom of the heater straight up to its top, creating a strong initial draught that sucks in enormous quantities of oxygen for a thorough, clean burn. Although this feature is central to the Finnish designs, they diverge at this point into two separate versions: the wraparound and the fountain. In the former, flue gases above the fire travel down one side of the heater, pass underneath the firebox and exit at the top of the other side — the flue passage, true to its name, actually wraps itself around the fire. In the fountain style, flue gases travel down both sides (like a fountain, or a whale spouting), meet under the firebox and exit at the back through a common chimney flue. Of the two, the latter is preferred because it throws an equal heat from each side and is less subject to the strains of uneven expansion and contraction.

These designs are unique in that they have two masonry shells. The inner shell, made of refractory cement, forms the firebox, and the outer one, which can be made of brick, stone or tile, provides an attractive façade for the front and forms the outer wall of the shallow 3-inch flue passage on each side. The fountain style is often called a contraflow heater because hot gases running down between the two shells travel against the grain of the gases in the fire chamber as well as against the rising convective current of room air on the outside of the heater.

In addition, the Finnish stove is notably more efficient and cleaner burning than other masonry heaters. This is partly due to the long, vertical flame path, but the design of the firebox itself plays a role as well. Some 20 to 24 inches above the bottom of the firebox, both the back and front walls start to slope inward until they form a narrow 3-inch-wide throat. The turbulent rush of superheated gases and oxygen through its narrow opening assures complete combustion, and the throat becomes a crucible, with temperatures approaching 2,000 degrees F. The design is so efficient at retaining heat in the stonework that, according to Norbert Senf, a metal stovepipe exiting at the back of the stove is only warm to the touch.

For all their benefits, masonry heaters will not solve all the problems of the world, or even of North American wood burners. To begin with, they are not suited to all home designs. Their dependence on natural air circulation necessitates an open house plan, rather than one that breaks up into many small rooms, and for the heat to reach every corner, the stove should be located centrally within the house. Traditionally, perhaps to offset their large floor-space requirements, masonry stoves are installed as part of a room divider, often between the kitchen, where they are fuelled, and the living room, where solid brickwork or colourful tiles radiate a steady, clean warmth.

Masonry stoves are more readily suited to new houses where the structural stresses of the massive stonework can be accounted for in construction. Fitting an older home with a main-floor masonry stove weighing five tons can mean pouring a new slab in the basement and building a foundation up to the floor level to support the weight of the stove, adding up to $1,000 to the installation cost.

Expense is another factor that may cause undecided metal-stove owners to count their blessings. Prices for a tile Kachelofen, installed, start at around $4,000 and know no upper limit — beauty, convenience, safety and efficiency do not come cheap. Of course, glossy ceramic tiles, although elegant and expensive, are no more effective at holding heat than plain brick. Both the Hearns and the Baldwins were able to have their heaters built for about $3,000, partly because they were able to do some of the work themselves.

One aspect of life with a masonry stove is the need to light many fires. Unlike the old airtight come-on of "all winter on one match," a masonry heater is always fired from scratch, usually once in the morning and once at night, to give an even heat during the dead of winter. That means crumpled newspapers and kindling, followed by small sticks and then larger logs — twice a day. For the person who does not mind throwing a couple of logs on an existing blaze but who tires easily of the ritual of lighting new fires, that can be a substantial deterrent — so can wood splitting. With a masonry heater, the overnight log is as passé as getting up in the middle of the night to stoke the fire. Short, hot fires require logs no more than four or five inches in diameter, and this, combined with the increased need for kindling, means that although the size of the woodpile needed to get through the winter is reduced, the time spent on the end of a splitting maul is not.

For Canadians who wish to have a masonry stove built in their home, the choices, although increasing, are still not great. Most commonly available is the Kachelofen, with a handful of masons across the country importing tile (*kachel*) from Europe. Baumhard, who has built seven tile stoves in Ontario, says, "They work best with an open-concept floor plan, but generally, they can be built in any house." Although it only takes eight working days to construct the heater, and his stock of tiles is growing, a special order of tiles can involve a delay of three months.

According to Baumhard, the owner-built Kachelofen is not out of the question for homeowners with a background in masonry — if they have a set of plans. Thus far, the only literature available on Kachelofen design is written in German. Christian Koussis, a Toronto-area mason who studied heater construction in Germany — where stove building is as much a trade as welding or pipefitting and where there is a one-year waiting list for Kachelofens — served a three-year apprenticeship before getting his papers. He stresses that an improperly designed stove can be dangerous as well as inefficient. Among the many twists and turns of the complex flue passage, it is vital — particularly with a coal-fired unit — that there are no dead corners. "Flue gas can collect in these corners," he says, "and like a gas pocket in a mine, it could explode."

Senf was born in Germany and studied the literature on Kachelofens but, in the end, decided to go with the Finnish contraflow. He lives beyond the reach of hydro and telephone lines in the wooded hills north of Shawville, Quebec, and knows that the Finns are serious about wood heat. "There's a certain amount of national chauvinism involved, but they feel that the trend in Kachelofens has been toward good looks — that their efficiency hasn't improved in the last 200 years." In Finland, where 50 percent of the national production of bricks goes into masonry heaters, a new home is not qualified for a government mortgage if it does not contain a contraflow heater. "It's the state of the art," says Senf. "I haven't built anything else since I discovered them."

Since that discovery, he has built 15 Finnish heaters, the first an experimental model in his own house. "I couldn't believe the difference," he says. "With the wood stove, our feet were always cold because the heat went straight up, but the first time I lit up the contraflow, I put one thermometer on the floor and another up at the ceiling, and there was only half a degree difference."

Senf learned his construction techniques from Finnish experts imported for a workshop in Maine by Albie Barden, who built the heaters for the Baldwins, his neighbours, and the Hearns in Prince Edward Island. Barden is the man responsible for bringing the Finnish technology to North America, and he says that although a background in masonry (or at least carpentry) is a big asset, anyone who can follow instructions can build a Finnish heater. "In fact," he adds, "a novice may be as well equipped to build one as an accomplished mason, who may be hampered by certain biases and attachments that the novice may not have." Without a doubt, masonry-heater construction is unconventional. Says Barden, "Some of the details may make a mason very nervous. They don't want to believe that a modest firebox and 20 or 30 feet of convoluted flue passage will not only draw flawlessly but also produce ample heat from small loads of wood."

The special techniques involved in the construction of a masonry heater are necessary in order to accommodate the movement of the massive stonework caused by the temperature fluctuations of the stove. Essentially, a Finnish heater is two different structures resting on the same base, an inner firebox made of firebrick laid with refractory cement as the mortar and an outer skin of ordinary brick. Across the front of the stove, a single row of brick backed by a ¼" blanket of mineral-wool fibre covers the firebrick; the rest of the outer skin is a double layer of bricks. The 3-inch-wide heat-exchange channels keep the outer skin a safe distance from the inner box on each side, but across the back, the outer bricks are again separated from the firebox by a layer of compressed mineral fibre. Resting on top of the inner box is a slab of castable refractory cement which deflects the rising heat from the fire down each side channel and which, aside from the throat of the firebox, takes the most severe punishment of any part of the stove. It must be able to take a large initial expansion or, in Senf's words, "have complete freedom of movement." The castable refractory slab rests loosely on a shelf, where it is packed in mineral wool and covered with a concrete slab that is also set on a bed of mineral-wool fibre. This design allows ready access to the heater's innards in case repairs are needed, another unique feature of the Finnish stoves. The chimney, a single row of bricks around a tile flue liner, stands about an inch away from the stove proper.

The outer skin, although not subject to intense temperatures like the firebox, nevertheless has special needs because, as the medium that passes the heat of the flue gases to the relative cool of the room, it is subjected to a substantial temperature difference from one side to the other. Around three sides of the stove, it is a double skin; that is, two rows of bricks, partly for extra mass and partly because most Canadian fire codes require it. Normal mortar, though strong and weatherproof, is too brittle and unyielding to take the sort of constant movement that occurs in these walls. The Finns use a clay-based mortar (clay, sand and water), which seems to be the only viable solution — it allows the bricks to move without the mortar cracking. This mixture is so soft that, in mason's parlance, it must be raked and repointed — partially scraped out and then covered — with a more conventional mortar when the stove is complete.

Barden sells bags of clay-based mortar imported from Finland because he feels that it contains the only clay he can be sure of, but Senf, with a background in both engineering and masonry, has successfully mixed his own mortar using the Blue Leda clay common throughout the Ottawa Valley, even mixing in 10 percent Portland cement to avoid the tedious raking and repointing process. He has also used Redart terra-cotta clay, available from pottery-supply stores, very successfully.

Barden, in addition to building the heaters himself and sponsoring workshops for other masons, sells detailed plans for three sizes of contraflow heaters and imports the hardware to go with them. Senf has just begun importing the cast-iron doors and other accessories into Canada. On either side of the border, the cost of a heater, using imported castings and local

masonry materials, is about $2,000; labour adds another $1,000. Those figures are for the stove only — the foundation and chimney above the top of the heater are separate. A substantial investment, especially for an appliance that is decidedly not portable. Senf is concerned that with a lack of public awareness of their advantages, the installation cost may not be reflected in the resale value of a house equipped with a masonry heater. "On the other hand," he says, "nobody is going to steal it."

Once it is installed, the proud new owner of any type of masonry stove, whether it be a Kachelofen or a contraflow, has a final, essential task to perform before abandoning himself to the joys of masonry heat: the heater must be cured. Before subjecting the stove to any violent temperature swings, the mortar must be thoroughly dried. Both Senf and Baumhard agree that

The Baldwin's contraflow heater offers a slow but steady warmth, while a built-in cookstove provides quick heat when needed.

while the curing process is not difficult, it is absolutely critical that the correct procedure be followed to avoid cracks in the heater. They recommend lighting two small fires a day for the first week to set up a gentle but fairly constant flow of warm air that will slowly draw moisture out of the stonework. The emphasis is on small and gentle — use softwood only. During the second week, the fires may gradually be increased in size and intensity until the stove is working at its capacity.

If cracks develop in the heater, they may seriously impede its efficiency, allowing warm room air to rise through the heater and up the chimney like a convenis pollution-free, safe and, above all, comfortable. Comparing her experiences with a cast-iron wood stove and her new masonry heater, Liz Hearn says, "The smoky air, the soot, worrying about creosote, cleaning out the stove, taking apart the pipes and cleaning them — well, no more." Says Norbert Senf, "Heating your house with a pile of hot bricks is a great idea." ∎

Charmaine Gaudet is a freelance writer based in Halifax who specializes in travel and energy-related issues. Michael Webster is an associate editor of Harrowsmith.

Sources

Eric Hayes

Curled up on a cherrywood warming seat, Patty Baldwin soaks up the gentle warmth held by the 5-ton mass of a Finnish-style masonry heater.

tional fireplace. For this reason, it is desirable to have airtight doors on the heater, even though the fire is always burned with the dampers wide open. Most stoves are fitted with a chimney damper that slides in and out to cut off the flow of air up the chimney when the fire is out. Traditionally, the damper was shut as soon as the flames had died in the firebox so that all the heat from the bed of coals remained in the stove, but because of the danger of carbon monoxide poisoning, this is no longer a recommended procedure.

After the curing period, the masonry-stove owner is set for life with an attractive heater that will squeeze every calorie of heat out of each fire log and transfer it into a gentle, constant, long-lasting warmth which

Books

THE BOOK OF MASONRY STOVES
By David Lyle
Brick House Publishing

KEN KERN'S MASONRY STOVE
By Barbara and Ken Kern
Charles Scribner's Sons
144 pages
340B — hardcover, $25.50
Available from Harrowsmith Books, Camden East, Ontario K0K 1J0.

Kachelofens

CANADIAN CERAMIC WOODSTOVES
69 Tecumseh Drive
Aurora, Ontario L4G 2X2
(416) 727-2241
Contact: Ulli Baumhard

E.H.L. KACHELOFEN CERAMIC LTD.
4630 Kingston Road
Scarborough, Ontario M1E 4Z4
(416) 282-7411
Contact: Erwin Lindner

HAUSOT MASONRY AND HEATING
Box 1780
Prince George, British Columbia
V2L 4V7
(604) 564-0347

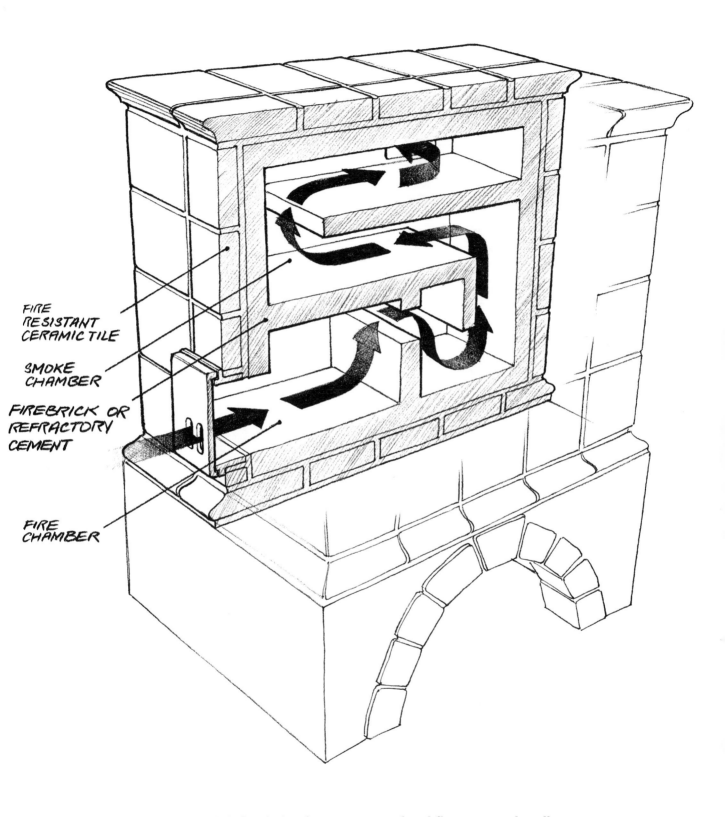

FIRE
RESISTANT
CERAMIC TILE

SMOKE
CHAMBER

FIREBRICK OR
REFRACTORY
CEMENT

FIRE
CHAMBER

A typical Kachelofen design features a convoluted flue passage that allows the masonry to soak up heat like a sponge and radiate it to the room for hours after the fire is out.

Ian S.R. Grainge

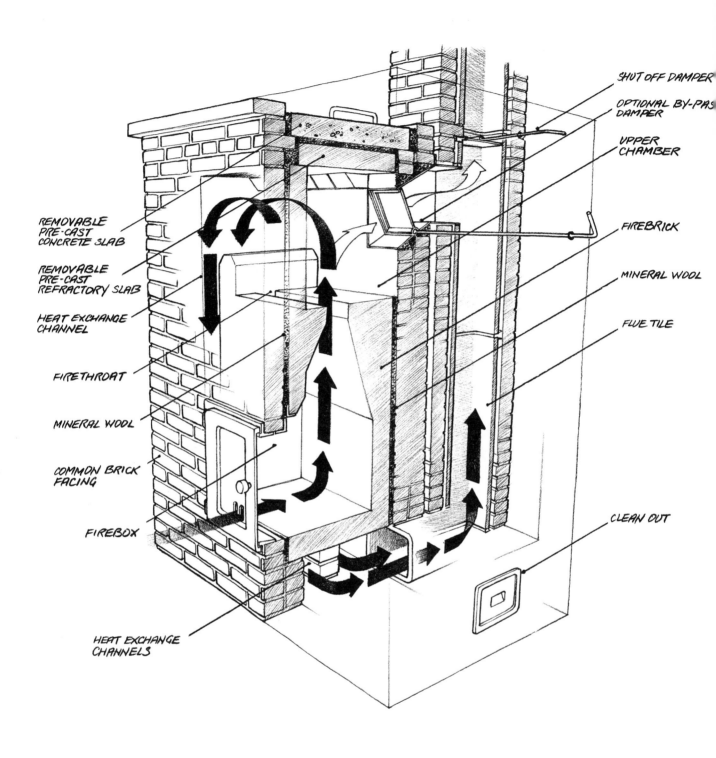

SHUT OFF DAMPER

OPTIONAL BY-PASS DAMPER

UPPER CHAMBER

FIREBRICK

MINERAL WOOL

FLUE TILE

CLEAN OUT

REMOVABLE PRE-CAST CONCRETE SLAB

REMOVABLE PRE-CAST REFRACTORY SLAB

HEAT EXCHANGE CHANNEL

FIRETHROAT

MINERAL WOOL

COMMON BRICK FACING

FIREBOX

HEAT EXCHANGE CHANNELS

The long, vertical flame path and turbulence created by a narrow fire throat ensure complete combustion in the Finnish contraflow heater, while flue passage channels down each side transfer the heat of the fire to the massive brickwork.

Ian S.R. Grainge

Courtesy Ulli Baumhard/Canadian Ceramic Woodstoves

Elegant tile stoves like this replica of a 19th-century Swedish heater are now being made in Canada with imported tiles by a growing number of European-trained masons.

PETER FENDLER
161 Daniel Johnson Boulevard
City of Laval, Quebec H7V 2E1

THERMO HEAT LTD.
3616 Logan Crescent S.W.
Calgary, Alberta T3E 5Z5
(403) 242-4176

RAINER TRIEBE MASONRY AND
KACHELOFEN HEAT
R.R.1
Carlsbad Springs, Ontario K0A 1K0
(613) 822-2889

Finnish Heaters

MAINE WOOD HEAT COMPANY
RFD 1, Box 640
Norridgewock, Maine 04957
(207) 696-5442
Cast-iron doors, dampers and clean-out doors. Plans for small contraflow heater (12" x 12" doors) $10. Plans for large contraflow heaters (16" x 18" and 18" x 22" doors) $15. Payable in U.S. funds. Contact: Albie Barden.

MASONRY STOVE BUILDERS
RR5
Shawville, Quebec J0X 2Y0
Contact: Norbert Senf. Send $2.00 for information packet and prices for cast-iron parts.

Bramble Culture

Raising Canes: A primer in the planting and care of raspberries

By Jennifer Bennett

It is a ritual as soft and hazy as summertime itself, the rekindling of a debate time-honoured among gardeners and always delectably vexatious: Does the raspberry taste better than the strawberry, or does its extreme fragility simply make it seem that way? No less an authority than Carl Linnaeus, father of the scientific system of classifying plants and animals, entered the horticultural fray and penned this opinion about an 18th-century raspberry of his acquaintance: "As to its flavour, it has such a delicate mixture of the sweet and acid, as is not equalled by the best of our cultivated Strawberries." There are those who would today challenge the Swedish botanist's words, but when the discussion takes place in midsummer over a forehead-high row of ripe raspberries, anyone who would defend the honour of the strawberry will find his horn of the dilemma a prickly one. Raspberries cupped gently in the hand, raspberries deliquescing on the tongue, raspberries nestled in the bucket: surely this must be the most ephemeral delicacy in this, or indeed any gardener's, climate.

Certainly, there are some with little good to say about the fruits of the bramble, and most are to be found in the realm of megahorticulture, where the tender raspberry squeezes reluctantly into a world of mass cultivation, mechanical harvesters and 18-wheeled trips to distant markets. Fresh raspberries are an increasingly scarce commercial commodity; when found, they command a fruit lover's ransom. Meagre half-pint cartons were seen in Toronto markets priced at $1.79 in the summer of 1982, and many produce vendors today simply avoid this, the most notorious of perishable commodities.

As with all things complex, however, there is a simple side: five or six dollars will buy a package of five good raspberry plants. True enough, these canes will themselves yield little more than a half-pint of berries in a season, but they do carry a genetic potential. In a 1939 experiment at the University of Manitoba, 14 raspberry plants produced another 157 plants by their first fall. Three years later, there were 13,230 plants — enough, at commercial spacing rates, to cover six acres. It is no wonder that John Wallace of Beaverlodge Nursery in northern Alberta calls the raspberry "the most satisfactory fruit which can be grown in northern locations."

Throughout the colder reaches of North America, the raspberry has legions of followers and, we can speculate with some degree of confidence, has always had, for this is a berry which thrives wild from coast to coast and north even beyond the tree line. As if to gild the undomesticated lily, improved varieties of berries that produce bigger fruit in larger quantities than their untamed forebears will survive in almost every garden in Canada and the northern United States.

It uses the relatively brief summer here to such advantage — the canes shoot up about an inch a day in midsummer — that wild raspberries have formed almost impenetrable thickets of brambles here and there over much of the continent. The European wild raspberry, *Rubus idaeus vulgatus*, is the forebear of most North American domestic berries and looks much like

them: prickly, about six feet tall, and producing red or yellow berries that are smaller and rounder than those on most cultivated canes. The wild North American raspberry, *Rubus idaeus strigosus*, is also part of the genetic heritage of many domesticated cultivars.

There are several low-growing, wild North American varieties as well, notably the hairy raspberry, *R. pubescens*, the trailing raspberry, *R. pedatus*, and the dwarf or arctic raspberry, *R. arcticus*, which Carl Linnaeus praised. The cloudberry, *R. chamaemorus*, is also less than a foot tall, but has large, yellowish fruits that are somewhat sour.

Used in the development of domestic black raspberries is the wild blackcap, *R. occidentalis*, or its western version, *R. leucodermis*. Another relative, the thimbleberry, *R. parviflorus*, has bright red fruits that are softer and more shallowly cupped than those of the common berry. *R. spectabilis* is the salmonberry, a tall, prickly West Coast variety that produces large, gold or red, watery fruits, and is used in breeding extra-early cultivars. All of them are closely related to the blackberry and its kin, which differ from the raspberries primarily in the way their fruit remains attached to the receptacle, or core, when it is picked. Raspberries leave the receptacle on the stem, and so the picked fruit is cup or cap shaped.

The fruit itself is really a cluster of many small fruits called drupelets, each of which begins its life as an individual ovary within the blossom. Thorough pollination is thus required if the fruit is to develop fully, rather than being one-sided or crumbly. Raspberries are mostly self-fruitful, but sometimes two different varieties or cultivars grown together will produce more berries than either cultivar alone, and a nearby hive of bees will almost certainly increase the yield of well-formed fruit.

This fruit, whose flavour is its ticket to new ground via the digestive passages of birds and mammals, appealed likewise to the native Indians, who made use of the raspberry, root to fruit, in medicines, dyes and foods long before Europeans settled North America. Twigs of the common red raspberry were peeled and eaten raw by the Iroquois and were boiled for hot tea by the Ojibwa, who also made a decoction of the roots for the treatment of dysentery and soaked the inner bark of the root to make a soothing eye bath. The Cree infused the leaves, which are high in tannin, in boiling water to treat infant cholera. The berries, of course, were eaten fresh and, according to the early 17th-century journals of Samuel de Champlain, "The savages dry the berries for use during the winter, much as we in France dry prunes for use during Lent." On the West Coast, Captain James Cook wrote more than a century later, "The only fruit trees I met with [were] some Raspberry, Currant and Gooseberry-bushes."

When Europeans settled in North America, they brought some of their own berries and must have been dismayed by their lack of winter hardiness. In *The New American Gardener* of 1843, Thomas G. Fessenden noted that "there are only two sorts of any great value — the white *Antwerp* and the red *Antwerp*." But native raspberries were abundant, and an espe-

Betty Lowden, wife and business partner of raspberry breeder and former mail-order nurseryman Edward Lowden, harvests a crop of organically grown fall-bearing raspberries.

cially good strain of these, known as the *Common Red*, was the favourite until the mid-19th century, when the raspberry, last of the common fruits to attract the attention of plant breeders, seemed suddenly to attract everyone's attention at once. A few of those interested were D.W. Herstine of Pennsylvania who released his *Herstine Red* of 1870; Mr. Older of Independence, Iowa, with his *Older* of 1872; Thomas Cuthbert of New York who announced his *Cuthbert* which, after beginning to be distributed in 1880, became exceedingly popular in the northeast; A.M. Smith of St. Catharines, Ontario, who introduced his *Smith Giant* of 1888. These early breeders must have taken a parental pride in watching their vegetal progeny appear in nursery catalogues and government reports, sometimes well into the 20th century when the publicly sponsored breeding of raspberries took over.

LOCAL SUCCESS

Most Canadian cultivars have come out of the Agriculture Canada research stations in Agassiz and Vancouver, British Columbia; Morden, Manitoba; Ottawa, Ontario; and Kentville, Nova Scotia, with each station producing for a different climate and market. British Columbia breeders work within Canada's best raspberry-growing climate, with mild winters that will allow the growth of such cultivars as Oregon's *Willamette* or British Columbia's *Haida*, too tender to survive almost anywhere else in the North. These berries are tall and so prolific that 80 percent of all the raspberries grown commercially in Canada are produced within a 30-mile radius of Clearbrook, in British Columbia's Fraser Valley. Here, a grower averages 6,000 pounds (8,000 pints) of berries per acre, whereas the Ontario average is a quarter as great. Raspberry growing is big business in British Columbia and two northwestern states, Washington and Oregon. Although virtually all these berries are processed, a rapid rise in raspberry popularity has meant skyrocketing prices: in 1976, the bulk wholesale price of a pound of raspberries was 32 cents; two years later, it was 90 cents.

In Ontario and Quebec, where nearly 20 percent of Canada's raspberries are produced, winters are harsher, the acreages are smaller and there is a larger proportion of pick-your-own operations, most of them in the warm, southernmost parts of the provinces. Sam and Carol Turturici are fairly typical of this area's growers. On their part-time, 26-acre farm near Brampton, Ontario, eight acres are dedicated to pick-your-own raspberries of two types, *Festival* and *Comet*. Last year, the Turturicis charged $1.45 a quart for their berries.

In the Maritimes, the farms are very small and most berries are grown in home gardens. Dr. Don Craig, who heads the Berry Crops section of the Kentville research station, says, "Here, we're comfortable with an acre or two of pick-your-own. *Festival* survives our kooky winters, this freezing and thawing business. People with *Festival* are doing well, making six to eight thousand dollars an acre for pick-your-own." One such grower is Bob Aucoin whose farm, Blueberry Acres, located about five miles from the Kentville experimental station, produces 82 acres of blueberries and two acres of *Festival* raspberries. Last year, pick-your-own brought him 90 cents a pint. The raspberries that were left over sold on local fruit stands for $1.35. Aucoin hopes that eventually he will be able to ship his raspberries to the lucrative American markets the way he already does with his blueberries: "Because of the climate, we're so late in the season, even after Michigan. We started around August 25 with blueberries and shipped till October 11 last year, and we were pretty well alone on the market in Boston."

But it is their perishability that is mostly to blame for the scarcity and high price of fresh raspberries,
which will keep for only about two days in cold storage. Craig says, "Here, you can't even get them to the markets in Halifax if the weather is hot and humid in August when most of the shipping is done — so you might be lucky once and the next time the wholesaler phones you up and says, 'Your load of raspberries has moulded overnight.' " The answer to the supply-and-demand problem for city dwellers is often the pick-your-own patch. Anyone with a little more land might consider growing his own; a sunny, fertile spot of ground 10 feet by 6 feet can produce up to 10 quarts of berries a year.

The type of raspberry one wants is the first choice to be made. Virtually all the domestic raspberries grown in Canada are standard, summer-bearing reds. But there are several other domestic types. One, a variant of the red, which produces a yellow berry, is generally considered to be milder and sweeter than the red. Edward Lowden, an Ontario berry breeder who sold Canada's largest mail-order selection of raspberries before he retired, describes the yellow berries: "Nicer than the reds when you eat them fresh, but when you cook them the flavour's gone."

There are also purple- and black-fruiting types, both of which are more susceptible to disease and less winter-hardy than most of the reds and yellows. Says Don Craig, "We've gone through the gamut of black, purple, *Boysen* and the rest and all were more tender and more subject to disease. Lots of reds grow wild here, so we know they will do well."

Within the red and yellow colour groups, there are also everbearing or fall-bearing selections. These bushes produce one crop during the regular summer season, another on different canes in late summer or early fall. The summer crop is inferior in quantity and berry size to that of most standard cultivars, but the fall harvest produces big berries in good quantity — if any berries ripen at all. As Edward Lowden points out, "Fall-bearing raspberries require the right kind of climate, one that escapes hard freezing till late fall and is not subject to excessive and continuous wet weather in the fall." Fall-bearers, then, will not produce a fall crop in most of the North — ripe raspberries, says Lowden, "freeze as easily as tomatoes."

Although techniques exist for helping canes overwinter, nothing can save a berry that is simply too tender for its environment. Winter-damaged canes may fail to bud entirely in spring, or they may start to grow normally, but as the season progresses, the leaves gradually turn yellow, dead spots appear, and finally the canes die.

Not every standard berry will crop in the North. Frost hardiness varies considerably with cultivar, as is noted on the accompanying table. It varies, also, with location. In 1970, M.C.J. Van Adrichem of Agriculture Canada's Prince George, British Columbia, experimental station reported the results of a countrywide raspberry-hardiness experiment. "At all locations, *Chief* was placed in the hardiest group. All northern locations listed *Honeyking* as the hardiest cultivar tested, while the southern locations, Brooks and Morden, rated *Chief* and *Latham* hardier than

Honeyking. . . . Although *Comet* rated high for hardiness at Ottawa, it was one of the least hardy at Morden, Prince George and Beaverlodge." Raspberry shoppers, then, are wise to choose among cultivars developed nearby, or carried by local nurseries and used by local growers — many of which will have been introduced after Van Adrichem's report was written. Says Lowden, "I have learned that a variety that is best on one property may not be so on another, so I advise testing more than one if you have room."

There are other important differences between cultivars as well. Some have very short canes which require no support but will likely produce a smaller harvest that the picker will have to bend for. Some canes are spiny and some are not. Spineless canes are especially important in the pick-your-own market, but most home gardeners also prefer them. On the other hand, spines may help deter porcupines bent on nibbling canes to their roots.

Disease resistance varies considerably as well. Fungal diseases such as moulds, mildews and blights as well as viral diseases are the most troublesome, causing the production of crumbly, uneven berries, or no fruit at all. Transmitted to plants by aphids, viral diseases such as mosaic, says Don Craig, are evident on wild raspberries everywhere he goes in the northeast: "I never see many aphids but there are a few; I've had them identified. There are enough to carry the disease." On the West Coast, he says, aphids are "tremendously abundant. You find aphids roped on the tips of wild berries, but here you never find that. I think it must be because our winters are more severe."

In relatively benign areas, then, where viral epidemics have wiped out entire raspberry crops time and again, erasing most of the old cultivars from recommended listings, the major thrust of breeding has been the development of cultivars that resist aphids. Of the five summer raspberries named at England's East Malling research station since 1970, four carry one or more genes for resistance to the raspberry aphid, *Amphorophora idaei.* All of the new western cultivars, too, have inbred aphid resistance.

Diseases will not necessarily kill plants, but will almost certainly lessen the harvest and the longevity of the canes, so even backyard growers should choose canes resistant to diseases prevalent around them, and then manage the plants in a way that will minimize disease problems. Raspberries should not be planted near wild brambles, most probably infested with aphids, nor should they be planted near or in a place previously occupied by *Solanaceae* such as tomatoes, peppers and potatoes, which are vulnerable to some of the same diseases. Healthy raspberries are better able to resist diseases than are unhealthy ones, so plants that are sufficiently winter hardy for one's area, that

Top*, after they have been pruned, trained raspberries on a commercial B.C. acreage reveal the neat rows that encourage the growth of healthy plants. Wire supports,* **middle***, keep rows orderly and improve their exposure to the air and sun.* **Bottom***, the raspberry is actually composed of many small individual fruits, whose full development is the result of a cooperative effort between berry breeders, berry growers and the bees.*

are planted in good, deep, well-drained soil in full sun, and kept weeded and pruned, are likely to be as healthy as their genetic means will allow. Old plants, too, tend to become diseased. Commercial growers may replace a field of raspberries in less than 10 years; a backyard patch may bear for a lifetime, but the harvest is bound to lessen and berry quality decline as the roots age.

Because some diseases can be carried in vegetative material — domestic raspberries are reproduced not from seeds but with cuttings from other raspberry plants — most canes are now grown by certified or registered growers, as seed potatoes are grown. Don Craig says that his 1981 release, *Nova*, is now being propagated by nurseries which must follow the guidelines developed by the province in order for their plants to be certifiable. "It is simply an agreement between the provincial department of agriculture and a nursery — there is no real law of certification nationally." Bountiful Ridge Nurseries of Maryland, some of whose raspberries are marked 'registered' in their catalogue, notes, " 'Registered' raspberry plants are grown from foundation stock originally indexed virus-free and produced in screen-houses. The 'Registered Plants' are grown under isolation from this originally virus-indexed stock on fumigated soil under University of Maryland supervision. An approved spray schedule for insect and disease control is followed and the plants are inspected regularly."

Bucking the spray schedule is Edward Lowden, whose organically raised stock was certified in the 1920s, but who says that since the certification regulations were changed in 1965, "We have made no attempt to grow certified stock, as one of the conditions for certification is that you must do a lot of spraying. We are strictly organic growers and have never sprayed raspberries in our lives, and don't intend to start now."

Also varying from cultivar to cultivar are berry quantity, size, flavour and colour (even within the colour groupings). *Royalty*, a purple-red cultivar released in 1982 from the Geneva, New York, experimental station, has berries that tend to weigh approximately a quarter of an ounce each — about 80 berries to a pound — whereas Craig's *Nova* produces the more normal one-eighth-ounce berries. Dr. Elizabeth Keep writes from East Malling, "Commercial growers appreciate large-fruited varieties because hand-picking costs are reduced for a given weight and pick-your-own growers, also, are finding that their customers prefer extra-large fruit." For the home grower, however, flavour is usually more important than size. And flavour is a subjective issue, although the Ontario Ministry of Agriculture and Food (OMAF) has rated the popular berries for flavour. These ratings appear in the accompanying table.

The choice of an appropriate raspberry cultivar, or better, cultivars, is one of the most important preparations the berry gardener will make. This may be a lifetime investment, so a run to the neighbourhood shopping mall for generic canes will likely be a waste of a good deal of effort to come. But there are other important preparations as well. Again, keep in mind that this is a long-term project. After the first full crop

of berries in a year or two, your patch of raspberries may be around for as long as you are. It is important, then, to choose a suitable berry site, and to prepare it well.

This spot should not be located in the middle of the vegetable garden, as raspberries are tall and notoriously invasive. In a battle between berries and beets, the beets will surely lose. Better have the raspberry patch on its own, preferably surrounded with mowed grass or a perimeter of tilled earth to keep the canes within bounds. This spot should be in full sun and sheltered from strong winds, with soil that is well drained but not bone dry. If you must use a wet spot, try a tolerant cultivar such as *Gatineau*.

If the future raspberry patch is now weedy and overgrown, begin the site preparation six months ahead of planting; this spring for fall planting, or any time this year for planting next spring. If the spot is already quite clear, however, the roots could be planted this spring, after any necessary fertilization.

ORGANIC SITE

In the Agriculture Canada publication, *Growing Red Raspberries in Eastern Canada*, Don Craig writes, "Organic matter plowed into the soil is really its life blood. It provides plant food, improves the physical properties of the soil, promotes the growth of helpful soil organisms and increases the water-holding capacity of the soil. To prepare the soil before planting raspberries, plant a row crop followed by a green-manure crop such as rye, buckwheat, oats or millet. Weed-free animal manure (15 to 20 tons per acre) is another way to improve the organic matter content of soil. Lesser amounts of poultry manure (5 to 10 tons per acre) can also be used in the fall. Raspberry roots in contact with fresh poultry manure will be severely injured. Weeds, particularly quack grass, must be eliminated before planting."

The backyard grower, of course, does not measure his fertilizer in tons, nor has he such an overwhelming task as the would-be commercial grower. In a small patch, a spade or rotary tiller will break up weedy areas, which should then be combed with a rake to remove weed roots. About an inch of compost or manure (three or four bushels to 100 square feet) may be incorporated into the patch.

The amount of space the plot will occupy will depend in part upon the planting system used. The following systems take into consideration the fact that pickers must have access to all plants, that cultivation must take place between rows, and that disease is least likely to occur in a spacious, well-weeded plot. Many home raspberry plantings become unhealthy, unproductive and unharvestable thickets because the gardener tried to save space by crowding plants.

The first system, the linear, is the most popular among commercial growers of tall canes. Plants are set about two feet apart in single rows, and each plant is allowed to develop 5 to 10 canes, forming clumps at intervals along the row. Suckers that sprout else-

RECOMMENDED RASPBERRIES

BOYNE

Early mid-season (July 9); medium-tall canes that are very strong and spiny; very hardy; heavy yield of somewhat small berries that Voakes says have "the best flavour of any we grow," while OMAF rates flavour "fair to poor." Introduced in 1960 from Morden, Manitoba.   A, Bo, D, L, Mc, S-Mc, Pa, R, V

CHIEF

Early; short, vigorous canes; very hardy; small fruit of good flavour. Alberta Nurseries & Seeds calls it the "finest for this climate." Considered by most commercial growers to have been surpassed by *Boyne* for the Prairies. Introduced in 1920 from the University of Minnesota.   A, Bo, L

COMET

Early mid-season (July 10); tall, sturdy, spiny canes; hardy (Sears-McConnell calls it hardy to zone 3); moderately susceptible to mildew; OMAF rates the flavour "fair." Introduced in 1954 from Ottawa.   S-Mc

FESTIVAL

Mid-season (July 12); erect, short, nearly spineless canes; very hardy; resistant to mildew; flavour rated "very good" by OMAF; recommended by D.L. Craig of Kentville for areas with greatly fluctuating early spring temperatures. Introduced in 1972 from Ottawa.   No mail-order source.

GATINEAU

Very early (July 6); short canes; hardy, very susceptible to anthracnose; fairly tolerant of wetness. Flavour rated "fairly good" by OMAF. Introduced in 1972 from Ottawa.   D, R

HERITAGE

Everbearing; first crop mid-season (July 18); second begins around late August; sturdy, upright short canes that need no support; moderately hardy (Burpee calls it hardy to -20 degrees F, while Sears-McConnell calls it hardy to zone 3B). Voakes reports that in early September his fall crop began to produce "an enormous crop of large, firm berries with very good flavour." Introduced in 1969 from Geneva, New York.
          D, Ma, Mc, S-Mc, R, V

KILLARNEY

Early mid-season (July 9); medium-tall, sturdy, very spiny canes; very hardy; recommended for Prairie growers by the Manitoba Department of Agriculture. OMAF rates it "very productive" but the flavour "poor." Introduced in 1961 from Morden, Manitoba.   Be, Bo

LATHAM

Mid-season (July 17); canes medium-tall (about five feet), slender; popular but does not compare well with many newer cultivars; berries tend to be crumbly. Flavour rated "poor" by OMAF. Introduced in 1920 from Minnesota experimental station.   D, G, Ma, Mc, S-Mc

MUSKOKA

Mid-season (July 14); medium-tall, spineless canes somewhat susceptible to winter injury in most areas; a very heavy producer. Flavour rated "good" by OMAF. Introduced in 1950 from Ottawa.   Bo

NEWBURGH

Mid-season (July 14); medium-tall, somewhat spiny canes; moderately hardy; susceptible to viral diseases but resistant to fungal diseases; fruit hard to pick unless fully ripe, tends to crumble. Flavour rated "good" by OMAF. Introduced in 1929 from Geneva, New York.   D, R

SEPTEMBER

Everbearing; first crop early mid-season (July 9), second begins in mid-September in Vineland and coastal British Columbia; tall canes susceptible to wind damage and to winter injury; OMAF rates the flavour "only fair." Introduced in 1947 from Geneva, New York.   D, V

SKEENA

Second in importance, after *Willamette*, in the giant British Columbia raspberry industry, *Skeena* produces larger, brighter berries in greater quantities than does *Willamette*. It also has especially sturdy, smooth, upright canes. Considered winter-hardy in Ohio, in Michigan and in limited tests in Ontario. Introduced in 1978 from Vancouver. No mail-order source.

TRENT

Early (July 8); canes short (about 4½ feet tall), upright, spiny; hardy; susceptible to mildew, anthracnose, spur blight. Lowden reports, "The berries are produced on the outside of the bushes where they are easily seen, making them a favourite with pickers." Beaverlodge notes, "This remains our standard of excellence for adaptability, yield and quality." Introduced in 1943 from Ottawa.   Be

WILLAMETTE

Mid-season (July 15); tall (about 10 feet), spiny canes; large, firm fruit becomes dark red when ripe; will not tolerate poor drainage; very susceptible to winter injury; the major cultivar grown commercially in the warmest areas of British Columbia and Washington. Introduced in 1943 from Oregon.
          D, V

Canadians who wish to import raspberry canes from the U.S. and Americans who want Canadian plant materials must write to their own federal department of agriculture for the requisite forms and information.

(The date listed in brackets denotes the average first date of ripening at Vineland, Ontario. Actual ripening dates will tend to be later in cooler areas and earlier in warmer areas.)

Code letters following each raspberry indicate nurseries carrying this type — see Sources.

Robert Kaufman

where are pruned away. The canes can then be tied in small bundles to double-cross wires, forming a V-shaped row.

In the hedgerow system, the suckers that grow between the original plants are maintained if they grow within the row, which may be as wide as 2½ feet. If tall canes are involved, this system also benefits from support wires. Best suited, however, to short, sturdy canes that do not require support, the hedgerow system makes good use of limited space.

The third system involves growing groups of 5 to 10 strong canes around a single support. This is the hill system, best in a small garden where only a few plants can be accommodated, or in a large acreage where space is not a problem — mechanical tillage can then be used between rows and between plants.

Whatever the planting system used, commercial acreages usually have rows 10 feet apart at most — the taller the canes and the wider the cultivation equipment, the wider the paths should be. In a backyard plot, paths may be as narrow as five feet. In the hedgerow system, suckers will be allowed to fill in between the plants in the row but will not fill in between the rows.

Raspberries are planted in either spring or fall, with early spring the favoured time in most of the North. In southern Ontario, the West Coast and parts of the northern states, however, fall planting is often preferred. The nursery plants will be about a year old and dormant at the time of purchase. They must be planted immediately or else stored in a cool, moist place for a short time before being planted.

In a hole two to three feet from the next one in the row, set each plant slightly deeper than its present soil mark. As soon as it is planted, prune it to about four inches in height and water it well. Because no berries should develop the first summer (this would utilize plant strength that could better be used to grow strong roots), remove blossoms as they appear. Given about an inch of water a week the plants should thrive, so that by the third year there will be a solid row of canes.

This is because red, yellow and some purple raspberries produce suckers from their roots and shoots, 6 to 15 a year per plant, from the base of their canes. Although the plant roots are perennial, these suckers and shoots are biennial; they will grow to their full height during the first year, when they are known as primocanes, overwinter, and then, the following season, when they are called floricanes, they will produce fruit, never to do so again. (Fall bearers are slightly different, as we shall see.) There are two very important pruning times, then, for the raspberry grower; one is late summer or fall when mature floricanes that have produced fruit are removed. The other takes place in very early spring, when all dead, weak, damaged or unwanted canes are removed, and tall-caned cultivars are shortened to 4½ feet or about 6 inches above the support wires. In all cases, unwanted canes are snipped off at ground level, an operation most easily done with long-handled pruning shears.

One very important pruning exception occurs with the everbearing or fall-bearing raspberry. Its summer crop is produced lower down on canes whose tips produced fruit the previous fall; thus, from cultivars such as *Heritage* or *September*, the removal of canes that produced fruit in fall would result in no crop the following summer. After the summer crop, however, the fruiting canes should be removed. Some growers, especially those who have both standard and everbearing raspberries, prefer to allow the everbearers to produce only a fall crop which, in this case, will be larger than it would otherwise be. These growers mow the entire plot of canes after the first hard frost, the system followed by Edward Lowden.

Two further pruning jobs are required with purple and black raspberries. In early summer, when the shoots are 2½ or 3 feet tall, the tips of the shoots are pinched off, forcing the growth of side branches. In early spring, when the weak and undesired canes are removed, the side branches should be shortened to about a foot long.

The most ambitious pruning job of all comes to the gardener who has fallen heir to an overgrown plot of raspberries, or who has left his own pruning work untended. If the berries are old and unproductive, it is wise to cut all the canes at ground level and plough or dig up the roots, removing shoots later as they appear. Then start fresh with a new raspberry plot in a new place. If, however, the plants seem to be in good condition, again cut all the canes back to the ground, then till paths between what will be the new rows and zealously prune out suckers as they appear in the paths, while keeping the plants in the rows thinned to the strongest canes. After this, prune as usual.

Cane growth will be especially lush in fertile soil, but this can be too much of a good thing. Edward Lowden says that one of the most common errors made by backyard raspberry growers is using too much manure. "There's been no manure on my berries in 40 years. If they pile manure on them they'll grow canes instead of berries. And that's what a lot of people do." A yearly application of mulch and, if available, compost, will maintain a small plot that was initially well prepared.

Mulching also keeps weeds down and, along with occasional passes with a rotary tiller, or the cultivation of lawn grass in the paths, is one of the best systems for keeping raspberries in control. Jim Manchester, a pick-your-own grower in Vermont, told *Gardens For All* newsmagazine, "We try to keep leaf mulch constantly around our plants." Farther north, about six inches of straw, hay, sawdust or other organic material should be applied to the pathways after tillage during the second spring of growth of the canes. Every spring thereafter, the mulch is reapplied after cultivation.

Growers wishing to expand their plots can transplant suckers elsewhere, moving them with the same care and methods as were utilized originally. Black and purple raspberries, which produce few or no suckers, are normally propagated by tip layering. In late summer, bend the mature canes and poke their tips vertically into the soil about three inches deep. The following spring, one or more small plants should appear around the buried cane, which is cut about six inches above ground level to provide a handle with which the tip plants can be held and moved to the desired spot. Each plant is placed in a hole six inches deep, and the roots are first covered with about two inches of soil — roots too deeply covered are likely to rot. Clip off the "handle" of old cane at the soil level and, as the plant grows, fill in the hole around it.

Where the season is too short for tip layering, tip cuttings are propagated in a greenhouse or misting frame. These propagation methods are time consuming and difficult, so tissue culture, the growth of new plants from a few cells of parent plants, is now being used to multiply some black and purple cultivars such as New York's new purple-red *Royalty*.

Winter protection is needed for black and purple raspberries throughout most of the North, and for red raspberries in the Far North and the Prairies, where John Wallace of Beaverlodge Nursery recommends that "protection of the canes by tip-covering during the winter is advised for all." Making the bend as close to the ground as possible, bend the canes down to the ground and cover their tips with enough soil to hold them in place. This is done mostly to protect the canes from desiccation, a major cause of winterkill. The uncovering should be done before spring growth starts, when minimum temperatures have risen to about five degrees F. Where the snowfall is heavy, cane breakage is a worse danger. In late fall, Bob Aucoin of Kentville, Nova Scotia, ties bunches of canes together, tepee style, with baling twine, and snips the twine as soon as the snow melts in spring. "That's the easy part," says Aucoin. "The hard part is tying them all up in the fall." Amazing to what lengths a Northerner will go to produce a crop of decidedly better berries. ∎

Jennifer Bennett is an associate editor of Harrowsmith.

Sources

Bracketed letters following each company name correspond to references in "Recommended Raspberries" chart (previous page).

LAKESHORE TREE FARMS LTD. (L)
R.R.3
Saskatoon, Saskatchewan S7K 3J6

PATMORE NURSERY SALES (Pa)
Brandon, Manitoba R7A 5Z7

ALBERTA NURSERIES & SEEDS (A)
Bowden, Alberta T0M 0K0

W. ATLEE BURPEE CO. (B)
Warminster, Pennsylvania 18974
Also *Thornless Red Mammoth* standard red; *Indian Summer* everbearing red; *Fallgold* everbearing yellow; *Bristol* black; *Cumberland* black; *Brandywine* purple.

BEAVERLODGE NURSERY LTD. (Be)
Box 127
Beaverlodge, Alberta T0H 0C0
(403) 354-2195
Also *Honeyqueen* gold, a very hardy, yellow-fruited cultivar.

BOUGHEN NURSERIES VALLEY RIVER LTD. (Bo)
Valley River, Manitoba R0L 2B0
(204) 638-7618
Also *Wyoming* black, "quite hardy with us, heavily fruiting and a mild flavour."

DEAN FOSTER NURSERIES (D)
Hartford, Michigan 49057
Standard reds: *Canby, Early June, Fairview, Hilton, Mammoth Red Thornless, Meeker, Summer, Taylor, Citadel*. Everbearing reds: *Durham, August Red, Indian Summer, Fall Red, Scepter*. Blacks: *Cumberland, Huron, Black Hawk, Bristol, New Logan, New Morrison, Allen, Jet*. Golds: *Fall Gold, Golden Queen, Forever Amber*. Purples: *Sodus, Clyde, Brandywine*.

GOLDEN BOUGH TREE FARM (G)
Marlbank, Ontario K0K 2L0
Catalogue $1.00.

MAKIELSKI BERRY FARM & NURSERY (Ma)
7130 Platt Road
Ypsilanti, Michigan 48197
(313) 434-3673
(313) 429-9355
Also *Canby* and *Scepter* red raspberries; *Lowden, MacBlack, Munger, Bristol, Cumberland, Logan* black raspberries; *Brandywine, Royalty, Lowden Sweet* purple raspberries.

McFAYDEN SEED CO. LTD. (Mc)
Box 1800
Brandon, Manitoba R7A 6N4
Also *Tayberry*, a frost tender blackberry/raspberry hybrid; *Logan* black raspberry.

LE REVEIL DE LA NATURE (R)
R.R.1, St-Philibert
Beauce, Quebec G0M 1X0
(418) 228-1268
Catalogue $1.00.

SEARS-McCONNELL NURSERIES (S-Mc)
Port Burwell, Ontario N0J 1T0
(519) 874-4405
(or through any Sears catalogue outlet)
Also *Black Hawk* black, "hardy in zones 4-9."

VOAKES' BERRY FARM (V)
Box 368
Wheatley, Ontario N0P 2P0
Also *Hilton* standard red, "very hardy"; *Mammoth Red Thornless* standard red; *Canby* thornless standard red; *Sentinel* standard red; *Black Hawk* and *Morrison* black; an unidentified yellow.

Predator Patches

Seeding the winds of insect war in the pest-plagued home garden

Article and photography by Adrian Forsyth

That my first garden produced anything at all was no small horticultural coup. Hacked out of a vacant city lot, my plot-to-be consisted of stiff, sun-baked clay mixed with quack grass roots, broken bottles, rusting Volkswagen parts and an unexplained quantity of discarded undergarments. To my surprise and delight, religious application of compost was enough to produce a profusion of greenery even from this soil — if that is not too kind a description. But at the same time, my unlikely patch produced a second, not nearly so delightful bumper crop: a horde of leaf-chewing and sap-sucking insects that, for a time, appeared intent on reaping all of my hard-won bounty.

Although the same literature that had wisely recommended the copious application of compost had also asserted that this practice, coupled with crop rotation and avoidance of pesticides, would make most insect problems vanish, the verdant, promising days of spring turned into a summer of hand-to-hand combat with an advancing army of earwigs, aphids, cutworms, flea beetles and swollen, wiggling caterpillars. True, many of these pests can be controlled with organic products such as rotenone and *Bacillus thuringiensis*. But both have drawbacks. *B. thuringiensis*, a virus that attacks caterpillars, simply has too short a life to be completely effective. And I suffer violent reactions when exposed to rotenone. This reduced me to a losing campaign of seeking out and hand picking pests.

As the summer progressed, I began to notice that my labours were being assisted by other insects, which proved to be a good deal more efficient than my clumsy fingers. Occasionally, I would come upon a lethargic cater-

Aesthetic as well as utilitarian, the spreading platforms of hundreds of miniature blossoms on plants such as the cow parsnip and other members of the large Umbelliferae family both beautify the garden and provide rich sources of vital nectar for beneficial wasps.

pillar, its back festooned with the white woven silk cocoons of parasitic wasps. Because the prospect of having someone or something else doing the killing had considerable appeal, I started to investigate ways in which the effects of beneficial parasitic insects, particularly small wasps that are harmless to humans, could be enhanced in my garden.

The solution, I found, is both functional and beautiful. Because wasps require nectar to flourish, they can be attracted to any garden that boasts stands of such diverse, easy-to-grow and useful plants as carrots, Jerusalem artichokes, daisies and dill.

The parasitic wasps are a rich and widespread group of thousands of species that prey primarily on other insects. Few insect groups are not parasitized by some type of wasp. In most instances, the female wasps inject their eggs into other insects, and the resulting larvae literally mine the innards of their hosts until they die. The various types of parasitic wasps attack all life stages of their victims: eggs, larvae, pupae and adults. In the garden, they prey on aphids, bean beetles, cutworms, grasshopper eggs and the notorious green caterpillars of the white cabbageworm moth.

But, despite their diversity, most parasitic wasps are extremely small, only a few millimetres long. Some groups, such as *Trichogramma*, are mere pinheads, able to grow to maturity within the confines of a single butterfly egg. Even the most humble backyard garden plot is a vast continent to these tiny hunters. To them, the leaf of a tomato or sunflower must appear as a spacious plain, thick with a forest of plant hair. The trunk of an apple tree must seem a brown world of rough canyons and crevices. They have limited visual powers to aid them in their search for food. Theirs is a time-consuming olfactory quest, and as they trundle across the foliage, their antennae drum incessantly in an alternating rhythm sifting for the chemical signatures and traces of their prey. Some of the victims of these wasps are easy targets: insect eggs and pupae require nothing more than a jab of the egg-laying ovipositor. Caterpillars, however, sometimes demand a battle.

To the small parasitic wasps, a caterpillar is a huge and powerful bull-like grazer. Many thrash violently as soon as they feel the tickle of wasp feet, and some rear back, gushing acrid orange regurgitations over their attackers. Still others have long poisonous structures hidden behind their heads, which come lashing out like whips at their foes.

The wasp's hunt, then, is a tiring business, and this is the crux of its difficulties in a garden. In the wild, the exhausted wasp female is easily revived by a suck of flower nectar, but because of her tiny size, she relies on plants with easily accessible nectars. The nectar in

Even the smallest backyard garden is a vast continent to tiny parasitic insects who pass their days in an exhausting and dangerous search for prey. **Top**, *a female giant ichneumon wasp undertakes the energy-demanding task of seeking out horntail larvae in tree bark by sensing their vibrations, then inserting her ovipositor through several inches of wood. A beneficial ant,* **centre**, *drives a harmful fly off the blossom of a Rocky Mountain sunflower.* **Bottom**, *a feeding* Polistes *wasp.*

the flowers of vegetables like peas, beans and even smaller blossoms like tomatoes or various trees is recessed beyond the reach of minuscule tongues, and many wasps risk starvation within a vegetable garden or orchard. In the wild, parasitic wasps depend primarily on shallow flowers such as Queen Anne's lace. This species is an umbel; that is, it belongs to the family Umbelliferae. Umbels are designed for tiny pollinators such as beneficial wasps, and their spreading platforms of hundreds of miniature blossoms are exceptionally attractive. One study found that a single umbel species in German woodlands attracted 168 different species of insects, most of them parasitic wasps.

Work done by Agriculture Canada shows that *Orgilus obscurator*, a wasp that attacks pests such as the white cabbageworm moths, tent caterpillars and pine shoot moths, is attracted exclusively to umbelliferous flowers. Other species of parasitic wasps are also primarily attracted to umbels, but they will also feed on milkweed, catnip and buckwheat. When orchards with and without populations of appropriate wildflowers were compared, it was found that the wildflower orchards had much higher levels of parasite action against tent caterpillars and codling moths.

Work done by Paul Syme of the Canadian Forestry Service on the effect of nectar availability on the longevity of *Orgilus obscurator* showed that nectar from Queen Anne's lace enabled adults to live five times longer than unfed individuals. This allows the female to make full use of her total egg supply. Potentially, she can lay 160 to 200 eggs, but her maximum rate is only 10 per day, a limitation that presumably evolved because of the large search time required to find prey. She can survive the three weeks needed to use all of her eggs only if nectar is available. Syme was impressed enough by this relationship between nectar and parasite effectiveness to recommend plantings of wild carrot along with buckwheat, milkweed and catnip in pine plantations as a means of augmenting biological control of pine shoot moths. This practice is already in use in Russian fruit orchards.

The availability of umbelliferous plants has affected the success of other biological control programmes. Efforts to introduce a parasitic wasp (*Tiphia popilliavora*) into the United States from Asia to control Japanese beetles were most successful where stands of wild carrot occurred.

These studies and my own observations suggest that plantings of umbels are an ideal pest-control tactic that not only lures in and sustains populations of parasitic wasps but also adds to the culinary and aesthetic value of the garden. In our eastern Ontario garden, we have successfully grown the usual umbels (carrots, celery, parsnips and parsley) but also anise, caraway, chervil, coriander, cumin, dill, fennel and lovage. All of these are pleasing to the eye and palate, easy to grow and relatively pest-free. If your garden suffers from carrot maggots, be aware that caraway, fennel and long-rooted parsleys sometimes are affected by this fly. Thus, one may wish to avoid these and stick to anise, cumin, lovage and other fibrous-rooted umbels. I prefer to disperse the different umbels according to their grow-

On a hot summer afternoon, the author's interplanted row of buckwheat and Jerusalem artichokes hums with the activity of beneficial wasps, attracted by nectar easily obtained from both plants' leaves. This sort of planting is ideal for sandy and gravelly soil, into which the buckwheat can be lightly raked after the artichokes have sprouted.

ing habits, but massed plantings in border areas are very attractive. Plantings of domesticated umbels such as coriander are recommended over the use of wild plants such as Queen Anne's lace. In some areas, this species and others are considered noxious weeds subject to weed-control ordinances, requiring their removal upon the threat of county herbicide spraying.

Umbels are not the only plant species that attract parasitic wasps. Many plants have highly accessible extrafloral nectaries, glands on leaves or stems that ooze nectar. Nectaries in flowers serve to seduce pol-

Exhausted by the quest for caterpillar victims that will become hosts for her offspring, a female thread-waisted wasp alights for a restorative draught of nectar from the composite flower of a black-eyed Susan.

linators, but these extrafloral nectaries also attract plant protectors. Often, these protectors are ants. The Rocky Mountain sunflower, for example, uses extrafloral nectaries to attract ants to its flowers. The ants, being pugnaciously defensive about sweet things, indiscriminately chase off all other insects, including certain flies which infest the seeds. The plant thus relies on the ants' self-interested aggression to keep itself clean of other insects. Extrafloral nectaries also attract large numbers of parasitic wasps that destroy parasite caterpillars after they feed. In our garden, the extrafloral nectaries of cherries and elderberries allure many parasitic wasps during spring. In summer, these nectaries dry up, and the activity switches to the foliage

of Jerusalem artichokes. On a hot summer day, a patch of these yellow-flowered tubers interplanted with buckwheat fairly hums with wasps and bees. This sort of planting is ideal in sandy, gravelly soil. Once the Jerusalem artichokes have sprouted, buckwheat can simply be broadcast between the rows and lightly raked in.

In late summer, composite flowers such as black-eyed Susan, the common daisy and goldenrod act as attractants for the larger predatory wasps. Many of these insects, such as *Polistes* paper wasps, rear their young on caterpillars. Where *Polistes* are common enough, such as in the southeast United States, they have been used to control tobacco and tomato hornworms, and when I lived in Arizona, I found them effective at destroying cabbage moth caterpillars. In Ontario, our composite flowers are frequented by thread-waisted wasps (*Ammophilia*). Females of this species build nests in sandy, open ground and pack them with a food supply of caterpillars. One female alone can drag home dozens during a day to feed a new generation of caterpillar-hungry thread-waisted wasps.

The composite blossoms also lure many equally beneficial flies such as the brightly striped *Syrphidae* flower flies. The adults visit the flowers to feed on both nectar and pollen, while their larvae roam garden leaves consuming herds of aphids.

One can, of course, purchase beneficial insects of all sorts: ladybugs, lacewings, praying mantids and parasitic wasps. I personally find the expense of buying beneficial insects unattractive and generally think it unnecessary. Nurturing natural resident parasites and predators is more interesting, and planting the flowers they need requires only a trivial investment. A few patches of flowering umbels or composites can provide nectar for dozens of flies and wasps, each capable of destroying hundreds of harmful insects.

Exactly how successful this tactic is in controlling garden pests has not been scientifically determined. However, my own qualitative observations suggest that parasites can be very effective against certain caterpillars. I commonly find the caterpillars of white cabbageworm moths bristling with pupal cocoons of braconid wasps. I have encountered aphids whose brown mummified appearance indicates that the former pests had become no more than housing for developing parasitic wasps. Frequently, I stoop to pick up sluggish cutworms with tiny black holes in their backs, the telltale signatures of wasps' ovipositors.

This is not to claim that patches of umbels and composites are a panacea for pest problems in the garden. Much of what determines an insect's abundance is simply the vagaries of weather and not the biological pressures of parasitism, predation and competition. Thus, pest problems are inevitable. Agricultural ecosystems are, of necessity, disturbed and simplified plant communities. During domestication, the panoply of natural plant defences — the spiny armour, the poisonous oils and alkaloids and the tough fibre of food plants — have been converted into palatable, succulent and therefore vulnerable forms.

Gardening calls for a mixture of pest-control techniques if the yield is to be pristine vegetables. The establishment of plants appropriate for parasites and predators is only part of the arsenal, but it is one of the few weapons that not only looks good but also increases the biological richness of the garden.

Occasionally, as I discovered, parasite patches can bring other, definitely nonhorticultural rewards. I garden with my stomach in mind; my wife, a botanical illustrator, gardens with an eye for colour and form. The difference, at one time, resulted in disputes over relative square footage allotted to vegetables and flowers. We were happy to realize that flowers in the garden can gladden not just the beholder's eye but, ultimately, his palate. ∎

Adrian Forsyth, a biologist, is co-author of Tropical Nature *and lives in Chaffey's Lock, Ontario.*

PLANTING TIPS FOR THE PREDATOR PATCH: A BRIEF GUIDE TO GROWING EDIBLE UMBELS

Angelica: This is a large biennial which can reach six or seven feet in height. Normally, it flowers in its second year. Seeds should be sown in the fall beneath one-half inch of rich, moist, yet well-drained soil. Plants need two to three feet of spacing and prefer partial shade. They do not transplant well. Seeds lose viability rapidly, so they should be kept refrigerated if overwintered.

Anise: An annual, anise is normally grown by direct sowing in sunny areas with good drainage. The seed should be sown in the spring after the heavy frosts are over. It should be covered lightly. Thin plants to eight inches. Anise flowers early in the summer.

Caraway: An annual, caraway prefers well-drained clay soils and cool temperatures. Seeds are broadcast early in the spring and require little thinning. It flowers in midsummer.

Chervil: Chervil is grown as an annual in partially shaded areas with light, well-drained soil. Broadcast seed and cover lightly. Thin seedlings to eight inches.

Coriander: This umbel needs full sun and rich, well-drained soil. It is grown as an annual and flowers in midsummer. Plants should be spaced 12 inches apart.

Cumin: An annual, cumin is grown like coriander but is more sensitive to frost.

Dill: Another annual, dill grows well in almost any soil. Plant seeds 12 inches apart. Dill flowers in midsummer.

Fennel: Fennel is a perennial normally grown as an annual. It does not fare well under acid or shady conditions. Broadcast the seeds in the fall and thin seedlings to one-foot spacing in the spring. Flowers in midsummer.

Lovage: This large perennial grows up to seven feet tall. It prefers partially shaded, moist soil. Plants require three-foot spacing. They can be transplanted, with care, and can be propagated through root division. Seeds are best sown in midsummer as they ripen. Overwintered seeds, however, retain viability. Flowers during the summer after two or more years of growth.

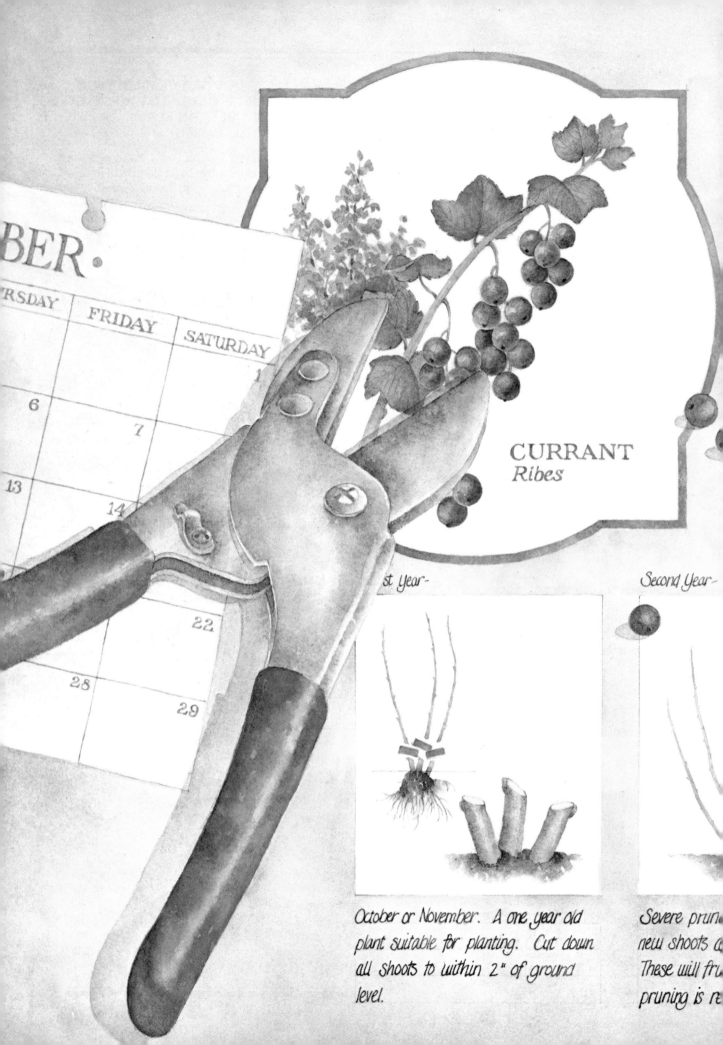

CURRANT
Ribes

BER.

TRSDAY	FRIDAY	SATURDAY
6	7	1
13	14	
		22
28	29	

st Year

Second Year

October or November. A one year old plant suitable for planting. Cut down all shoots to within 2" of ground level.

Severe prun new shoots These will fr pruning is re

Productive Pruning

Cutting comments: the art of plant propagation without seed

A Harrowsmith Staff Report

Joanne T.L. Fitzgerald

Chivers Olde English preserves must take the credit, in a roundabout way, for our first really dramatic experience with vegetative plant propagation, a technique that started in the black currant patch but that has since greatly expanded our gardening horizons. The imported British jams had acquainted us with the grand, sophisticated taste of black currants, which can fairly be said to produce a truly adult preserve — not too sweet but laden with flavour. Eager to expand our plantings without purchasing additional canes, we were determined to try cut-and-multiply gardening despite the fact that we had previously done little but the usual propagation of coleus and impatiens, whose cut stems will quite reliably root even when abandoned in a glass of unadulterated water.

And so when, in the fall, just after the leaves had dropped, we cut some of the old, woody growth out of the currants — part of our annual pruning chores — we set aside some of the cane tips. Extensions of the older wood, these were the shoots of new, green growth from the just-completed growing season and

Third and following years-

The bush fruits on last year's wood. New basal growths develop.

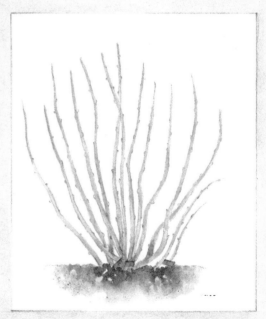

October or November. Cut out approximately one-third of the fruited branches. Also, cut out damaged or weak growths.

sulted in strong
from the base.
wing year. No
this point.

The point of union between the current season's soft growth and last year's hardened stem is the best place to take a cutting from a woody plant such as this bay laurel. Pruning convention dictates that all base cuts be made on an angle and that all top cuts be made straight across so there will be no later confusion about which end is up.

As soon as possible, prepare the cutting for planting, first by trimming off the lower leaves. Only a few leaves remain at the top, enough so that photosynthesis continues, but not so many that the stressed plant will lose too much moisture from its foliage. In this case, the pruned bay leaves are saved for use in cooking.

A tea made of pounded soft willow shoots blended with a little water contains rooting hormones that enable it to be used alone or in combination with purchased rooting hormones in the preparation of cuttings. Gardeners using the tea should immediately place the prepared cutting upright in it, leaving the cutting to soak for a day or two.

Now the cutting is planted in a container or flat of a moistened sterile potting mix — in this case, one-half peat moss, one-half vermiculite. Water the medium with willow tea or tepid water, and until the cutting roots — as long as it remains green — make sure that it is never allowed to dry out entirely. A plant such as bay will take about one month to root.

A moist greenhouse atmosphere which ensures that the cutting will not dry out quickly is obtained by enclosing the pot in a polyethylene bag. A straw or chopstick holds the plastic off the leaves, and the bagged pot is placed by a north-facing window or away from direct sunlight. Rooting has commenced when the cutting will not move if gently tugged.

the requisite material for propagation. We cut the shoots in 8-to-12-inch lengths, leaving a butt of old wood at the base of each as directed, and buried them vertically in the garden, leaving only two or three inches and a bud or two exposed at the soil surface. We then mulched the bed with a few inches of straw. Late next spring, new growth emerged from the tops of about half of the buried shoots. We had created new berry bushes, just like that; so much for paying five dollars apiece for nursery plants. A year later, they were producing fruit — black currants, only on wood produced the previous season. We could have pruned and propagated red or white currants in the same way, although they would have begun fruiting a year or two later, on two- and three-year-old wood. Dormant cuttings taken in fall but propagated indoors include those of banana, date, fig, filbert, mulberry, olive, quince, pineapple and pomegranate.

In theory, all plants can be coaxed into producing roots from stem cuttings, a means of propagation described as vegetative, or asexual. From a single plant, then, a poor but patient gardener can produce an entire hedge, fruit garden or woodlot. But in practice, some plants, such as most evergreens, are very difficult to root while others, like currants, root quite easily. Some plants, too, reproduce vegetatively on their own, so there is normally little point in the gardener going to all the trouble of taking cuttings. The roots of raspberries, lilacs and Saskatoon berries, for instance, produce suckers that can easily be planted elsewhere; low bush blueberries send out rhizomes that produce new plants; strawberries develop new plants at the ends of runners; blackberries produce new shoots from stem tips layered against the ground. Only in the laboratory is the use of cuttings of such plants routine. At Kemptville, Ontario, for example, a programme researching the possibility of growing low bush blueberries as an eastern Ontario cash crop utilizes hundreds of cuttings from New Brunswick plants. In such a case, cuttings enable many clones of a desired parent plant to be produced rapidly.

TRUE BLUE

That is one attribute of vegetative propagation that sexual propagation (from seed) does not have; plants grown from seed may vary in their genetic makeup. In plant nurseries, this is critical not for low bush blueberries but for plants such as the Colorado blue spruce, which may vary in colour from a striking blue to a dull green if grown from seed. Cuttings taken from a blue specimen are, however, always blue — and commercially valuable. Nurseries, then, that deal in perennial plants depend almost entirely upon vegetative propagation. Vegetative propagation is especially useful for plants that are difficult or time-consuming to grow from seed. And it can often be done as an adjunct to pruning when crowded or crossed branches that are removed can support shoots ideal for propagation. Still, fruit trees, most nut trees, maples, oaks, birches, lindens and beeches are more easily propagated from seed, grafting or budding than from cuttings.

Generally the easiest of all plants to propagate from cuttings or "slips," herbaceous or nonwoody plants often reward even the most negligent gardener with a healthy root system within weeks. House plants such as coleus, begonia and impatiens, and herbs such as scented geraniums, lemon verbena, lavender, rosemary, marjoram, sage and winter savory can be propagated whenever succulent new shoots become available for cutting. Most of these will root without the use of rooting hormones (described later), but the use of the techniques described for softwood cuttings will help ensure success with prized plants.

Tomatoes are good examples of nonwoody plants whose cuttings root easily. Any sucker that forms in a leaf axil or crotch throughout the summer can be snapped off at its base and buried two-thirds deep in the garden or in potting soil indoors. Kept wet until roots form in two or three weeks, they reward the gardener with a late harvest of the same type of fruit produced by the parent, whether open-pollinated or hybrid. As these suckers are usually removed as a matter of course in the pruning of staked plants, their production of added fruit is a bonus for good gardening.

Suckers brought indoors in fall and rooted in plant pots can be used to overwinter a favourite hybrid variety, perhaps one whose seeds are expensive or difficult to obtain. In spring, again take cuttings from the plant, which will by then be tall and gangly. Root them in individual pots and then treat them like any other vegetable transplant, hardening them off before planting them outdoors.

The new, spring growth of deciduous trees and shrubs, called softwood, also roots relatively easily in many cases, though a little more patience and care is necessary than with most herbaceous plants. Taken in fall just after leaf drop, such cuttings of wood developed that year are called semi-hardwood. Most plants can be rooted at either time, but the success of the timing will depend upon the weather that year and the climate and conditions in one's own house or garden. Among the easiest woody plants to root are willows, currants, gooseberries, figs and vining plants such as hops, ivy and grapes. Only slightly more difficult are euonymus (burning bush or winter creeper), forsythia, honeysuckle, cinquefoil and mock orange. One of the more difficult plants, sugar maple, was propagated in early June by Bill Langenberg, an Ontario government horticulturist seeking to multiply especially promising trees by measuring the sugar content of the sap of a grove of trees and taking cuttings from those whose sugar content was highest. Langenberg says, "The same as we do with dairy cows, we are trying to come up with an ROP, a record of performance, and we hope eventually that we can create clones of super-sweet maples."

The process Langenberg uses is much the same as that used with all cuttings. It was once thought, he says, that the best success with maples came with the use of semi-hardwood cuttings — those taken in fall when the new growth had begun to harden — but new research in the United States on cuttings rooted from January through December indicates that the best time to cut is just after the leaves have fully opened. Ninety percent of the cuttings taken at this time, he says, will root.

Langenberg selects healthy cuttings from choice trees, and makes his cut just below the joint between the new and old wood. This is quite a clear demarcation on all woody plants; the new wood appears shiny, bright and supple, whereas last year's wood will have hardened and dulled. The joint is the best place for rooting to take place. The lower cut is made on an angle, whereas the top cut, if there is one, is made straight across, a pruning convention that ensures that the gardener can always tell which end of the cutting is up, essential for success. Each of Langenberg's cuttings is about a foot long, and includes several buds or leaf joints. All the leaves are removed from the lower two-thirds. Langenberg wets the base and then dips it in rooting hormone powder and, shaking off the excess — too much can be harmful — buries the treated stem several inches deep in wet perlite. The planted shoot then goes into a greenhouse, where it will be sprayed several times a day with an electronically controlled misting device.

The rooting hormone that Langenberg uses in this particular instance is Stim-root, manufactured by Plant Products Limited in Bramalea, Ontario. Like many brands of rooting hormones, Stim-root comes in several concentrations labelled, in this case, One, Two and Three. The lowest number, containing the smallest percentage of hormones, is formulated for easily propagated plants such as common shrubs and houseplants; the middle number is for semi-woody or woody plants and easily propagated evergreens; and the highest number treats the most recalcitrant plants such as semi-hard or hardwood cuttings of azalea, rhododendron, maple and difficult conifers. Because he is working with softwood cuttings of maples, Langenberg chooses the middle strength, Stim-root Two. With brand names such as Hormodine, Hormex, Seradix, Rootone and Plantaide, all the commercial rooting substances contain synthetic copies of the natural hormones produced by plants themselves in forming adventitious roots (those that do not develop normally from nodes). At least one brand is available at most garden shops, but some are also available by mail order.

WILLOW TEA

A recently discovered alternative or addendum to the use of commercial rooting hormones is willow extract, whose efficiency in promoting rooting was first reported in the early 1960s by Dr. Makota Kawase, then at the Agriculture Canada experimental station in Morden, Manitoba. The extract easily promoted the production of more than 100 roots on a section of mung bean stem, the usual test plant for such experiments, while control sections produced only four or five roots. "Alone," wrote Kawase, "it seems to have the ability to stimulate rooting unmatched by any previously known rooting substance, including the plant hormones. . . . Combined with plant hormones, the substance is able to increase rooting far better than the traditional recipe of one or two plant hormones." In one experiment, yellow birch cuttings, previously described as "almost impossible to root," produced no roots when treated with Hormodine No.2 alone, but invariably rooted when treated with the commercial powder combined with the willow rooting substance, which has also proved effective in stimulating the rooting of the softwood cuttings of bittersweet, forsythia, peach and spirea.

In Kawase's original experiment, cuttings of new growth were taken from mature white willow trees between mid-June and mid-September, and the liquids were extracted by centrifugation, a spinning process. Bob Hill, who works with Kawase at the Ohio Agricultural Research and Development Center, says that a home gardener who wants to try working with willow extract "could try putting some stems in a blender and using the juice." We found that sections of very green, supple end shoots of willow, leaves removed, first pounded between two sheets of wax paper, then blended with enough tepid water to cover them, left

By taking softwood cuttings of the current season's growth of selected trees in June, Bill Langenberg hopes to "create clones of supersweet maples" for the Ontario government. Langenberg dips the base of each cutting in water and then in a commercial rooting hormone powder before setting it in damp perlite. The flat of cuttings is then kept warm and moist under an electronically controlled misting device in a greenhouse.

to steep several hours and strained through a sieve, produced a green soup that we used in rooting bay laurel cuttings. Hill says that about "90 percent" of all willows should be effective. Considering its price and availability, willow extract is certainly worth a try. The gardener using it should place cuttings upright in a couple inches of extract for a day or two before planting them in a rooting medium, which can then be watered with the tea.

There was a time, of course, when neither rooting hormones nor willow extracts were used by gardeners, yet cuttings of woody plants nevertheless sometimes rooted. Early propagators, however, had to pay particular attention to the environmental demands of cuttings which, when denied easy access to water and nutrients through roots, are in a condition of stress. In the early 19th century, English gardener J.C. Loudon wrote that "Too much light, air, water, heat or cold are alike injurious." He instructed that cuttings be planted in a shady spot outdoors and covered with a glass jar "enclosing an atmosphere over the cuttings" which could be further shaded with screens, if necessary, or removed entirely if the temperature were high. This is a slow, imperfect procedure with a fairly high failure rate, in part because it demands at least daily vigilance on the part of the gardener, and yet it is effective enough that cuttings such as those of apple can often be induced to root.

Loudon described the apple cuttings, taken in spring, as consisting of young wood with a small portion of old wood at the lower end. All the buds except two or three at the top are removed, and the cuttings are placed three or four inches deep in sandy loam, "pressing the earth firmly to them, watering, and covering with a hand glass . . . the glass should not be touched, excepting to give water, till the shoots have sprung an inch or two. Shade during the midday sun and begin to harden by giving air in July; finally, remove the glass in August; and in October, transplant to nursery rows, or in pots, according to future intention." Working in England, Loudon had a long season in which to root his cuttings taken "early in February." Where the growing season is shorter, the cuttings will have less chance to develop a sturdy root system before freeze-up and should usually be rooted indoors. Newly rooted cuttings are often less hardy and less able to survive winter than more mature plants.

Fruit trees grown from cuttings will grow to standard, large size, though their fruit will be the same as that of the parent tree whether it was dwarf, semidwarf or standard. Fruit trees, then, are normally propagated by grafting, a practice the gardener can copy should his fruit tree rootstocks produce suckers. These can be propagated as cuttings and used as rootstocks to receive scions of favoured varieties.

With better growing facilities than Loudon had and less sophisticated ones than Langenberg has with his large greenhouse and automatic misting system, the home gardener can make the best of his own situation in other ways. Virtually any plant is worth a try, although, as we shall see, old conifers and most grafted trees are better avoided.

The procedure is simple, and similar to that utilized by both Loudon and Langenberg. Because the plant should be constantly moist — lacking roots, it can easily dry out and die — the gardener should use a sterile growing medium. This helps control the spread of dampness-loving fungus diseases. Langenberg uses perlite alone, but perlite, vermiculite, or peat alone or mixed are all possible choices. Vermiculite alone does tend to pack down, and peat alone may be somewhat acidic, but all have been successful in some cases. The best medium for home use is an all-purpose mixture such as half peat, half vermiculite. Before it is placed in pots or flats deep enough to hold four to six inches of medium, it is first wetted by kneading or stirring it with water. Pour it into the container and make holes with a pen or knitting needle wherever a cutting will go.

The cuttings themselves must never be allowed to dry out. The best procedure is to prepare and plant them as soon as you cut them. If this is not possible, either set them upright in a few inches of water, or prepare them for winter storage (described later). If you are taking cuttings from the wild or from a friend's

garden, leave them in a plastic bag in a cool, shady place until they reach home.

Individual cuttings may be placed one per pot, the base of the cutting against the bottom of the pot, and left in place even after they root. However, the gardener who finds it possible to take many cuttings — a better practice as some may not root — can place them in rows in flats or large pots, each cutting about a half-inch from the next, the rows about two inches apart. The growing medium should be firm around each cutting. The entire pot or flat can now be enclosed in a polyethylene bag or covered with plastic wrap. Place supports in the growing medium so that the wrap does not rest directly on the plants. The entire unit is now placed out of direct sunlight in enough light to keep the foliage green, but not so much that the cutting wilts and the growing medium dries out quickly. A north-facing window sill is fine; otherwise, the plants can go inside a fairly bright room, away from the windows. A temperature range of 60 to 85 degrees F suits most cuttings best. If the plants are placed in a greenhouse, do not cover them with polyethylene, but with a light cloth or several layers of cheesecloth that can be removed on dark days and at night if you choose. The growing medium should always be damp.

CONIFERS

A fabric cloak that reduces the light level by half protects thousands of black spruce cuttings being grown in a species-improvement project at the Ontario Ministry of Natural Resources Forestry station in Orono. This cloak is doubly useful, because the researchers there have found that by watering the fabric rather than the soil medium, fungal problems, the greatest hazard with slow-rooting cuttings such as conifers, are minimized. More easily rooted conifers include cedar, arborvitae, yew, retinospora and some junipers, their cuttings taken in late summer or fall. A University of New Hampshire publication states that in New England, yew or arborvitae cuttings are best taken in August, with the grower taking the lower cut at the base of the current year's growth. These take 6 to 10 weeks to root after treatment with Hormodine 2 or 3 for yew, or Hormodine 3 for arborvitae. Chinese juniper cuttings taken in August rooted in four months; Savin juniper cuttings taken in July or August, in 6 to 10 weeks. Both junipers required Hormodine 3.

Bernie Phillion, superintendent of the Orono station, recommends that home gardeners take cuttings of spruce in January or February. It is more difficult to root cuttings taken from summer growth of some conifers. Cuttings should be taken from trees that are less than five years old, he says, and trees less than three years old will produce even better rooting success.

"If a home gardener wants to do this he should work with material that's as young as possible. If he's got something like a blue spruce, it will probably have been grafted, and he won't know how old it is," says Phillion. Also, it is most difficult to propagate cuttings from grafted ornamental trees. "If it was possible to grow the plant from a cutting, the nursery would have done it." Propagating cuttings is far cheaper for the nursery than grafting, a painstaking manual procedure. Search, then, for a graft, a callused ring at the base of the stem or trunk, before taking cuttings.

The spruce cuttings from Orono averaged about two inches long and about an eighth of an inch across at the base. They were inserted about a half-inch into the growing medium, without removing the basal needles. Phillion wrote in a recent report that "It has recently been shown that the removal of the lowermost needles from the base of black spruce cuttings prior to planting is unnecessary and is often detrimental to rooting ability. . . . The same study showed that planting depths between .5 and 2.5 cm into the rooting medium had little effect on the rooting of black spruce, as long as the cuttings were well planted initially."

A medium of half peat, half vermiculite was used "because it is sterile, capable of retaining sufficient moisture to meet the cutting requirements and also porous and well drained so that oxygen is readily available for root development." No rooting hormone was necessary — spruce, like some junipers, seem unresponsive to the packaged hormones.

The station's conifer cuttings were taken from both laterals and upright shoots. But, as American horticulturist Thomas Fessenden noted in 1843, "When you intend to propagate trees for timber or for a tall, stately growth, be very particular never to take cuttings from horizontal branches, for they will ever have an inclination to grow in a spreading manner; always make choice of perpendicular shoots and particularly those that terminate the branches; these will produce the straightest trees." The cuttings from laterals "can take years to straighten," says Phillion.

Phillion explains that the planted cuttings are placed under the shade cloth, which diffuses light and retains moisture. The temperature is maintained, as much as possible, at about 70 degrees F, although in the greenhouse it often rises above that on sunny days. Every two weeks, the cuttings are treated with the fungicide Benylate, a treatment optional for home gardeners. With this regimen, black spruce seedlings root in as short a period as three weeks, with the average taking a month to 40 days. After 10 weeks, 97 percent of 35,700 cuttings planted in 1982 had rooted.

A home gardener can test whether seedlings have rooted by giving them a very gentle tug; as soon as roots begin to form, the cuttings will resist being pulled. The formation of callus tissue at the base of the cutting is a good sign: Cells in the callus may reorganize into growing points, some of which become roots. But the sure sign of success is growth. The first growth produced by his rooted black spruce cuttings "looks like hang," says Phillion, because the soil medium lacks nutrients. So, as soon as growth commences, fertilization does as well. At this time, the home gardener can use a fish fertilizer diluted according to the manufacturer's directions. In a couple of weeks, plants can be hardened off for planting outdoors or, if appropriate, can be moved into permanent pots.

The length of time it will take cuttings to root depends not only upon the type of plant — and it is generally true that the more expensive a plant is at the nursery, the harder it will be to root — but also upon the gardener's choice of whether or not to use a rooting hormone, and the environmental conditions he can provide. Under close to ideal conditions, Langenberg's maple cuttings root in three or four weeks and are then planted in potting soil. In two years, they will be ready for field planting. As long as any cutting looks healthy and green, it should not be discarded. Have patience; some plants such as silver fir may take a year to root.

Before they can be planted permanently outdoors, cuttings rooted indoors must be gradually accustomed to outdoor conditions of bright light, variable temperatures and wind. Take off the polyethylene covering or, if there is shade cloth, remove it late in the afternoon, as Phillion does with the rooted Orono station plants. He covers the plants again so that they are not exposed to the morning sun, then gradually moves the afternoon uncovering time forward so that in about two weeks the plants are exposed to full light all day. Plants can then be moved outdoors for gradually increasing durations. For a home gardener, an outdoor cold frame used as a temporary shelter can ease the transition of plants to life outdoors.

WINTER STORAGE

In some cases, cuttings are not rooted immediately but are taken in fall and, in areas where the winters are harsh, are stored in a cool, damp place over the winter, to be planted as soon as the soil can be worked in the spring. Such cuttings include willow, lilac, *Multiflora* rose, locust, poplar — and currant and gooseberry where winters are especially severe. Grape cuttings, too, can be taken just after leaf drop in fall, from well-matured canes of that year's growth. Roughly nine inches long and including three buds, each grape cutting ends just below the lowest bud, and its top cut is about an inch above the top bud. Pack bundles of the cuttings in moist sand, sawdust or peat moss buried under about three inches of sand or sandy soil in a well-drained spot in the garden, and mulch the bed with about a foot of fallen leaves, straw or grass clippings — or pack the cuttings in damp sand and store them in a very cool basement. As soon as the soil can be worked, plant each cutting so that its top bud is just above ground level, the other two buds underground. Pack the soil firmly around the cutting and keep it watered until growth begins.

Using various techniques in our work with cuttings, we have been able to share some of our favourite plants with other gardeners, and their cuttings have swelled the ranks in our own gardens, for free. By taking enough cuttings to allow for experimentation with schedules and methods, we are finding that vegetative propagation is as important a part of the gardening routine as producing our own home-grown transplants from seed. And we no longer have to turn to Chivers for black currant jam. ∎

Sources

C.A. CRUICKSHANK LTD.
1015 Mount Pleasant Road
Toronto, Ontario M4P 2M1
Stim-root and Seradix available in three strengths. Stewart propagators, plastic trays with fitting polystyrene covers. Catalogue $1.00 deductible from first order.

W.H. PERRON
515 Labelle Boulevard
City of Laval, Quebec H7V 2T3
(514) 332-3610
Roots gel rooting hormone; Seradix in three strengths. Merrygro miniature greenhouse. Catalogue $1.00.

MELLINGER'S
2310 W. South Range Road
North Lima, Ohio 44452
(216) 549-9861
Plant products to U.S. addresses only; Hormex in six strengths; Rootone. Catalogue free.

Fruit Within Reach

With dwarf fruit trees, small is both beautiful and practical

By Jennifer Bennett

Grand as they were, those old fruit trees left plenty to be desired. In my childhood backyard in Vancouver, there was a *Bing* cherry whose upper branches could be seen well above the roof peak from the front yard. Although that tree must have borne bushels of fruit in its good years, we were never able to pick more than a few quarts, only what we could reach while teetering on the corner of the roof or by climbing the tree — almost pointless, as little fruit grew near the mammoth trunk or scaffold limbs — or by standing on tiptoe and manipulating a long bamboo pole tipped with a wire loop that was once a coat hanger. Someday, that giant will make a beautiful table, but in the meantime, its fruit is so far flung as to be mostly unharvestable except by the birds.

The most remarkable change in orcharding in this century has been a drastic reduction in the space between the fruit crop and the earth. Trees that once grew to 30 or 40 feet are now 10 or 20 feet at maturity, and yet their fruit is much the same as before, sometimes even bigger and better. Among the best of these small trees for home gardeners, especially for those in cities and sheltered suburbs, are the dwarfs — pint-sized trees, usually less than 10 feet tall. They are small for any of several reasons: because they are grafted to a dwarfing rootstock, because of genetic inclination or because of pruning or a severe climate. But all of them offer the home gardener several advantages, the greatest of which is fruit within reach. As Ontario gardener I.B. Lucas wrote in *Dwarf Fruit Trees for Home Gardens* (Dover Publications), "We appreciate what a luxury it is to be able to prune, spray, thin and pick while both feet remain firmly and comfortably planted on the ground."

That small size brings other attributes with it as well. Dwarf trees can be placed as close to one another as five feet, whereas standard trees usually require about 20 feet all around. So not only does one tree fit easily into a spare corner of the backyard, but there may even be room for more than one tree where previously only one would have fit. That is especially useful with the kinds of trees that require cross-pollination to bear a full crop: apples, Japanese plums, pears and sweet cherries (except *Stella*). Check the neighbours' yards before planting two of a kind. If there is another cultivar of the same fruit type within 200 feet, your pollination needs may be met. Also, dwarf trees produce little shade and will not interfere with the neighbour's suntan or your own vegetable garden; nor is the tree's own fruit overly shaded and thus slow to ripen. That fruit, which is often borne earlier than on standard trees, will not arrive in overwhelming quantities. About 100 pounds of apples a year per dwarf tree will suit a family nicely, but double or treble that harvest — the fruit of a standard tree — can be too much of a good thing. As well, if the harvest is too great and the fruit is left on the tree, it is less likely to turn into pulp after a 10-foot fall than it would from 40 feet.

It is this impressive list of attributes, especially the efficient use of space, that has altered the appearance of commercial orchards significantly in the last decade. The move toward small trees will likely continue for quite some time as new, increasingly cold-resistant dwarfing rootstocks are developed and as old, standard orchards decline and are replaced with smaller trees. In New York State, for instance, the expected average apple harvest of 400 bushels per acre in 1970 has now more than doubled, largely because many more dwarf trees can be squeezed into an acre — as many as 1,350 compared with 35 to 70 standard apple trees. Very slender dwarf trees, some little more than fruit-bearing stems, can be concentrated as heavily as 5,000 to the acre.

More efficient fruiting aside, commercial growers, like home gardeners, also appreciate the way dwarf trees can be easily pruned, sprayed and harvested from the ground. Ultimately, it is the commercial orchardists' interest in smaller trees that will benefit the home gardener, as horticulturists work to enlarge the orchardists' profit margins while extending the dwarf tree growing areas northward.

Appropriately, then, it is home gardeners in or near commercial fruit growing regions who now have the best success with trees on dwarfing rootstocks, some of which are more cold-tender than their larger counterparts. A check through most of Canada's tree-nursery catalogues reveals that those located outside the country's fruit belts — Quebec's Sursum Corda, Ontario's Golden Bough, Manitoba's Boughen, Alberta's Beaverlodge — do not even stock dwarf trees. And yet Canada's largest mail-order nursery, Sears-McConnell of southern Ontario, reports that almost three-quarters of its fruit-tree sales are dwarfs. Both Sears-McConnell and the other nurseries are following perfectly sensible policies, selling the types of trees that will do best for most of their own customers.

However, because many home gardens are in protected situations, with walls, fences and buildings to contain heat, decrease wind and trap snow, the region for possible success with garden dwarf trees extends farther north than for the same trees in exposed commercial orchards. I.B. Lucas grew nearly 1,000 dwarf trees — apples, pears, cherries, peaches and plums — on less than an acre of land near Georgian Bay "in the centre of an area which is declared to be too cold for any except the hardier varieties of apple." Protected parts of cities are often a full climatic zone higher (and hence considerably more benign) than the surrounding countryside, and the gardener who makes the best use of southerly exposures, insulating mulches and sheltered corners can further increase his chances of success. Dr. Kenneth Taylor, a Quebec fruit grower whose *Van* sweet cherry thrives next to a south-facing wall, says, "You never know. You have to test the trees in your own backyard. Sometimes they don't turn out to be what they're supposed to be." It is unlikely that a dwarf peach will survive the winter in Edmonton or even in downtown Sudbury — peaches along with sweet cherries being the most cold-tender of northern fruits — but beyond extremes, almost anything is worth a try in a protected spot. In the countryside, however, where trees are exposed to cold winds, growers should check with local tree nurseries to find out what is reliably hardy. As Bill McKentley of St. Lawrence Nurseries in Potsdam, New York, says, "Apples grafted onto MM dwarfing stock in our location have either died or, at best, lingered on pallidly with little growth or predictability."

THE ROOTS OF DWARFISM

Most home gardeners know little or nothing about rootstocks, such as the MM stocks to which McKentley refers, and the little knowledge grudgingly offered by many nurseries is not always useful in any case. It is worth knowing, however, that all domesticated fruit trees have been grafted onto some type of rootstock — the ring of callused bark above the roots is evidence of that grafting — and that the best selection of dwarfing rootstocks available is for apples. For all types of tree fruits, however, there is at least one dwarf option, although the amount of dwarfing that occurs is variable, as is the rootstock's influence upon other tree characteristics: size of fruit, time of blossoming and age of first bearing.

The MM stocks mentioned by McKentley were developed in England, in research stations at East Malling and Merton (hence the "M" designation). Suited to the English climate, some of these rootstocks are not equal to the climatic rigours of the northern North American fruit growing regions. Malling 9 (M9), one of the most popular apple dwarfing rootstocks, is not recommended for use in Quebec, although it has been found sufficiently hardy for southern British Columbia, the Montreal area and southeastern Ontario. A tree on this brittle, shallow rootstock must be staked throughout its entire lifetime, which, like the tree, is abbreviated. Apple trees on M9 are expected to bear for only about 30 years, while a standard apple might easily bear twice that long. Nevertheless, M9 trees are comfortably small — about 8 to 10 feet tall — and produce fruit that is larger than that on most other roots. Dean Foster Nurseries of Michigan utilizes M9 on all their dwarf apples.

Although about 20 feet tall, an 18-year-old Compact Stella *sweet cherry in Summerland, British Columbia, shares the dwarf characteristic of high yield per unit of surface area.*

Malling 26 (M26) trees, though slightly larger at 8 to 12 feet, are better adapted to Canadian conditions. They are much hardier and do not require staking after the first year or two, although, as James Cummins of the New York State Agricultural Experiment Station says, "Experience indicates that the grower who has his orchard staked sleeps much better during the storms of September." These trees usually bear fruit within three or four years of planting. Bountiful Ridge Nurseries of Maryland and Sears-McConnell graft many of their dwarf apples on M26, which is recommended in all northern commercial fruit growing regions.

Ottawa 3, developed in Ottawa, is an even more cold-hardy apple rootstock. Edward Dugas of north-

ern Maine reports that his Ottawa 3 trees have survived minus 47 degrees F, although another winter's dip to minus 37 degrees caused some damage. Winter hardiness is a variable commodity, affected not only by minimum temperature change but also by duration of cold, snow cover, wind velocity and other factors. Ottawa 3 is now available from a few nurseries, but as rootstock propagation techniques improve, there will be more trees available to home gardeners on Ottawa 3 stock. These trees grow to 8 or 10 feet and have been shown to bear about a half bushel of fruit apiece by the third season and a bushel by the fifth.

An interstem, a section of dwarfing trunk grafted between a cold-hardy, vigorous rootstock and the tree above, further extends the range of dwarf trees northward. Bountiful Ridge Nurseries, for instance, offers apples with an M27 interstem. M27 is a very dwarfing stock that produces a tree only half the size of M9 but which would winterkill even in the northeastern United States if used as rootstock. On hardier roots, however, the M27 interstem dwarfs the tree but does not inhibit its ability to survive cold winters. Although interstem trees are more expensive than others — two grafts are required rather than just one — they may be the answer for growers with limited space. Bountiful Ridge rates its M27 interstem *Jerseymac, Spurmac, Imperial McIntosh* and *Molly's Delicious* as hardy to U.S. climatic zone 4, which includes the entire St. Lawrence valley, the southern and coastal areas of the Maritime provinces and Newfoundland, all of southwestern Ontario and all of southern and south-coastal British Columbia.

MIXED FRUITS

Pears are often dwarfed on the roots of quince, which is unfortunately less hardy than pear and can only reliably survive to about minus 18 degrees F (though under mulch, it has been known to survive minus 30 degrees). Not all pears do well on quince roots, but those that do produce a tree about 8 to 15 feet tall that bears larger-than-usual fruit. Raymond Granger of Agriculture Canada's St-Jean, Quebec, research station says that they are experimenting with native hawthorns (*Crataegus*) as possible cold-hardy dwarfing stocks for pears. Native plants are sometimes used with plum and apricot as well. Plums on the Western Sand cherry or *Hansen's* bush cherry, which grow to about nine feet, are hardy to about minus 18 degrees without mulch. Sears-McConnell's *Harcot* apricot is grafted on *Hansen's* bush cherry, its plums on the *Nanking* cherry.

Besides being used as rootstocks, wild or bush cherries will yield fruit that in some cases, such as *Hansen's* bush cherry, is similar in flavour and size to that produced by pie cherry trees and can be successful even in cold prairie gardens. These bushes, including the Sand cherry, *Mongolian* cherry and *Nanking* cherry (all of which have been subjected to selection for especially large, sweet fruit), can be grown as hedges that produce flowers and fruit. They grow to about six feet, are easy to tend and should be planted about four feet apart.

Among the domesticated fruit trees, there are also naturally or genetically dwarfed specimens that are fully as hardy as their standard counterparts. In fact, regardless of rootstock, some cultivars have a greater tendency to form a big tree than do others. The *Northern Spy* is a notoriously large tree on any rootstock, while *Golden Delicious* on M26 may be smaller than *Delicious* on M9 because the latter is a more vigorous tree. The *Idared*, a naturally small tree, needs only a little annual pruning to keep it to dwarf size. The *Noret* apple, developed at Beaverlodge, Alberta, grows to 8 to 10 feet, according to Irene Wallace of Beaverlodge Nurseries.

One type of naturally small tree is the spur-type, although, as Dr. David Lane of Agriculture Canada's experimental station in Summerland, British Co-lumbia, says, "The size of the tree is probably the same as a standard, so we don't think of it as a dwarf, but it's much easier to prune and produces much more fruit compared to the amount of woody matter." Spur-type trees, which are now sold by most large mail-order nurseries, have less twig or branch between clusters of fruit and tend to be more vertical in shape; some of them, such as the Wycik spur-type strain of *McIntosh* developed in Kelowna, British Columbia, are virtually fruiting trunks. Grafted to dwarfing rootstocks, spur-type trees make the most efficient use of space and can be grown in trellised rows somewhat like grapes.

The *Compact Lambert* sweet cherry is a similarly concentrated bearer, although this tree is not a natural but a man-made mutation, the result of irradiating a standard *Lambert* cherry with X-rays. *Compact Lambert* grows to only about six feet, fruits early and bears heavily. It needs very good soil and care, however, or both tree and fruit will be undersized. *Compact Stella*, similarly developed, is not truly a dwarf, growing to a semidwarf size of about 15 to 20 feet, but it has one outstanding attribute: It is the only self-pollinating popular sweet cherry; a home gardener need plant only one.

Sour, or pie, cherries, however, are regularly self-pollinating, and the most promising small version of these is the *Northstar*, developed at the University of Minnesota. It is capable of surviving to minus 25 degrees F without mulch and, according to Sears-Mc-Connell, is hardy to Canadian climatic zone 4B, about the same as U.S. zone 4 previously described. Kenneth Taylor of Quebec says, "If I recommended a cherry for a backyard, *Northstar* would be it. It stays only about six feet tall and has a nice shape." *Meteor*, another naturally small sour cherry, grows to a slightly larger size than *Northstar* but is similarly cold-tolerant. Sour cherries can be grown considerably north of the range of sweet cherries.

NATURAL DWARFS

Cherry plums, which produce delicious, sweet, plumlike fruit slightly larger than a cherry, also tend to be small trees, about eight feet tall, and are often hardy enough for prairie growers. Boughen Nurseries in Manitoba sells several of these, along with a small pear, *Ure*, a product of the Agriculture Canada experimental station in Morden, Manitoba. Along with Beaverlodge Nurseries, Boughen describes several of their offerings as naturally small or semivigorous. According to Dr. B.B. Chubey of Morden, "In north Saskatchewan, the trees are probably two-thirds the size of here. Depending on where you are on the prairies, you don't need dwarf trees because they're all small." Irene Wallace of Beaverlodge agrees: "We have a *Heyer 12* apple that is 40 to 45 years old, and it's fairly broad, but it's not more than eight or nine feet tall. Some of them are trained that way, but otherwise, they just get killed back."

Aside from such climatic rigours, keeping most dwarf trees from being killed back is, first, a matter of proper site selection and the choice of a suitable type of fruit and rootstock for one's area. For any fruit tree, the best site will be one with full sunlight or as much light as possible, without which fruit will not ripen properly if it forms at all. Warmth and shelter from strong winds are also important; if you do not have a protected spot, choose a hardier tree, perhaps a semi-dwarf, which will grow to 15 or 20 feet but will be considerably more vigorous than most dwarfs. Avoid planting in a hollow, at the base of a hill, or anywhere that frost is likely to settle. The soil should be fairly fertile, but more critically, it should be well drained. Standing water, flooding or water seepage will probably kill the tree.

AGAINST THE WALL

Some trees, especially peaches and sweet cherries, will do best near sun-reflecting walls. I.B. Lucas writes: "It is not merely a controversial or academic opinion but a thoroughly tested conclusion that peaches are very desirable subjects for the home garden in any climate where the hardiest apples will succeed. I simply train them as fans against walls that face in any of the 16 points of the compass from east to west with due south being best, and if cold enough to warrant it, with the added protection of wooden covers." These Lucas leaned against the wall to shade the trees. Apples or pears, which may be successfully grown close to walls in cloudy areas, do not do well there throughout most of North America, where an abundance of summer sun can bake these trees. As any trees against walls are more likely to dry out, they must be checked frequently. Do not plant trees closer than nine inches to a wall.

Although fruit trees may be planted in fall after the leaves have dropped but before the soil freezes, early spring planting, as soon as the soil thaws, generally gives a tree its best chance for a good start. Prepare a generous-sized hole for the tree — about two feet wide and a foot and a half deep — discard the subsoil and wet the hole thoroughly. Next, pound an 8-foot cedar post treated with wood preservative into the edge of the hole so that it extends six feet above the soil surface; all dwarf trees should be staked or otherwise supported for at least the first two years. Discarding weeds and stones, combine the removed topsoil with an equal amount of organic matter such as peat moss, well-rotted manure or compost. Form part of this mixture into a mound at the bottom of the hole, high enough to support the roots and to hold the graft well above the soil surface. If allowed to do so, most trees will root from above the graft, growing to their full potential size.

Have a friend hold the tree straight while you arrange the roots over the mound, then cover the roots completely with the soil mixture. Press the soil down firmly with your foot, fill the hole with water, let it soak in and then fill the remainder of the hole with soil mixture, leaving a slight depression in the surface. Mulch the bare soil around the tree with about six inches of leaves, grass clippings or straw. This will moderate the soil temperature while limiting weed growth, the most frequent cause of problems in home-garden dwarf trees. Tie the tree to the stake with loops of cloth, willow whips or pieces of old garden hose or bicycle tire.

Dwarf trees need to grow unhampered for the first two or three years, so they require more fertile soil and more careful tending, especially at the outset, than do larger trees. As Dr. John Sanford of Cornell University says, growing a dwarf tree is like shooting photographs with a Leica. If you do not do it properly, you may end up with nothing, whereas with a Brownie, you will always get a picture. Dwarf trees will suffer if they have to compete with weeds, or even with flowers and vegetables, for nutrients and water, so plant the tree at least 10 feet from a standard tree, and keep the area directly under the branches (a radius of about a foot) clear and covered with mulch. Unless it rains heavily, water the tree every week until the soil freezes, at which time the mulch should be reapplied. Mulch provides a good home for small rodents, so let it disintegrate gradually through the following summer.

Snow, too, protects delicate root systems and can mean the difference between success and failure where winters are cold. J.N. Cummins of Cornell University says, "As long as the orchard is covered with 6 or 8 or 10 inches of snow, we are not going to get winter damage to our roots." If the snow cover is light, pile what there is around the trees to help protect the roots from damage. Lucas enhanced the winter ability of his trees by shovelling extra earth around the trunks in late fall and by wrapping his tenderest trees entirely in burlap, removing the burlap after the soil thawed in spring. Fertilize only in late spring or early summer, when an inch-thick layer of compost or well-rotted manure and a sprinkling of bone meal should be placed on the soil surface under the branches, not quite touching the trunk. Never fertilize in fall, as the tree's winter hardiness will be hindered.

SPECIAL TREATMENT

Especially in winter, dwarf fruit tree trunks need to be protected from predators. Plastic tree guards, available from tree nurseries, are suitable for larger trunks, but a wrapping of aluminum foil will protect very young trees. A cylinder of hardware cloth left around the trees all year is useful where cats are in search of scratching posts or where mice and rabbits are especially prevalent.

Naturally dwarfed trees like *Northstar* cherries or *Noret* apples are pruned like any other fruit trees of the same type; provincial departments of agriculture and Agriculture Canada offer free advice and publications on pruning fruit trees. Trees on dwarfing rootstocks, however, require more selective treatment.

Although Dr. Sanford advises, "Try to keep the pruning shears quiet in the first two or three years," he also says that some pruning is necessary at the outset for the tree to fruit optimally. Deadwood must always be removed to the nearest live bud as soon as it is spot-

ted, and any shoots or suckers that appear below the graft must be trimmed off flush with the trunk or root. The newly planted tree, says Sanford, should be headed off 30 to 36 inches above the ground, and the side branches trimmed to about five buds each. After that, he advises that the fruit grower keep a careful eye on his tree and rub off buds that develop in unwanted areas, rather than waiting for them to grow into branches that will have to be pruned off: "As soon as you put pruning shears to the tree, you have interrupted the fruiting system." And although some dwarf trees may produce fruit buds the first or second year after they are planted, the patient grower should remove them so the early energy is channelled into the production of a strong framework rather than fruit. Grafted dwarf trees are not vigorous, and if they do not grow strongly in their first few years, they will not make up the loss later.

Dwarf apple or pear trees are well suited to espalier systems, in which the tree is trained to grow flat, assuming a geometric shape. Those that will be trained along fences can utilize 4 wires, each 18 inches apart, stretched horizontally between posts, the top wire 6 feet off the ground. Trees trained in the oblique palmette system, one of the most popular North American espalier techniques, have their limbs at 30-to-45-degree angles from the horizontal, tied at intervals to the wires. The branches from neighbouring trees intermesh, forming a fruit wall. Plums, cherries and peaches do not adapt to flat systems easily.

While an acre of traditional orchard might include 35 to 70 standard trees, a young, productive Quebec orchard features 1,350 McIntosh *and* Spartan *apples per acre.*

It is not only their need for greater and more precise care that is a drawback of trees grafted onto dwarfing rootstocks. Raymond Granger of Agriculture Canada's St-Jean, Quebec, research station, who is generally in favour of the small trees, admits, "There is always a good side and a bad side, of course." He points out that because the dwarf tree bears most or all of its fruit lower down than does a standard tree, it is more susceptible to damage from deer and frost. Frost damage is especially dangerous in spring after the blossoms have opened, and can make a significant difference to the fruit harvest in bad years. Also, because of those low branches, says Granger, "Snow breakage may be a problem in some years. You have heavy snow on the trees, then a thaw perhaps in January, then it freezes again and pulls very hard. It can even pull fences apart. Or sometimes you have a thaw under the snow, and the snow caves in and breaks the branches." Granger points out that if branches are properly pruned and trained, especially if they are tied to wires or other supports, the threat of snow breakage can be lessened.

"Also," he says, "I heard a comment from a picker that the apples were *too* low, they don't like to bend to pick the fruit. But I don't worry too much about that. It's a lot better than having to take ladders around." ∎

Raymond Granger, Ariculture Canada

Sources

Developed by Agriculture Canada scientists in Morden, Manitoba, the Ure *pear is a breakthrough, producing sweet, full-sized fruit on a small tree hardy enough to survive in many prairie gardens.*

Associations

**INTERNATIONAL DWARF FRUIT TREE
ASSOCIATION**
c/o Dept. of Horticulture
Michigan State University
East Lansing, Michigan 48824-1112
(517) 355-5200
Publishes a newsletter and holds annual conferences
and summer orchard tours. Commercial membership,
$40; educational membership, $25; retired orchardists
and students, $15.

Publications

**DWARF FRUIT TREES FOR
HOME GARDENS**
By I.B. Lucas
Dover Publications, Inc.
Unfortunately now out of print, this guide was first
published in 1946 by A.T. De La Mare Company, New

York. As such, some of its information is out of date,
but the book is still valuable in that it was written by
an Ontario gardener who devised many techniques for
seeing dwarf trees through cold winters.

PRUNING
By Christopher Brickell
Simon & Schuster
96 pages
213A — comb bound, $11.50
Available from Harrowsmith Books, Camden East,
Ontario K0K 1J0. Published in cooperation with the
Royal Horticultural Society of England, Brickell's fully
illustrated book includes directions on several espalier
techniques.

Nurseries

**NEW YORK STATE FRUIT TESTING
COOPERATIVE ASSOCIATION, INC.**
Geneva, New York 14456
Thirty-two apple cultivars on M9 rootstocks; 52 apples
on M26; 9 apples on M9 interstem with hardier
MM106 roots; the rootstocks themselves are also avail-
able. Send a donation to help pay for the catalogue.

Agriculture Canada

FOUR WINDS GROWERS
42186 Palm Avenue, Box 3538
Mission San Jose District
Fremont, California 94538
(415) 656-2591
Specialists in dwarf citrus: nine oranges, seven tangerines, four lemons, two grapefruit, three limes, two tangelos, three kumquats. Orders from outside the U.S. receive a $10 surcharge. Catalogue free.

KELLY BROS. NURSERIES INC.
Dansville, New York 14437
Dwarf plums, pears, peaches, apricots; *Northstar* cherry; *Hansen's* bush cherry. Catalogue free.

J.E. MILLER NURSERIES
Canandaigua, New York 14424
Dwarf apples, plums, apricots, *Northstar* cherry. Sells to U.S. addresses only. Catalogue free.

DEAN FOSTER NURSERIES
Hartford, Michigan 49057
Seventeen apples on M9; 13 dwarf peaches, 11 dwarf plums, 10 dwarf pears; also apricots and nectarines. Red- and gold-fruited *Hansen's* bush cherry. Catalogue free.

PACIFIC TREE FARMS
4301 Lynnwood Drive
Chula Vista, California 92010
A good source for almost anything your heart desires (including the genetic dwarf almond *Garden Prince*). Catalogue free.

HALLMAN ORCHARDS AND NURSERY
Box 1218
Ganges, British Columbia V0S 1E0
(604) 537-9316
Dwarf apples, cherries and plums. Wide variety of dwarf rootstock. Catalogue free.

SURSUM CORDA
Scotstown, Quebec J0B 3B0
Northstar cherry, *Ure* pear, *Idared* apple, tree guards.

McFAYDEN SEED COMPANY LTD.
Box 1800
Brandon, Manitoba R7A 6N4
Nanking cherry, Sand cherry, *Sapacherry* plum, dwarf *Pembina* plum, tree guards. Catalogue free.

BOUNTIFUL RIDGE NURSERIES, INC.
Princess Anne, Maryland 21853
(301) 651-0400
"One of the largest growers of dwarf fruit trees in the country." Apples, pears, plums, peaches, apricots, nectarines, *Nanking* cherries, *Black Velvet* bush cherries, *Sub-zero* bush apricot, *Manchurian* bush plums, *Oka* dwarf cherry plum, *Northstar* and *Meteor* cherry. Catalogue free. Planting guides available $1.00.

HASTINGS
SEEDSMEN TO THE SOUTH
434 Marietta Street, N.W.
Box 4274
Atlanta, Georgia 30302
Five genetic dwarfs: *Garden Delight* nectarine, *Garden Sun* peach, *Garden Annie* apricot, *Garden Delicious* apple and *Garden Bing* cherry. Shipping season starts in January. Catalogue free.

BEAVERLODGE NURSERIES LTD.
Box 127
Beaverlodge, Alberta T0H 0C0
(403) 354-2195
Noret apple, *Mongolian* cherry. Catalogue free.

BOUGHEN NURSERIES VALLEY RIVER LTD.
Valley River, Manitoba R0L 2B0
(204) 638-7618
Native and bush plums, cherries, cherry plums, *Ure* pear. Catalogue free.

CALIFORNIA NURSERY COMPANY
Niles District
Box 2278
Fremont, California 94536
Dwarf citrus: *Bearss Seedless* lime, *Eureka* and *Meyer* lemon, *Ruby* grapefruit, *Nagami* kumquat, *Ruby Blood* and *Torocco* orange, *Dancy* and *Algerian (Clementine)* tangerine. Orders over $25 accepted only. Catalogue free.

SEARS-McCONNELL NURSERIES
Port Burwell, Ontario N0J 1T0
(519) 874-4405
(or through any Sears catalogue outlet)
Dwarf apples, plums, peaches, nectarines, apricots, *Northstar* cherry, *Hansen's* bush cherry, tree guards. Catalogue free.

Herbal Homegrowns

Starting right with the culinary basics — inexpensive, worry-free and fresh for the picking & drying

By Jennifer Bennett

It may have been *The Graduate*, with Simon and Garfunkel's subliminal herbal message camouflaged under the angst of Benjamin Braddock's love life, that began to turn the collective North American mind toward parsley, sage, rosemary and thyme in the late 1960s. That was when Richters, now North America's largest mail-order herb seed house, was just putting down its Ontario roots, when whole-food stores were starting to open up in small towns — "We used to have to go all the way to Peterborough," says herbalist Ross Parlette of Herbs for Health in Cobourg, Ontario, "and then there were stores all over" — and when seasoning began to mean more than just salt, pepper and Adolph's tenderizer. Whatever the change, few indeed are the kitchens today where the cook does not have an array of bottled or bagged seasonings close at hand, where virtually nothing — from spaghetti sauce to Hollandaise — would be the same without the essential flavourings of herbs. Suddenly to realize that these trusty little jars and tins and recycled bags may contain some of the agricultural world's most notorious health-threatening contaminants is profoundly disturbing.

Even in long-established North American gardens, herbs are often noticeably absent, and John Balf of British Columbia's Tansy Farms says that most Canadian and U.S. gardeners can be divided into two distinct groups: those who are intimidated by the mystique of these plants and those who think of herbs as mere weeds that will practically raise and harvest themselves.

Melvin Grey/Octopus Books Ltd.

154 GARDENING

Both attitudes contain an element of truth. What is important, as Benjamin discovered in *The Graduate*, is one's choices. Some herbs, such as catnip, horseradish and mint, do indeed resemble weeds in tenacity and invasiveness. Parsley, sage and thyme are usually vigorous but cooperative plants, while rosemary and other tender perennials must be coaxed along, brought indoors over the winter and set out again after the weather has warmed in spring.

When home-grown, all can save a cook money as well as providing known quality and an unshakable peace of mind. With commercial products fetching upwards of $2 for 32 grams — roughly a handful of dried leaves or seeds — a gardener should be able to recoup his or her investment in plants or seeds in a single season.

SEEDS OR PLANTS?

Herbs are becoming sufficiently popular now that most neighbourhood greenhouses and nurseries carry a small selection of plants every spring, and there are mail-order plant and seed salesmen who offer almost everything a herb gardener could want.

As a general rule, it is best for the beginning gardener to plant annual herbs from seeds, and perennials from transplants. While a commercially grown plant will be more expensive than the same herb grown at home from seed — a packet of about 500 parsley seeds costs about 50 cents, while a single parsley plant can cost $2.50 — the obvious advantage in buying plants rather than seeds is that plants save the gardener time and trouble, providing him with an instant garden. If only one or two plants of a particular herb are wanted, it makes sense to buy transplants. This may even cost no more than seeds when all expenses are considered. That is simply a matter of preference, but some herbs really must be grown from roots or plants. French tarragon, lemon verbena, horseradish, some thymes, mints and scented geraniums can be reliably reproduced only with cuttings or transplants. Other herbs, such as rosemary, can be grown from seed, but they take so long to reach harvestable size that most gardeners willingly pay extra to pare a few years from the growing process. In the case of hardy perennials, another advantage in purchasing plants that have been grown by the nursery is that the gardener will know the plants are hardy when he buys them — useful information, because most perennial herbs can be purchased in a number of strains with varying degrees of hardiness. Irene Dinel of Foxrun Farm, near North Bay, Ontario, grows about 105 herbs outdoors year-round, including lavender, which she says "does exceptionally well. Of course, there are lavenders that are frost-tender, but my English lavender does very well."

Winter survival is not an issue with annual herbs, such as summer savory, dill and basil, which are replaced each spring. With these plants, many of which germinate readily in warm soil, it is a waste of money to buy transplants, provided the gardener has any success at all in working with seeds.

Almost all types of herb seeds, annual or perennial, can be sown directly where they will grow in the garden, but many, such as marjoram or thyme, have tiny seeds that become tiny seedlings, which are easily desiccated, overwhelmed by weeds or overlooked by the gardener. These herbs, then, and slow-growing seeds, such as parsley and lovage, are best started indoors in a sunny place on flats of damp soil mix. Parlette prefers a soil mix of one-half homemade compost, one-quarter peat moss and one-quarter vermiculite, whereas Balf, who sells herb seeds and plants in Abbotsford, British Columbia, prepares a mix of 45 percent finely screened sphagnum peat, 45 percent perlite and 10 percent of "our own sterilized compost, which is very old compost that's almost soil, and a small amount of dolomitic lime — lawn-and-garden grade, because you would need twice as much of the coarser grind — about a cupful to a garbage pail of mix." Balf sterilizes the compost in small batches by heating it to 160 degrees F for half an hour to kill harmful organisms and weed seeds. Gardeners who do not have their own compost can buy it bagged from a garden supply store or can substitute a purchased sterilized potting mix for the Parlette or Balf mix.

The mix should be kept slightly damp — spray it with a vaporizer whenever the surface is dry — until the seedlings are about half an inch tall, when they should be thinned to stand approximately an inch apart. When they are an inch tall, carefully move them into individual containers, retaining as much soil as possible around the roots. After a week or two, harden the transplants by gradually introducing them to outdoor conditions, finally leaving them outdoors all day and night, allowing the soil medium to dry out between waterings. They will then be ready to move to a permanent location.

Because they are grown in small quantities by most home gardeners, herbs occupy little space and provide free rein to the imagination of a gardener who wants to work in circles or knots or who has always wanted a garden shaped like a pretzel. Annual herbs, however, can easily be grown in the vegetable garden, while perennials may be tucked in flower beds, along pathways or in dedicated herb gardens, where their various colours, shapes and textures can be highlighted.

John and Karen Balf write: "We have had good luck in our heavy clay soil growing herbs in raised beds. Most of the herbs are fairly shallow-rooted; if the top foot of the soil is well drained, this should suit them." Catnip Acres Farm in Connecticut recommends that in areas with poor drainage, the gardener dig out the site of the proposed herb bed to a depth of two feet, pour in six inches of rock and then refill the hole with the removed soil. "The resulting bed, slightly raised, should provide better drainage. Roots kept in standing water will rot quickly." Annual herbs tend to favour full sun and fertile soil, whereas hardy perennials are more tolerant of partial shade and poorer-quality soil. If both types of herbs will be grown, give the annuals the sunniest, most fertile soil. Every spring, the annual bed can be fortified with compost or manure and, if necessary, with limestone and rock phosphate. The pe-

Any gardener with patience, some skill and a sunny window can grow from seed such plants as thyme, a hardy perennial with minuscule seeds.

rennial bed should receive occasional small additions of fertilizer. Writes Balf, "Most herbs benefit from extra lime being worked into the soil around them and a dressing of compost or other low-nitrogen high-phosphate fertilizer."

The beginner's culinary herb garden we will describe consists of annuals and perennials that may be planted apart or in a single bed about 3' x 10'. Parsley, though actually a biennial, is considered an annual in this instance, as it will not be kept for seed production by most gardeners. And some herbs that are perennial in more southerly gardens — sage, oregano, thyme — will be grown as annuals or overwintered indoors in more northerly ones. Nevertheless, if a gardener lives where the climate is not much harsher than that of Edmonton — which has average spring and fall frost dates in late May and mid-September and is located in Agriculture Canada's climatic zone 3 — and has a plot of fairly fertile, well-drained, weeded soil, he may purchase all of the following herbs:

BASIL — Order 2 packets of seeds of each of 2 different types to grow 6 plants of each type
CHIVES — Order 1 plant (1 clump) of regular and garlic chives or 1 packet of seeds
DILL — Order 1 packet of seeds to grow 12 plants
LOVAGE — Order 1 packet of seeds to grow 1 plant or order 1 plant
MARJORAM — Order 1 plant
MINT — Order 1 plant of each of 2 types
OREGANO — Order 1 plant of each of 2 types
PARSLEY — Order 1 packet of seeds of each of 1 or 2 types
SAGE — Order 1 plant of each of 2 different types
SAVORY, SUMMER — Order 1 packet of seeds for 3 plants
SAVORY, WINTER — Order 1 plant
TARRAGON, FRENCH — Order 1 plant
THYME — Order 1 plant of each of 2 types

BASIL

The popularity of pesto (a flavour-rich sauce for pasta or salad dressings), says Waltrout Richter, has made basil one of Richters' best-selling items. But long before it became associated with pine nuts and noodles, basil was considered a pleasant partner to tomatoes in all forms, raw and cooked. Those who grow it come to appreciate its assertive, cloverlike flavour with other vegetables, as well as in meat pies, stews and teas. There are many types, including the most popular culinary form, sweet basil (*Ocimum basilicum*). Richters offers seeds for 16 other kinds, including lemon basil, the magenta-leafed dark opal basil and lettuce-leaf basil, with leaves as large as four inches across.

An annual member of the mint family that grows one to two feet tall, basil quickly produces big crops of flavourful, heavily scented leaves if its seeds are sown on warm soil, directly where they will grow. Wait until night temperatures are predictably above 45 degrees F, then sow the seeds in a sunny, fertile place, covering them lightly. The seeds sprout in a week at temperatures of 68 to 86 degrees F. As they grow, thin the plants to stand six inches apart — use the thinnings in cooking — and from the time they are about four inches tall, harvest when needed by pinching off the tops of the plants. If not regularly harvested, the plant will cease to produce leaves and will go to seed, developing edible flowers that Hedgehog Hill Farm in Maine uses, along with a few leaves, to produce an especially attractive herb vinegar. Harvest basil entirely before the first fall frost — the plant is not at all frost-hardy — or bring a few plants indoors for winter.

CHIVES

Attractive, delicious, hardy and disease-free members of the onion family, chives (*Allium schoenoprasum*) deserve a place in every herb garden. The dark green, onionlike leaves grow in a foot-tall clump, and the lavender flower heads shoot up a few more inches in summer. A flat-leafed, taller and less bushy species, garlic or Chinese chives (*Allium tuberosum*) are just as easy to grow but have a distinctive garlic flavour.

This variety develops a white flower that is edible, as is that of common chives.

Like other onion seeds, chive seeds germinate best in darkness, so after spreading them in a thin layer on a flat of damp soil medium, cover them with a quarter-inch of soil. The seeds will germinate in about two weeks at 60 to 70 degrees F. As soon as the ground can be worked in spring, set the transplants outdoors, two inches apart, or sow the seeds directly outdoors at that time. When you wish to divide or enlarge the chive bed, remove single bulbs or clumps of bulbs in spring, and plant them elsewhere. Chives can be brought indoors in winter, provided they have first been exposed to heavy frost.

Once the plant is established, cut or pinch off a few outer leaves as needed. Purple chive flowers are excellent for drying for winter arrangements and are attractive in herb vinegars. The chopped leaves can be used anywhere that green onions would be found or wherever a delicate onion or garlic flavour is desired.

DILL

Besides its well-known use in pickles, dill adds a distinctive, refreshing flavour to stews, vegetables, sauces, dips and herbed butters, as well as to eastern European dishes. Around the last spring frost date, sow dill seeds outdoors in a sunny, fairly fertile, well-drained spot. Thin the seedlings to stand about four inches apart. The leaves, seeds and seed heads are all useful and have the characteristic dill flavour. Dill often self-sows in the garden if allowed to go to seed, producing two- or three-foot-tall seed heads. Like other members of the Umbelliferae, including coriander, anise, lovage and parsley, dill is a favourite food of the green and black parsley worm, larva of the swallowtail butterfly. Handpick these caterpillars.

LOVAGE

Related to dill, lovage produces similar umbrella-shaped seed heads, or umbels, hence the family name Umbelliferae. Lovage, however, is a hardy perennial, and it is a distinctive one, with celerylike foliage and stalks and seed heads that can reach a height of five or six feet. Give it a foot of space all around.

The flavour of lovage is similar to that of parsley and celery, so the leaves, stems, seeds and even the roots of the plant are useful wherever those flavours would be appreciated. Frederick McGourty, editor of the Brooklyn Botanical Garden booklet *Culinary Herbs*, writes that lovage, an "elegant sort of perennial celery," is his own favourite herb. "It is a bold accent plant, one worthy of a spot in the sunny flower border. A leaf will perfume a stew, and two will make, with grated zucchini or cucumber and chicken stock, a memorable soup. No freezer unit should be without 15 quarts." One lovage plant, however, is enough for most families. Sow seeds indoors or outdoors in the manner of parsley.

Harold V. Green/Valen Photos

Chives are hardy perennials but can be grown from seed as easily as their vegetable-garden cousins, the onions.

MARJORAM

Marjoram and oregano are closely related members of the *Origanum* genus, so confusion between the herbs has reigned since at least as long ago as 1640, when John Parkinson wrote that "there is much controversie among the Modern writers about these two herbs." Sweet marjoram (*Origanum majorana*) is a low-growing, fairly tender perennial shrub with a delicate flavour similar to that of most oregano species. As well, sweet marjoram is usually grown as an annual in the North, whereas some oreganos are hardy. Set the transplant outdoors in a warm, sunny, well-drained spot after the last spring frost, allowing it six inches all around. Pinch off the stems to use the foliage as needed, harvesting all that is left soon after the first fall frost and bringing indoors either a part of the plant — including roots — or stem cuttings to root over the winter, thus providing plants for the next year.

MINT

Vigorous and tolerant of shade, moist soil and cool weather, mint can be the ideal northern culinary herb if it is kept within bounds. All the hardy mint varieties

— including apple mint, orange mint, spearmint and peppermint, each of which exists in several strains — are invasive enough to take over a small herb garden in a few years. As is the case with all the perennial herbs, the variegated species such as ginger mint (which is green and gold) and pineapple mint (green and white) are less hardy than their plain-leafed relatives.

Either plant hardy mints where they can ramble, or remove the base from a large plastic bucket, setting it into the soil so that its rim stands about an inch above soil level, and fill it with fertile soil — a half-and-half mixture of soil and compost suits mint well. Set one or two purchased transplants or stem cuttings within each container.

Mint is such a sturdy plant that once established, it can be harvested almost as soon as it emerges from the soil. Pinch off the tops of shoots as they grow. If the roots are confined, it will need to be thinned every spring and then fertilized with a complete organic emulsion or with an inch of compost. Both flowers and leaves are used in desserts, candies, sauces, jellies and teas.

OREGANO

Sometimes called wild marjoram, *Origanum vulgare* and other oregano species, which grow up to a foot and a half tall in sunny gardens, are considered almost as important in Italian food as tomatoes. There are many strains — Tansy Farms sells nine different oreganos, including golden, with "gold-green crinkled foliage," and three ornamental oreganos "grown for their good looks rather than flavour." Mulch oregano in the fall, and bring stem cuttings or rooted clumps indoors over the winter if you are unsure of its hardiness.

PARSLEY

Parsley is so well known that it is often considered more a vegetable than a seasoning. Many gardeners regularly include it in the vegetable garden, although it is attractive enough to use as an edging plant in herb and flower gardens. There are three different types of parsley and several cultivars of each of the first two: moss-curled parsley; plain-leafed, or Italian, parsley; and parsnip-rooted, or Hamburg, parsley, which is grown primarily for its parsley-flavoured root, used in soups and stews.

Provided it survives the winter, parsley, a biennial, will go to seed in its second year, when it produces the characteristic seed heads of the Umbelliferae. Gardeners who do not want seeds for sowing or for culinary use grow the plant as an annual only. As soon as the ground can be worked in spring, parsley seeds can be sown directly outdoors in a fertile, moist, sunny or partially shady place. It germinates and grows slowly and may not be ready for a first harvest for two months. To get a jump on the season, start the seeds indoors six weeks early, and transplant them outdoors when they are no more than an inch tall — they transplant poorly when larger — setting the plants a foot apart. Plants can be dug up and potted for indoor use during the winter.

SAGE

There are so many different types of sage that Tansy Farms remarks, "Collecting the different *Salvias* could be a lifelong hobby." Their catalogue lists 19, not all of them culinary, including candelabra sage, with "large, purple, orchidlike flowers," and the frost-tender pineapple sage, with "a delicious pineapple scent and vivid scarlet flowers just before frost. It grows to quite a size during one season, so you may want to take cuttings, which root easily in water or moist soil, instead of digging up the parent plant for winter."

Salvia officinalis, garden sage, is a relatively hardy, woody perennial member of the mint family that will overwinter in most Canadian gardens. Where it is not hardy, it may be grown as an annual, either from seeds or from purchased transplants or from cuttings taken in the fall. After the first fall frost, take sage shoots about three inches long, dip their bases in rooting hormone powder (available at garden shops), and root them in damp sand or vermiculite. Marjoram, oregano and thyme can also be propagated in this way.

Even where sage is hardy, it sometimes delays the production of its grey-blue leaves until early summer, so do not replace plants unless they have not reappeared by mid-June. Pinch leaves from the stems as needed, or cut entire stems for drying in fall. Its flavour is strong and distinctive, so use sparingly at first. Traditionally used in poultry or pork dressing, sage is also good in dips, cheeses and teas.

SAVORY

Also mint family members, summer savory (*Satureia hortensis*), the annual species, and winter savory (*S. montana*), the hardy perennial, are similar in their peppery flavour and in their appearance — shrubs with narrow, shiny, thymelike leaves. Winter savory, however, is the smaller, slower-growing plant and is generally considered to have the stronger but less esteemed flavour. Both savories are called bean herbs because they complement the flavour of all types of beans, hot or cold. They also marry well with other vegetables, homemade sausages and poultry dressings.

Both savories do best on well-drained soil in full sun. Sow summer savory seed outdoors in late spring, pressing the seeds lightly into the soil and keeping them moist until they germinate in about a week. Savory transplants easily. Allow each plant a foot all around.

TARRAGON

Although not specified, when tarragon is called for

Parsley, sage, rosemary and thyme are basics, but even in the midst of a Canadian city, literally dozens of different herb plants can flourish.

in a recipe, it is certainly French tarragon (*Artemisia dracunculus sativa*), a plant that does not set viable seed and so can be grown only from cuttings or from purchased plants. When tarragon seed is sold by a seed house, it is Russian tarragon (*A. dracunculus*), a plant generally considered so lacking in true tarragon flavour that it is almost worthless.

When planted in moderately rich, well-drained, partially or fully sunny soil and mulched in fall, French tarragon should be hardy in most gardens. Allow it six inches all around. Tarragon grows about two feet tall and has slender leaves that complement salads, eggs, cheeses, meats and fish. The subtle anise flavour is largely lost in drying, so tarragon is often preserved

in vinegar for winter salad dressings. To propagate the plant, take stem cuttings of new growth in the spring, and plant them in a moist, shady place. Tarragon dies down in the winter and will begin to grow again in late spring.

THYME

Like mint, sage and oregano, thyme is a mint family member that comes in many forms: It varies in height from creeping to a foot and a half tall; in colour from grey to green; in flavour from caraway to lemon or camphor; in texture from woolly to smooth; and in hardiness. Some will survive winter in almost every northern garden, while others are reliably hardy only in the southern United States. Tansy Farms sells 26 thymes, including the quite tender pine-scented thyme

Marjorie & Ian Samson

and the fairly hardy common thyme (*Thymus vulgaris*). The Sandy Mush Herb Nursery in North Carolina sells 38, including the intriguingly named Pennsylvania Dutch Tea Thyme. All need well-drained soil and will do best in partial or full sun.

Many types of thyme have a creeping, matlike growth habit that allows them to fill in spaces between other plants in a herb garden. The hardiest of the species, such as wild thyme or mother-of-thyme (*Thymus serpyllum*), can be used to cover herb garden paths. Creeping thymes are best propagated by dividing the clump in spring.

The most popular culinary thyme is a shrub, garden or common thyme, a foot-tall plant that is not reliably hardy — a plant kept in the greenhouse at the University of Alberta Devonian Botanic Garden provides stem cuttings for replacement should their outdoor plants die over winter.

Common thyme is hardy, however, in most agricultural areas of the North, as is a surprisingly wide variety of herbs. Near North Bay, Ontario, Irene Dinel reports that the survival rate of hardy perennials "is excellent, particularly when we have a good snow cover. I do mulch with leaves, on occasion, but find the natural snow cover is less likely to smother plants. Even after the open winter we experienced in 1982-83, I lost only the more tender of the hardy perennials such as santolina and lemon and silver thyme.

"My hardy herbs came through with flying colours. I must point out that I did not mulch but left them to fend for themselves that winter." Among Dinel's hardy perennials, which she sells locally, are lemon balm, salad burnet, chives, comfrey, lavender, lovage, marjoram, French tarragon, nine mints, four types of oregano and four thymes. Some of the perennials that she must mulch include golden and Greek oregano, golden sage, creeping and winter savory and woolly and lemon thyme. Fallen leaves used alone as a mulch can mat down and smother plants if they are not removed promptly in the spring, so they are best used over a bottom layer of pine boughs or loose hay. Leaves shredded by a lawn mower are less likely than whole leaves to hinder the growth of herbs in the spring. Single plants can be surrounded with a wire tomato cage that is then filled with straw, grass clippings or shredded paper.

Fred Ashby mulches his perennials near Peterborough, Ontario, with sheets of plastic in the manner of row covers. "The herbs really don't need protection," he says, "but it warms the soil and allows us to get to work by about the first of March, instead of April or May." The plants that Ashby is able to overwinter and to sell by mail order include lemon balm, chives, salad burnet, lovage, oregano, sage, winter savory, French tarragon, sorrel, ten mints and four types of thyme.

If the hardiness of a particular herb is unknown, keep one plant or a few cuttings indoors for at least two winters so that the outdoor plant can be replaced if it dies. Planting the same type of herb in more than one outdoor location increases its chance for winter survival, as does a planting spot that avoids low areas or frost hollows and favours, instead, raised sheltered places where snow collects.

All of the herbs in the basic garden produce edible foliage that must be stored if it is to be used throughout the winter months. Although every preservation method produces a seasoning that is less desirable than the fresh herb — seasoned herbalists such as Ross Parlette and Pierre Burgoyne keep a few herb plants indoors under plant lights over the winter — each method does have its own advantages and disadvantages.

The least expensive and least bulky method of herb preservation is drying. The easiest way to dry herbs is to pick them on a dry, sunny day, tie the stems together, secure the bunch with an elastic band, and hang it from the ceiling of a warm, dark, well-ventilated room. Balf says, "We usually hang them upside down in bunches of a dozen or so upstairs, and we put the short-stemmed ones in Chinese wicker baskets — I think they're baby baskets — that let the air in underneath. We turn them every once in a while. The whole upstairs of our house — it's not an attic or anything, it's a real upstairs — is basically the herb area for drying. We leave the windows open at both ends and put on a fan on damp days." David Schmierbach of Dacha Barinka in Chilliwack, British Columbia, uses a similar system, but in his case, the drying room is part of an old barn with a black asphalt roof.

Schmierbach has allowed the 20th century into his herb-sales operation with the discovery that small amounts of herbs dry exceptionally well in a microwave oven. "Wrap them in a paper towel — I had a bad deal working with newspaper, which someone recommended, but it gave an off-flavour — or use a cotton dish towel, and put them in for just a few minutes, depending on the thickness of the stems. They have to be wrapped because the moisture is absorbed by the towel." Herbs can be spread in a single layer on cookie sheets in a standard oven preheated to 125 degrees F, where they will become crisp in about 20 minutes. Herbs are ready to store when they are cool and dry enough so that the stems snap, rather than bend, and the leaves crumble. Store them in airtight tins or in glass jars kept in a cool, dark cupboard.

Schmierbach also preserves herbs in vinegar, which he then sells at a local farmers' market. Any herb can produce a scented, flavoured, coloured vinegar that will transmit those qualities to dressings or pickles. The fresh, washed herb is placed in a bottle into which vinegar is poured. Leave the herbs in place indefinitely or until the vinegar attains the desired strength of flavour, and then strain the vinegar. Some especially good herb vinegars include those made with French tarragon, basil, dill, marjoram, oregano, sage and thyme. Try different herbs with different vinegars to determine which combination suits you best. In a variation of the same preservation method, Balf makes a sort of pesto base that can be frozen. "It's just basil leaves and oil. It works really well, like a basil concentrate. We might put a spoonful in a salad dressing or other sauces." Sage leaves store well in the same fashion.

Freezing is the preservation method of choice for Parlette, who prefers his herbs as close to fresh as possible, in flavour and fragrance. "The freezer is a great thing for us," says Parlette. "You pick the fresh leaves and put them in a plastic bag in the freezer, and then take the bag out the next day and crumble them — freezing makes them brittle. They then go back to the freezer — you can store a tremendous amount this way. They freeze easily, and you just keep adding crumbled herbs to the bag till it's full. The colour and the flavour are just about the same as when they're fresh out of the garden. But in drying, you lose colour and flavour."

For Parlette, herbs were a way of life even before Simon and Garfunkel wrote of parsley, sage, rosemary and thyme. But for most gardeners, the awareness of the habits of the herbs of *Scarborough Fair* is something quite new, turning them all into graduates of the subtle art of flavouring with home-grown seasonings. ∎

Sources

Publications

GROWING & USING HERBS SUCCESSFULLY
By Betty E.M. Jacobs
223 pages
228A — paperback, $13.25
Available from Harrowsmith Books, Camden East, Ontario K0K 1J0.

OLD TIME HERBS FOR NORTHERN GARDENS
By Minnie W. Kamm
Dover Publications, Inc.

THE HERB BOOK
By John Lust
659 pages
211A — paperback, $4.50
Available from Harrowsmith Books, Camden East, Ontario K0K 1J0. The lion's share of *The Herb Book* is entitled "A Compendium of Botanical Medicine," an alphabetical listing of herbs, their descriptions and curative properties. Also in the book are recipes for herbal medicines, dyes and teas as well as a list of botanical livestock feeds and insect repellents.

CULPEPER'S COMPLETE HERBAL
By Nicholas Culpeper
430 pages
202B — hardcover, $15.95
Available from Harrowsmith Books, Camden East, Ontario K0K 1J0. This colour-illustrated reprint of a 17th-century herbal describes the virtues and powers of hundreds of wild and cultivated plants in the quaint phrasing of an astrologer/physician of Cromwell's England. Of almost as much historical as botanical interest, it is a classic.

THE RODALE HERB BOOK
Edited by William H. Hylton
653 pages
21B — hardcover, $19.95
Available from Harrowsmith Books, Camden East, Ontario K0K 1J0.

Nurseries

ASHBY'S
R.R. 2
Cameron, Ontario K0M 1G0
Herb seeds to Canada and the U.S. Herb plants to Canada only. Wholesale prices available to horticultural societies and tradesmen. Catalogue $1.00.

HARBORCREST NURSERIES
4634 West Saanich Road
Victoria, British Columbia V8Z 3G8
Herb plants to Canada and the U.S. Catalogue $1.00.

LES HERBES FINES
DE SAINT-ANTOINE
480 Chemin l'Acadie
Saint-Antoine-sur-Richelieu
Quebec J0L 1R0
Herb plants and seeds to Canadian addresses only. Minimum order, four plants or, if ordering seed only, six packets of seed. French or English catalogue $1.00 refundable.

HERBS FOR HEALTH
Ross Parlette
R.R. 4
Cobourg, Ontario K9A 4J7
(416) 342-2188
Organically grown comfrey, garlic, chives, spearmint, French tarragon and lemon basil plants. Catalogue $1.00. Canada only.

RICHTERS
Goodwood, Ontario L0C 1A0
(416) 640-6677
Herb seeds, books, products. Catalogue $2.00.

TANSY FARMS
R.R. 1, 5888 Else Road
Agassiz, British Columbia V0M 1A0
(604) 796-9316
More than 300 herb plants to Canada and the U.S. Minimum order, six plants. Catalogue $1.50. Visit farm by appointment only.

WEST KOOTENAY HERB NURSERY
R.R. 2, Bedford Road
Nelson, British Columbia V1L 5P5
(604) 352-9479
Herb plants to Canadian addresses. Catalogue free.

Professionals' Pick

Six leading growers name their favourite herbs

"Basil, definitely. Bush basil. I grow tomatoes, too, so whenever I cook tomatoes, I use some basil. And I try always to have a few plants indoors in pots under lights, because dried basil isn't very good tasting. When I snip off some, it pinches it back. It still grows flowers, but that's okay."

— *Pierre Burgoyne*
Les Herbes Fines de Saint-Antoine
Quebec

"I have a few: I like rosemary and French sorrel and French tarragon. I love rosemary just because I like the way it looks and the way it flowers, and it is good for your circulation. Some people use it on chicken, but I'm not a meat eater, I'm a vegetarian, so I put it on vegetables. French sorrel, I just chop fine and put in a salad. Some restaurants wrap fish in sorrel leaves and bake it. With French tarragon, I make vinegar — almost everyone knows about tarragon vinegar — or I chop it fine in salad dressing with cider vinegar, water, sweetener (maple or rice syrup), a crushed clove of garlic, salt — just a bit, if you have herbs, you don't need much — and good oil."

— *Waltrout Richter*
Richters Herbs
Ontario

"Winter savory. It's just everything about it, the smell and everything. I use it in herb vinegar, with cider vinegar; or we get raspberry juice from the local producers and make raspberry vinegar with it."

— *David Schmierbach*
Dacha Barinka
British Columbia

"It changes all the time, whichever I've harvested most recently. I guess my favourite right now is Greek sage; it's nicer, more lemony, than regular sage. We use it sometimes in tea."

— *John Balf*
Tansy Farms
British Columbia

"Lemon basil. There are a lot of lemon herbs, but this one has a lemon fragrance and gives off its lemon flavour better than anything else. This is really a winner — it makes such a fragrant tea that people who usually don't think they like herb tea enjoy it. Even in the garden, you just bump up against it, and you smell the lemon fragrance. It's really delightful. We also use it to flavour fruit. We pack the fresh leaves in with peaches or pears in honey, with a little vitamin C to keep the colour of the fruit — about four cups of fruit to half a teaspoon of vitamin C — and store it in the freezer."

— *Ross Parlette*
Herbs for Health
Ontario

"I've got a lot of different favourites for different things. For fragrance, sage and lemon eucalyptus are two scents that are just beyond belief. For seasoning, Greek oregano and summer savory. Summer savory, I find, is one of the most versatile herbs. It has an oregano-thyme kind of flavour, so you can use it anywhere you'd use those herbs, in everything from scrambled eggs to soups and stews, tomatoes, spaghetti sauce and pizza."

— *Dean Pailler*
Catnip Acres
Connecticut

Cheating The Frost

All's fair in love and love-apples: new tricks for growing early tomatoes in the North

---

A Harrowsmith Staff Report

The Galápagos Islands are already well known for their curiosities of nature, but one story that arose from those Ecuadorian islands is more illustrative of the curious nature of wild plants in general. Charles M. Rick, one of the world's foremost authorities on tomatoes, and a colleague puzzled over their lack of success in germinating the seeds of wild Galápagos tomatoes in California. The only method that was significantly effective involved treating the seeds with household bleach, a success that puzzled them further. Clearly, the wild tomatoes could not have evolved to require soaking in Javex. After many more ill-fated attempts to germinate the seeds, the scientists fed wild Galápagos tomatoes to two Galápagos tortoises that had been brought to California. It took a full three weeks for the seeds to pass through the digestive tracts of the slow beasts, but once they emerged, the seeds germinated very well indeed — the tomato seed coats had eroded in much the same way as those that had been soaked in household bleach.

What this story illustrates is not just another curiosity of natural life on the Galápagos but a truth that applies everywhere: Plants evolve to suit the opportunities and difficulties presented by their surroundings. Like the Galápagos plants, our backyard *Beefsteaks* are genetically adapted to the native lands of their small-fruited ancestor, a perennial vine which thrives in a narrow belt from central Ecuador to northern Chile. There, equatorial mountain conditions include temperatures that seldom dip below 50 degrees F or rise above 100. Our garden tomatoes are so thoroughly domesticated that their seeds, like those of other food crops, germinate easily, but their genetically determined ability to thrive only in a climate similar to that required by their wild ancestors leaves many northern gardeners feeling like the California researchers without Galápagos tortoises. The northern spring is frequently cooler than 50 degrees, even during the daytime, causing tomatoes to grow slowly, delaying the harvest date. Prolonged temperatures a few degrees above freezing will kill the plants, as will even a short exposure to temperatures at or below freezing. Where and when warm weather is as scarce as tomato-eating tortoises, the growth of healthy plants often involves not bleach but bleach bottles and a host of other plant covers, plastic or glass protectors that concentrate the sun's heat directly around the plants. Whether purchased or homemade, individual plant covers or row covers can produce dramatic results. In an experimental plot in Kentville, Nova Scotia, in 1983, *Springset* tomatoes planted in plastic tunnels yielded, up to August 8, 11 times as many tomatoes as did uncovered *Springsets* growing nearby.

The force at work in these systems is the greenhouse effect, whereby the sun's heat is trapped within a transparent shelter, heating not only the plant but also the soil around it. The combination of a row cover and black plastic mulch has been shown to raise the soil temperature by six to eight degrees F, and warm soil is especially beneficial. In 1968, when G.A. Kemp

Most sophisticated and expensive of the individual plant covers, the 18-inch-tall Wall o' Water takes advantage of the insulating ability of water to keep tomatoes from overheating during the day and freezing at night.

worked at Agriculture Canada's experimental station in Lethbridge, Alberta, he wrote in the *Canadian Journal of Plant Science*: "The amount of root a tomato plant produces from seedling to first fruit set undoubtedly has a bearing on the number of fruit that set early and the number that the plant will be capable of supporting. Whether the plant develops from direct seeding or as a transplant, root development will be slower when soil temperatures are low than when they are high."

It is in part because plant covers help warm the soil that covered plants stay warmer at night than do uncovered plants, even though the greenhouse effect itself ceases to work at sunset. Optimal night temperatures for fruit set of tomatoes have been determined to lie in the range of 57 to 68 degrees F; if either higher or lower, fruit set slows and eventually stops entirely. Once pollination has occurred, however, tomatoes mature earliest with a night temperature of 79 degrees. Daytime temperatures in the range of 65 to 85 degrees are best. Although early tomatoes are genetically able to produce fruit in a shorter time than are other tomatoes, they are not necessarily more tolerant of low temperatures. In Agriculture Canada's *Growing Garden Tomatoes*, Calvin Chong writes, "Depending on length

or severity of exposure to chilling, the plants may be temporarily or seriously impaired by temperatures below 50 degrees. Exposures to chilling temperatures have a cumulative effect. Chilled plants may develop a purple coloration in stem and leaf veins, with possible subsequent stunting of plant growth and poor yield."

But the upper temperature limitation for healthy tomatoes is as important as is the lower limit. Overheating is an uncommon problem in most northern gardens, but it can easily occur in a closed shelter, where the greenhouse effect causes temperatures to soar to 100 degrees F on a sunny day when the ambient temperature hovers around 60 degrees. Not only is fruit set hindered by high temperatures, but tomato blossoms will burn if they are close to or touch the cover on hot days, and the red pigment may not develop if the tomato's skin temperature rises above 85 degrees. Higher temperatures can cause fruit blistering. Plant protectors, then, are not for everyone. They should not be used when and where the weather is generally hot and sunny, and when they are used, they almost always require ventilation. Lloyd Hausher of Alberta Agriculture says that after three years of tests throughout that sunny province, he does not recommend the use of plastic tunnels for tomatoes as "they produce real lush vegetative growth and delay fruit set, possibly because temperatures are too high." The use of temporary covers such as hot caps, however, has been recommended for prairie tomato growers who want a jump on the season, as we shall see.

Individual plant covers usually have an opening at the top through which hot air can exit, while the tunnels in the Kentville experiment were ventilated by a researcher lifting the plastic along one side whenever the inside temperature exceeded 95 degrees F. As well, once the weather is quite predictably warm and night temperatures are in the high 60s, the covers should be removed entirely or installed only on very cool or overcast days.

In general, plant protectors will allow the gardener to set transplants outdoors about two weeks earlier than usual or about two weeks before the approximate date of the last spring frost. Weed the place where the tomatoes will go, and put the protectors or a sheet of clear plastic in place about a week before the expected planting date so that the soil can warm. If the weather remains unremittingly cold and cloudy, however, delay the planting date, as the protectors are effective heat collectors only on clear or lightly overcast days.

When setting the plant covers out in the garden, be sure to install them securely, holding them in place with stakes, if necessary, and setting them, when possible, in an area somewhat sheltered from the wind. Wind, children and pets can all upset protectors, and knocked-over or broken plants can take weeks to recover.

The size and type of cover a gardener will use depends on how much he is willing to spend, the severity of the climate and the length of time he wishes to have the tomatoes covered: A hot cap six inches tall will cover a transplant for only about a week, whereas a foot-tall bleach bottle, its base and cap removed, may be in place for two, and a four-foot-tall polyethylene-covered wooden frame could protect plants for the entire season. All-season protection should be considered only where summer temperatures are likely to dip below 55 degrees F.

TO EACH ITS OWN

Individual plant covers are sometimes called cloches, referring to the glass bell jars used by French market gardeners to speed the growth of plants. The greatest advantage of such an individual cover is its portability. Whether large or small, most can easily be removed and installed from day to day as the weather changes, and they are just fine for the gardener growing one tomato plant by the patio, one by the garage and yet another by the Brussels sprouts. Homemade cloches assume almost every shape imaginable and utilize glass, polyethylene, rigid plastic and wax paper that may be self-supporting or attached to a frame of wood or chicken wire. Gardeners who customarily cage their

The combination of dark plastic mulch and a row cover, **top,** *can raise the soil temperature by six to eight Fahrenheit degrees, hastening tomato growth and ripening in areas where the ambient temperature is cooler than optimum.* **Bottom,** *in a tomato row-cover demonstration in Kemptville, Ontario, sheets of dark plastic mulch pierced to admit transplants were covered with nine-gauge wire hoops that were in turn covered with six-foot-wide plastic sheets.*

tomatoes can hurry spring growth by surrounding the cage with a sheet of clear polyethylene.

Commercial hot caps with such names as Hotkaps and Plantkeepers are among the smallest of the protectors. They cost about 25 cents each, are designed for one-season use only and are made of heavy wax paper that is pressed into the soil with a pasteboard setter shipped with the protectors. Charles Walkof was employed at Agriculture Canada's Morden, Manitoba, research station when he noted that with the use of this type of plant protector, tomato transplants could be set out around May 15 on the prairies, two weeks earlier than would be wise if they were unprotected. Walkof wrote, "Before using the protectors, ventilate them by cutting an opening three centimetres (one inch) in diameter at the peak. Enlarge the opening when the temperature goes above 24 degrees C (75 degrees F). When frost threatens, place a second protector over the first one. Do not let the plants become overcrowded and deformed in the protector. A deformed plant seldom produces good tomatoes. Allow the plants to grow out of the protectors freely, and finally, press the paper around the base of the plant where it will keep weeds down and conserve soil moisture."

Also available commercially are Sunhats, about nine inches tall but narrower than hot caps. Their greater cost, about 80 cents each, can be attributed to their durable heavy plastic construction, which allows them to be used for several seasons. Imported from Switzerland, the Sunhats have a vented top and green shading stripes to prevent overheating and to eliminate the need for daily attention by the gardener. The manufacturer also claims that Sunhats serve to protect young plants from snails, slugs and birds.

Accommodating an even larger plant is Tomato Grow-Film, which comes to the purchaser as a 2½-foot-wide, 33-foot-long tube of perforated, tinted polyethylene that can be cut into lengths sufficient to cover the plant for as long as an entire season. The cylinder is meant to be tied at the top to the tomato stake. Allowing four feet of plastic for each plant, one tube — which costs about $10.45 — could then cover eight plants at a cost of $1.30 each, more than the other plant covers but possibly worth the price for the gardener in a cool summer area with only a few tomato plants.

The most expensive individual plant cover of all, at $3 or $4 each, is Wall o' Water, the most sophisticated device, which is designed not only to raise the temperature around the plant during the day but also to provide insulation for it at night. Taking advantage of the fact that water heats and cools more slowly than air, Wall o' Water consists of a 10-inch-wide ring of 6-mil vertical clear plastic tubes that can be filled with three gallons of water and left around the plant for about a month. Its Utah inventors claim that the water insulation also keeps the plant from overheating on hot days. The 18-inch-tall protector can be closed into a tepee shape on frosty nights, or it may be covered with plastic or a blanket when the plant inside becomes too tall to allow reshaping of the Wall o' Water.

Because they cover more than one plant at a time, row covers are useful for cool spring gardens, where entire rows are devoted to such tender crops as tomatoes. Like individual covers, they can be small enough to cover the plants for only a week or two or tall enough to protect them until maturity. The largest of these are tunnel greenhouses, which allow the gardener to stand upright and to tend the plants within.

The disadvantages of all row covers include their generally greater difficulty of construction, greater cost, greater maintenance and greater susceptibility to wind damage. Row covers, however, have recently undergone a surge of popularity among northern commercial growers of tender crops, who usually combine the covers with black plastic mulch, which helps raise the soil temperature and retain soil moisture while preventing the cover from filling with weeds. Row covers allow tomatoes to survive five to seven degrees F of frost if not vented, or three to four degrees if vented, and they extend the season by about two weeks at one or both ends, depending upon their size.

In their pamphlet *Slitted Row Covers for Intensive Vegetable Production*, Otho S. Wells and J. Brent Loy describe how to make an effective row cover at home. This cover, which "should not be viewed merely as a frost-protection system but as a growth-intensifying system during cool spring weather," is meant to be in use for four to six weeks for one season only. Researchers from the University of New Hampshire Cooperative Extension Service devised this system:

• Over damp soil, lay 4-foot-wide strips of black plastic mulch as long as the row of tomatoes will be. Cover the edges of the plastic with soil to hold it in place, and cut holes about 1½ feet apart where the transplants will go.
• Set the hardened-off transplants in place, one in each hole, and then water.
• Cut 63-inch lengths of No. 8 or 9 wire for the hoops, which will be inserted about 6 inches deep at each end at 4- or 5-foot intervals along the row, piercing the buried edge of the plastic mulch. The centre of each hoop will be about 14 to 16 inches above the centre of the row.
• Dig furrows 3 or 4 inches deep on each side of the row outside the hoops.
• The cover consists of 1.5- or 2-mil clear polyethylene that has 3-inch-long slashes running parallel to the loops and to each other, at ¾-inch intervals along each side of the midpoint. On a calm day and with the help of an assistant, stretch the plastic over the hoops, and secure the edges and ends with soil, tamping it down to hold the plastic securely.

Several similar row covers are available commercially as kits. The Cover Up, for instance, includes 16 feet of black plastic mulch, five galvanized steel hoops and 20 feet of vented clear plastic for about $16.50. The Select greenhouse tunnel includes 13 feet of covering plastic and 7½-inch-tall hoops made of plastic, not steel, so its price is a modest $4.50 or so. Available from some suppliers are Rumsey glass clips from England, which hold two sheets of glass together in a lean-to shape. For gardeners with access to recycled glass panes, several of these clipped glass units can be placed

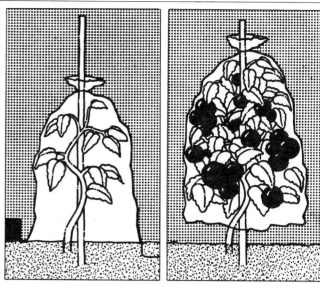

Individual plant covers, such as Sunhats, **below,** *may be small enough to enhance tomato growth for only a few weeks or, like another commercial product, Tomato Grow-Film,* **above,** *may be sufficiently large to cover plants to maturity. In either case, they utilize the greenhouse effect to concentrate solar heat around the plants. In Sunhats, excess heat exits through the top, while the Tomato Grow-Film is perforated for ventilation.*

together to form an attractive and inexpensive row cover.

A walk-in plastic tunnel, essentially a temporary greenhouse that will hold a row or more of plants to maturity, is most useful where the climate is only marginal for tomato culture and where fall usually brings the first crops of rock-hard green fruit. The Nova Scotia Department of Agriculture and Marketing has published plans for such a homemade tunnel, 14 feet wide and 80 feet long, which utilizes 4- or 6-mil polyethylene.

But such a cover, however large or elaborate, cannot guarantee a good crop of tomatoes. That is the product of a healthy, well-hardened transplant, which is then properly tended, watered and fertilized throughout the season and given the correct Andean temperature range. Of course, all of these techniques can be tested on other heat-loving garden vegetables, such as peppers, eggplant, squash, melons and many of the herbs. For the gardener who wants to experiment with creating microclimates around his vegetables, however, tomatoes are the most obvious starting point. Properly used, tomato protectors can help speed fruit to the harvestable stage and can easily recoup their cost in the first year by eliminating the need to buy commercial tomatoes for early summer salads. The lure of bringing in a basket of tomatoes weeks before they normally ripen might even tempt the gardener to further enhance their natural instincts with a performance of Ecuadorian flute music delivered to a tomato emerging from its hot cap into a garden half a world away from its native territory. ∎

Sources

Publications

GROWING GARDEN TOMATOES
Available from Information Services, Agriculture Canada, Ottawa, Ontario K1A 0C7. Publication #1558. Free.

A WALK-IN PLASTIC TUNNEL
Available from Nova Scotia Department of Agriculture and Marketing, Horticulture & Biology Services, Box 550, Truro, Nova Scotia B2N 5E3. Free.

Plant Protectors

ALBERTA NURSERIES & SEEDS LTD.
Bowden, Alberta T0M 0K0
Hotkaps.

DOMINION SEED HOUSE
115 Guelph Street
Georgetown, Ontario L7G 4A2
Sunhats, Tomato Grow Film. Canadian orders only.

CAVENDISH GARDEN PRODUCTS LTD.
300-1497 Marine Drive
West Vancouver, British Columbia
V7T 1B8
Rumsey Cloche Clips.

FIRESIDE & GREEN CONSERVER PRODUCTS
835C Broadway Avenue
Saskatoon, Saskatchewan S7N 1B5
(306) 665-6707
Wall o' Water.

GRO-TEK HOME GREENHOUSE SUPPLIES & SERVICES
RFD 1, 518A
South Berwick, Maine 03908
Wall o' Water, greenhouse supplies and materials. Catalogue 50 cents.

WALTER F. NICKE
Box 667H
Hudson, New York 12534
Rumsey Cloche Clips, Hotkaps, Glass Barn Cloche Fittings. Catalogue 50 cents to Canada; free in the U.S.

W.H. PERRON
515 Labelle Boulevard
City of Laval, Quebec H7V 2T3
(514) 332-3610
Select Tunnel. Catalogue $2.00.

STOKES SEEDS
39 James Street, Box 10
St. Catharines, Ontario L2R 6R6
Cover Up.

T&T SEEDS LTD.
Box 1710
Winnipeg, Manitoba R3C 3P6
(204) 943-8483
Select Tunnel, Plantkeepers. Catalogue 75 cents.

From *Common-Sense Compost Making* (1st edition)/Faber & Faber

That Old Black Magic

Composting: Horticultural prestidigitation turns wastes into nature's most perfect soil conditioner

By Jennifer Bennett

Dinner guests at Dr. Stuart Hill's Montreal home are occasionally taken aback at encountering a strategically placed bucket in the family bathroom. Even those full of bladder and well aware of the McGill University professor's international reputation as an advocate of ecological agriculture at times find themselves in a moment of unsettling hesitation: The bucket has been placed there to accept contributions for Hill's well-organized backyard composting system.

If he carries it a step further than most gardeners, Stuart Hill nonetheless typifies the increasing dedication and boldness of modern-day compost makers.

Compost itself is clearly in a period of ascendancy. The word makes its way into even the most genteel of party conversations; *New Yorker* artists work the subject into their sophisticated cartoons; Toronto department stores, catering to the carriage trade, now offer portable composting bins in their outdoor sections.

If composting is, as one city magazine recently referred to it, currently chic, it can hardly be called a new practice. One 18th-century farmer who developed a reputation for having unusual success with his crops was described in *The Farmer's Letters to the People of England* in 1771 as "almost constantly manuring one field or another."

This clever gentleman regularly hitched his team and drove four miles to the nearest town "for a wagonload of about one hundred bushels of manure, either cinder ashes, old mortar, hog-muck, rotten horse-muck, or clearing of the streets." The author of *The Farmer's Letters* remarked: "No farmer in the country better understands his business than this man; none raises better crops."

Three centuries later, we have a name for the farmer's technique — sheet composting, the spreading of organic matter directly on the field, where it is ploughed in and decomposes. But while most organic farmers today would applaud the fellow's ability to find some free fertility, many would say that he did not take the process far enough, that it was not composting at all. Applied this way, fresh wastes can wreak temporary microbial havoc on the soil, a disturbance that can be eliminated by first piling wastes to make finished compost.

Dr. Clarence Golueke of the University of California at Berkeley writes, "It is the application of control that distinguishes composting from the natural rotting, putrefaction or other decomposition that takes place in an open dump, a sanitary landfill, in a manure heap, in an open field . . . ."

In controlled compost making, wastes are handled and placed in a way that causes them to decay in a predictable fashion, producing a rich, earthy substance that is regarded by soil scientists both as an excellent fertilizer and as an earth conditioner.

Although compost, sheet or piled, has been around for centuries, the dynamic process that produces this material began to be understood only during this century, sparked by the research of British agriculturist Albert Howard, who would later be dubbed the "Father of Organic Gardening."

Howard was already a recognized agronomist when he embarked, in 1905, on a 30-year programme of research in India. There, basing his experiments on peasant methods already in use, and mightily impressed by the Eastern respect for recycling and waste utilization, Howard developed the "Indore method" of composting, named after the Indian state in which he worked.

The Indore method became the reference point for all later aerobic composting procedures. ("Aerobic" means that decomposition takes place in the presence of oxygen; its opposite is "anaerobic" composting, which excludes air.)

Aerobic composting is deceptively simple. Nature herself will accomplish the process as long as the gardener has a basic understanding of what is involved. His allies in the compost pile are an almost unimaginably large number of microorganisms. (An Ontario government report calls compost "a rather bizarre artificial ecosystem.") A single gram of wet, 158 degree F compost contains more than one billion bacteria and 10 million fungi. By the time the composting process is complete, about one-quarter the weight of the finished pile will be comprised of microbes, living and dead.

How compost reaches that temperature of 158 degrees is the core of the mystery, and the success, of the composting system. All the gardener really needs to know is that if the proper materials are piled in the proper fashion and kept moist, heating will occur naturally, breaking all the organic matter down into soft, dark humus in a matter of weeks or months.

Technically, what happens is very complex. The thousands of microorganisms — the ones that really do the work of composting — require oxygen, carbon,

Frequent turning, ensuring that vital oxygen penetrates throughout the compost, is essential in both the homemade bin and in its commercial counterpart.

nitrogen and moisture to live, multiply and produce carbon dioxide, water and heat — much as man's body heat is maintained by cells breaking down the food he consumes. While oxygen is provided by air circulation, carbon and nitrogen are really the "food" of the organisms, which prefer the two elements in the proportion of 20 or 30 to 1; that is, about 25 parts carbon to 1 part nitrogen. This is the C/N ratio, very important in soil science, in which the amount of nitrogen is always assumed to be 1, and so need not be mentioned. If a horticulturist mentions a C/N ratio of 60, for instance, he means 60 parts of carbon to 1 of nitrogen.

Carbonaceous materials are relatively dry, hard and fibrous, like straw, paper or sawdust, while nitrogenous materials are usually less fibrous in nature — manures, grass clippings, meat scraps. All of these materials actually contain both carbon and nitrogen; the assignment of some as nitrogenous is purely relative. While the C/N ratio of paper is about 173, that of grass clippings is about 20, of sewage sludge, 6. The latter, then, has six times as much carbon as nitrogen, but it is considered highly nitrogenous, and not much would be needed to get a compost pile "working."

Obviously, no gardener will know the precise C/N ratio of anything he dumps on the compost pile, from today's kitchen garbage containing potato peels, half a muffin, egg shells, coffee grounds and the remains of Junior's dinner, to the cleanings of the chicken house

— and even if he did, some complicated mathematics would have to be done before he would know how many pounds of straw to mix with the chicken manure to obtain the preferable 30:1 ratio.

Peasants in India knew even less about the chemical components of their compost piles, and yet they composted successfully. Taking a cue from their example, Howard made the Indore method fairly uncomplicated. He recommended that the gardener or farmer use two or three parts of relatively carbonaceous wastes to one part of relatively nitrogenous wastes, which include kitchen scraps, manure, fresh grass clippings and weeds.

Howard decided that the materials should be layered in piles and that individual components would have to be saved until there was enough material to form a layer on the pile. The completed Indore pile itself is usually six or seven feet wide, three to five feet high and seven to thirty feet long — a large-scale endeavour — with it sides tapered so that the base is about two feet wider than the top. The Indore method commences with the farmer spreading a six-to-eight-inch layer of carbonaceous material over the area to be covered and topping that with two to four inches of nitrogenous material, adding about an eighth of an inch of topsoil. The pile is watered, and layers added in the same sequence until the pile reaches the desired height, at which point the entire pile is covered with a layer of soil, hay or burlap to retain the heat.

The pile will be turned twice, the gardener ensuring each time that the outside material is put in the centre. The first turning occurs in two or three weeks, the second after a further two or three weeks. In summer, the Indore pile is estimated to take about three months to fully compost, but will not be ready until spring if constructed in fall. In a truly cold climate, the pile could require two years to fully compost.

The two- or three-to-one carbonaceous to nitrogenous ratio that Howard recommended is most important — the compost pile will heat less efficiently if it is not observed, a leading cause of failure in catch-as-catch-can compost piles. Some materials, of course, must be avoided altogether. The microbes can digest organic matter only, not glass, plastic or metal. Hard-to-digest material such as branches, leather, cardboard, bone, wood chips and large quantities of paper or sawdust should be set aside in a separate pile to decompose slowly.

If the pile is overly carbonaceous, it will take a very long time to compost; if overly nitrogenous, it will smell like ammonia, evidence that precious nitrogen is being lost into the air. (The accumulation of wastes in an outhouse, for instance, is overly nitrogenous.)

Another requirement of the compost pile is moisture. While the ideal moisture content would be 100 percent (complete submersion), with bubbles percolating upward through the mush, providing essential oxygen — the way "activated" sewage sludge is processed — the home gardener, having no such equipment, must ensure that the moisture level is low enough to leave critical air spaces throughout the mass but high enough so that the matter does not dry out. Agriculture Canada reports that "in districts of low rainfall, such as certain areas of the Prairie Provinces and British Columbia, it is very hard to get satisfactory results unless a supply of water is available for moistening the heap."

Fletcher Sims Jr., who composts on a farm-scale in Texas, says, "My rule-of-thumb measurement on this is to take a handful of the mixture and squeeze it firmly, and if water comes between my fingers, it is too wet. If, on opening my hand, the ball shatters, it is too dry. Somewhere in between, where it will remain balled up with tossing in the air a few inches once or twice, will indicate the approximate proper moisture."

Squeezing wet garbage may seem distasteful to the composting novice, but this is compost — not garbage — and getting a real feel for the compost is the best way to ensure its success. The best practical moisture level is from about 60 down to 40 percent — less will result in slowed decomposition, which finally stops at about 15 percent. Too much moisture and the process again slows, exuding the "rotten egg" sulphurous smell that denotes anaerobic decomposition.

Aerobic decomposition always releases heat; the fallen leaves on the forest floor, for instance, exude warmth as they decay, but because there is no mass, no insulation to retain the heat, it dissipates into the air. The compost pile, on the other hand, is designed to contain the warmth provided by the microorganisms as they utilize carbon and nitrogen. As long as the properly made pile is not frozen, it will, by its own devices, begin to warm. From 59 to 104 degrees F, the pile is in the mesophilic stage, so-called because of the type of microorganisms at work. In two to four days, it graduates past 104 degrees and becomes thermophilic. Now, the mesophilic organisms move to the cooler outward edges of the pile and are replaced in the hot interior by thermophilic microorganisms. The temperature stabilizes at about 158 degrees F for approximately two weeks — at this stage, harmful pathogens, weed seeds, pests and their eggs are destroyed. The pile is prevented from getting hotter, from actually catching fire, by the compost pile's lack of combustibility, its relatively small size and its moisture content. The heat tolerance of the thermophilic microorganisms is limited as well, and they begin to die when the temperature exceeds 160 degrees F.

pH DYNAMICS

During this dynamic chemical process, carbohydrates, the food of microorganisms, are reduced to their components, water and carbon dioxide, and the pH of the pile — its acidity or alkalinity — changes. (Neutral, neither acidic nor alkaline, is represented by the number 7; higher numbers are increasingly alkaline, lower, increasingly acidic.)

The pile is, at first, usually slightly acidic, and as composting begins, it becomes even more so, becoming about as acidic as a tomato, around 4.5. Then, as the pile heats up, it becomes more alkaline, 7.5 to 8.5 at its hottest, and is usually alkaline when finished. Adding limestone or wood ashes to the initial wastes will speed up decomposition somewhat but will also cause some loss of nitrogen as ammonia, a loss that is seldom worth the slightly faster composting time. Golueke writes: "In practical operation, little can be done, or, rather, should be done to alter the pH level prevailing in the pile." In other words, add the wood ashes directly to the garden, not the compost pile.

As food sources in the pile are metabolized and become more scarce, microorganisms in the pile die and the pile gradually cools. Thermophilic organisms are again replaced by mesophilic, and protozoa, nematodes (most of which are not harmful), ants, springtails, millipedes and worms begin to invade the pile.

Composting is "finished" when the centre is cool — although, in fact, the process of decomposition is not strictly over until all the organic material has been reduced to carbon dioxide, water and ash. But what the gardener wants is the fairly homogenous, dark, crumbly substance that typifies good compost. When cool, the pile will have shrunk to one-third its original size.

14-DAY COMPOST

To speed things up, researchers in California devised the "14-day" or "Berkeley" method in the '40s. The scientists realized that if all the matter were shredded or ground, it would be more accessible to both oxygen and microorganisms, and the entire mass could be composted quickly. Some type of shredding equipment, then, is necessary in this method. Commercial grinders, especially designed for just this job, are available (see Sources), but a power or manual lawn mower can be used as well, if the gardener lays his material on the ground and then runs the mower over it.

In the Berkeley method, the same C/N and moisture principles apply as with the Indore; there should be two or three times as much carbonaceous matter as nitrogenous. All of it is shredded or ground, and then it is piled, without layering, in heaps no higher than five feet (taller piles would compact, shutting out air). The pile is turned on the 4th, 7th and 10th day and should be cool and ready to use by the 14th — in California, that is. The process may take a little longer in Canada.

The Berkeley method obviously exacts a price in labour intensiveness for the speed of its processing and again demands that sufficient matter be present before composting begins — tests in California determined that a compost pile must have a volume of at least a cubic yard to heat properly. Again, suitable materials would have to be stockpiled, entailing some nutrient loss by leaching and oxidation, before the pile would be started.

Despite its small drawbacks, however, the Berkeley method is the fastest so far devised. Dr. Golueke explains, "Some purveyors of compost equipment name times as short as three to six days with their systems. However, if one studies their claims, he will find that the complete directions call for a two-to-six-week 'maturation' period after the 'active' composting has been completed in the digester. In reality, the material prior to 'maturing' is far from being ready for use or for storage."

In fact, one cannot stray too far from the Indore or Berkeley methods and still have a well-designed aerobic compost pile. Compost activators, sold by some garden outlets, contain microbes or nutrients that are supposed to speed composting or produce an especially good product. Some, like Rotocrops' *Quickrich*, are simply high-analysis chemical fertilizers that may, indeed, get things going. *Quickrich*, with an analysis of 32-8-8, would be a help to gardeners short of nitrogenous material. The effectiveness of herbal activators seems to be a matter of opinion. P.H. Hainsworth writes in *Agriculture: A New Approach*, "Whether biodynamic herbal activators are of real value in the compost heap is hard to say. Those who use them claim they are. My own experience is limited, but there does not seem to be any superiority over compost without the activator."

Rapidly gaining interest is another way of processing wastes, digesting, a term that indicates its affiliation with what goes on in the stomach. Digesting is anaerobic decomposition — without oxygen — and involves different microorganisms and a different process from aerobic decomposition. It is generally used in processing animal wastes alone. Interest today stems not from the process' compost-making ability but from one of its by-products, biogas, which consists of up to 70 percent methane, a colourless, odourless energy source.

Most anaerobic composting is done in tanks, bins or silos, where the matter is most easily kept airtight. Usually, the waste materials used are kept in a near-liquid state, which enables them to be pumped and excludes air. Although large digesters are commonly heated — decomposition works most efficiently at about 90 degrees F — even in the cryophilic stage, below 70 degrees F, slow breakdown will occur.

Two kinds of bacteria are at work. First, acid-producing bacteria break down the organic matter into acids, and then methane-producing microorganisms convert those acids into methane. The proper balance between the two types of bacteria, and hence the optimum for methane production, depends upon proper temperatures, the best pH (slightly alkaline) and good-quality raw materials. As well as methane gas, biogas contains carbon dioxide and small amounts of hydrogen sulphide (a noxious "rotten egg" gas), ammonium sulphide and water vapour. It is the tiny amount of hydrogen sulphide that gives anaerobic decomposition a malodorous reputation.

Anaerobic composting is time-consuming and is a delicate process, as the two types of bacteria must be in balance for it to proceed properly — a balance that changes with various materials, the moisture content and air temperature. Says John Martin of Cornell University's agricultural engineering department: "If I produce too much acid to be consumed, then the pH goes way down and it is toxic to the methane-formers. We just had this happen with some cow manure. The whole process stops, and it just sits and stinks. Eventually, over a very long period, it will come back again."

But besides its production of methane, digesting has

Nutrient Content of Common Organic Materials

	% NITROGEN	% PHOSPHORUS	% POTASH
Alfalfa Hay	2.45	.5	2.1
Blood Meal	15	1.3	.7
Bone Meal	4	21	.2
Cattle Manure (fresh, mixed with straw bedding)	.57	.15	.53
Coffee Grounds (dried)	1.99	.36	.67
Cottonseed Meal	7.00	2.5	1.5
Dried Blood	12 - 15	3	
Eggshells	1.19	.38	.14
Fish Scraps	2 - 7.5	1.5 - 6.0	
Grass Clippings	2.41		
Horse Manure (fresh, mixed with straw bedding)	.66	.23	.68
Leaves (freshly fallen)	.5 - 1.0	.10	.4 - .7
Meat Scraps	5 - 7		
Phosphate Rock		30 - 32	
Poultry Manure (fresh)	1.47	1.15	.48
Rabbit Manure (fresh)	2.4	.62	.05
Seaweed	1.6	.75	5
Sheep Manure (fresh, mixed with straw bedding)	.9	.34	1.0
Swine Manure (fresh, mixed with straw bedding)	.56	.32	.52
Wood Ashes		1.5	7

* From *The Encyclopedia of Organic Gardening* by Rodale Press, *The Biochemistry and Methodology of Composting* by the Connecticut Agricultural Experiment Station, and *Manures and Compost* by Agriculture Canada.

some other positive points: foremost, that little fertility loss seems to occur in the process. A report from the Biomass Energy Institute of Manitoba states that "approximately one percent of the original nitrogen in the manure is lost in the anaerobic digestion process. Virtually all of the phosphorus and potassium are still present in the digested manure. There are reports that digested manure is a better fertilizer than regular liquid manure, but all that can be said with scientific certainty is that it is at least as good as regular liquid manure." While a conventional, aerobic pile loses nutrients to the air and by leaching, and loses about half its weight, anaerobically processed materials commonly decrease by only one-quarter in weight.

Martin believes, however, that anaerobically composted wastes are probably not significantly better fertilizers than their oxygenated counterparts. "There are arguments both ways about whether fertilizer from anaerobic processing is better. The only reason its nitrogen content is higher is because you don't lose much ammonia in the anaerobic process, but that can be lost as soon as the fertilizer is spread anyway. If you surface-spread it, in 24 to 48 hours, half that ammonia will be gone."

Anaerobic composting, in any case, is quite impractical for home use. The gardener might place all his wastes in an airtight garbage bag, but biogas production will explode the bag if it is not vented off. If the gas does escape, it may be objectionable.

The solution, then, is a well-managed aerobic compost pile. Wastes need not be layered, and they can be piled as they become available (just remember to stop piling once there is a cubic yard of matter, and start on another pile), but the proper carbon-nitrogen ratio and moisture content should be observed. Eventually, perhaps in two years, the gardener will have something that looks and smells like good compost — that is, something very much like dark, fibrous topsoil.

It is because compost piles are so often imperfectly made that human and pet wastes should not be used in them, unless such compost is to be used only in the flower garden, around fruit trees and on the lawn. Dr. Raymond Poincelot of Fairfield University, Connecticut, who has done considerable research with compost, says about human wastes, "In China, they use them routinely, but I would not recommend it unless the composting operation was done exactly correctly. If done right, the compost pile will kill all the pathogens, but with a homemade pile, you might turn it too often, or not get the outside edge turned in or something." The result could be that a disease or parasite is preserved in the compost and transmitted to the garden soil. Parasitic worms, cholera and typhoid are often troublesome in areas where human wastes are not properly processed but are used in fertilization.

Even purchased municipal sludges like *Milorganite* should not be used on vegetables — not, in this case, because of pathogens, but because of city-borne heavy metals present in the sludges that may be retained in vegetables.

Hill, a professor of entomology, believes that human urine, which is normally pathogen-free, is a safe, nitrogen- and potassium-rich addition to the compost pile — as long as the donor is free of any bladder infection.

Compost, he points out, tends to dry out and is exposed to disturbance by animals if piled out in the open. As far as compost containers are concerned, Hill himself recommends "New Zealand" composting boxes, hand-built, three-sided wooden containers, four-foot-square, which are built in a series of three or four, so that piles in various stages can be kept in each section. One box will hold a ton of compost, says Hill, "enough for over 500 square yards of garden if put on to a depth of two or three inches."

All that is really required of the container is that it be somewhat rot-resistant, that it be permeable to air and big enough to contain a pile, allowing easy workability. Containers can be any shape and made of chicken wire, snow fencing, or a perforated oil drum or barrel from which both top and bottom have been removed.

Commercial designers offer a whole range of containers for those who can afford them — they can run as high as $500. The least expensive are bins, and the dearest, supported, horizontal drums, in which the compost is turned by rolling the container.

Unfortunately, although these composters may look more presentable than the homemade type, they make no better compost, and that, after all, is the crux of the matter. If the C/N ratio is not observed, the organic matter in that all-steel composter might just sit and stink. If all is done properly, any correctly designed container — however simple — can turn out top compost in two or three weeks.

What to do with that compost is of little concern to most organic gardeners. There is simply never enough. It can be used on and around anything that grows, as potting soil, as a fertilizer and as a conditioner. Hill, writing in *Composting for Farm and Garden*, says, "adding compost to soil represents one attempt to cooperate with the decomposers and enable them to supply nutrients to our crops. It also improves soil aeration, drainage, moisture and plant nutrient retention, soil stability, and it reduces the energy required for tillage. Compost can also lead to increased resistance in plants to pathogens and pests. What N-P-K fertilizer can claim to do all these things?"

Regular compost, after all, does not compete well with chemical fertilizer if analyzed numerically. The content of a chemical fertilizer is designated by percentages: N-P-K content, nitrogen, phosphorus and potassium are listed, say, as 32-8-8 on the label, meaning that the bag includes 32 percent nitrogen, 8 percent phosphorus and 8 percent potash. The remaining 52 percent is a mixture of other elements such as chlorine and sulphur.

LOW ANALYSIS FERTILIZER

The analysis of finished compost, on the other hand, generally hovers at about 3-1-2. But its analysis is only part of the story, seven percent of it, in this case. The balance of the mass is replete with micronutrients, soil conditioners and microbes, all of which contribute to soil health and almost all of which are lacking in chemical fertilizers. When compared with synthetic fertilizers of similar analysis, compost has increased yields by as much as 10 percent. Since most of its nitrogen is in organic form, it is released slowly, extending the availability of nutrients and lessening the problem of their leaching into waterways. Compost does not "burn" plants as raw manures and chemical fertilizers can do. Poincelot writes: "The Tennessee Valley Authority and the Public Health Service concluded that municipal compost improves aeration, tilth and water-holding capacity of soil. Addition of 50 to 400 tons of compost per hectare in vineyards increased moisture retention, pore volume and aeration of root areas." Furthermore, because compost can be applied as a mulch to the soil surface, discouraging weed growth, the development of beneficial plants is further encouraged.

According to Hill, "Compost gives all this plus the knowledge that by going the compost route you will not be unnecessarily using up our diminishing energy reserves, not adding to environmental pollution, and you will be cooperating with the ecological cycles, providing our plants with nutrients as they need them and building up your soil. Composting provides a way to make peace with your land." ∎

Sources

Equipment

W - W SHREDDER/GRINDERS
2957 North Market
Wichita, Kansas 67219
Canadian dealers:
WESTCAN HORTICULTURAL SPECIALISTS
1900-11th Street S.E.
Calgary, Alberta T2G 3G8
(403) 266-5688
and

GIBSON POWERCRAFT CENTRE LIMITED
727 Market Street
Victoria, British Columbia V8T 2E2
and
GOLDEN WEST SEEDS LTD.
915-23rd Avenue S.E.
Calgary, Alberta T2G 1P1
(403) 263-4200
and
HALIFAX SEED COMPANY LTD.
Box 8026
Halifax, Nova Scotia B3K 5L8
(902) 454-7456

**MIGHTY MAC COMPOST
SHREDDER-GRINDERS**
Amerin-MacKissic Inc.
Box 111
Parker Ford, Pennsylvania 19457
(215) 495-7181
Canadian dealer:
OTTO RICHTER & SONS EQUIPMENT
12 Heritage Road
Markham, Ontario L3P 1M4
(416) 294-1407

THE ROTO-HOE COMPANY
100 Auburn Road
Newbury, Ohio 44065
Canadian dealers:
MONNETT SALES
80 Town Line Place
Carleton Place, Ontario K7C 2E4
and

MACLEOD EQUIPMENT
36 Fielding Avenue
Dartmouth, Nova Scotia B3B 1E4
and
RINGHAM AGENCIES
4671 Tourney Road
North Vancouver, British Columbia V7K 2W2

**TROY-BILT ROTO TILLER-POWER
COMPOSTERS**
Garden Way Canada, Inc.
514 Carlingview Drive
Rexdale, Ontario M9W 5R3
(416) 674-1503

Publications

LET IT ROT
By Stu Campbell
152 pages
230A — paperback, $10.00
Available from Harrowsmith Books, Camden East, Ontario K0K 1J0.

THE RODALE GUIDE TO COMPOSTING
By Jerry Minnich, Marjorie Hunt and the editors
of *Organic Gardening & Farming* magazine
405 pages
217B — hardcover, $17.95
Available from Harrowsmith Books, Camden East, Ontario K0K 1J0.

MANURES AND COMPOST
Available from Information Services, Agriculture Canada, Ottawa, Ontario K1A 0C7. Publication #868. Free.

AGRICULTURE CANADA CLIMATIC ZONES

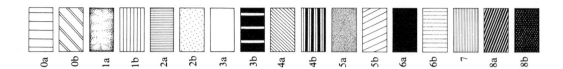

0a 0b 1a 1b 2a 2b 3a 3b 4a 4b 5a 5b 6a 6b 7 8a 8b

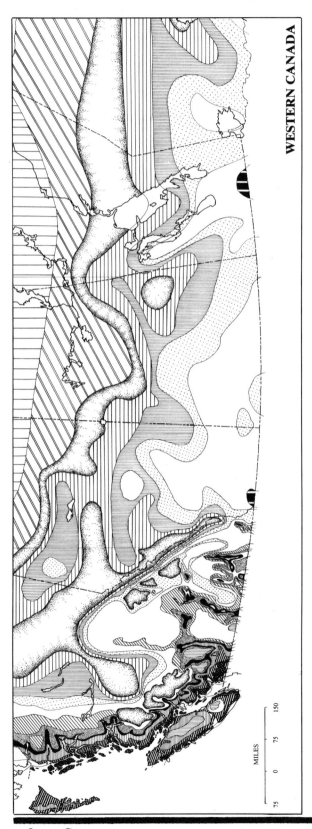

WESTERN CANADA

MILES
75 0 75 150

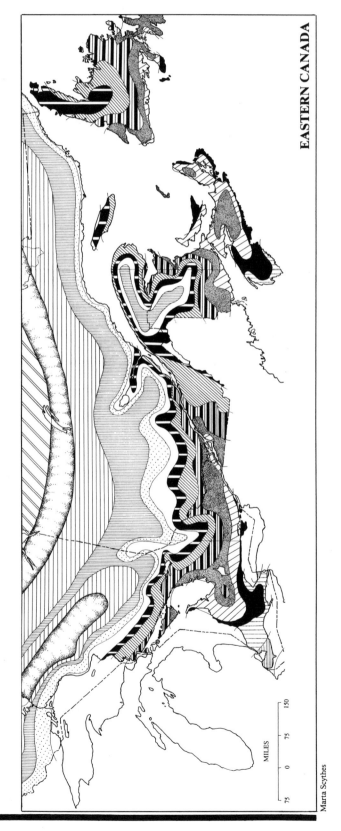

EASTERN CANADA

MILES
75 0 75 150

Marta Scythes

UNITED STATES DEPARTMENT OF AGRICULTURE CLIMATIC ZONES

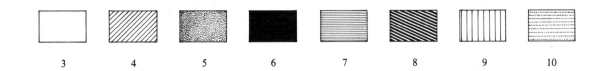

| 3 | 4 | 5 | 6 | 7 | 8 | 9 | 10 |

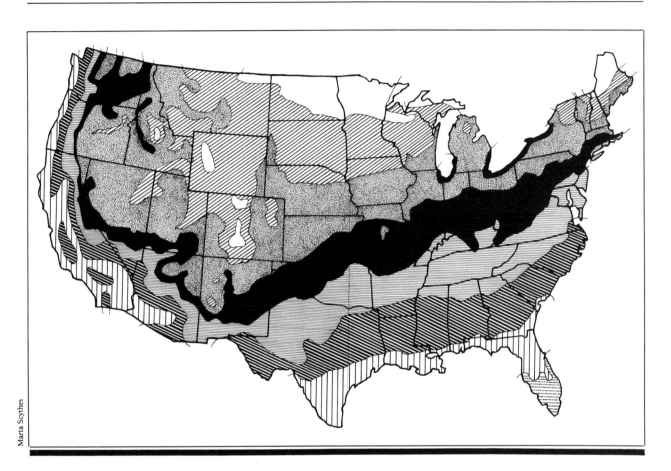

Marta Scythes

IMPORT PERMITS

Canadians who wish to import plant material (including seeds) from other countries must obtain a "permit to import" from the federal government. First, obtain the catalogues of companies selling plants that interest you. Then, write to the Agriculture Canada Permit Office to obtain an "application form for permit to import." The address is: Permit Office, Plant Health Division, Agriculture Canada, Ottawa, Ontario K1A 0C6.

Obtain one application form for each company from which you will order plants. Fill out the form, and send it back to the permit office. (Note: seeds of flowers and vegetables for the home garden do not require an import permit.)

A permit to import will be issued by mail. Unless otherwise specified, the permit is valid for one year from the date of issue and covers multiple shipments and unlimited quantities of the materials requested. The permit also provides details of any restrictions and prohibitions regarding the material you wish to import.

On receipt of the permit, you must send the enclosed instructions to the exporter. Send them with your order, along with your payment.

Well-Managed Meadows

Making the most of small farm pastures

By Michael Webster

"The best fertilizer is the farmer's footsteps."
— *Chinese Proverb*

A dairy cow and an 8-year-old boy have at least one thing in common — their eating habits. Given his head at the dinner table, the boy first drains his glass of milk, then dispatches his entire pork chop (after meticulously trimming off every scrap of fat), works through the potatoes with some enthusiasm and, pretending that the Brussels sprouts are not there, asks for more meat. If this bid is successful, he eats the meat and declares himself too full for his vegetables. Threatened with "no vegetables, no dessert," he complains bitterly that the Brussels sprouts are cold and secretly wishes that he could avoid this parental play by eating his ice cream first.

The cow, in her own way, is no different. Turned out to a lush May pasture for the first time, she kicks up her heels in heiferish enthusiasm, makes a quick tour of the fences to check for any obvious weak spots and settles down to a contented meal. But while grass is just grass to a less discerning eye, a cow is an epicure who sees not a pasture but a cornucopia of individual leaves, and given her choice, she wraps her tongue only around the most tasty and nutritious plants in the field. Having eaten her fill of clover and vetch, or whatever bovine equivalent to pork chops and ice cream is available to her, she finds a spot in the shade to ruminate. In a few hours, she is up again, selecting the tender leaves of her favourite plants from the spacious platter of green delicacies underfoot.

FIRST CHOICE

After several days, the cow has picked her way through the whole field and would have to turn her attention to the less tasty greenery, except that the warm spring rains have encouraged the plants which she ate on the first day to put out a few fresh leaves. Pleased with this fortuitous development, she makes another round of her favourites, and another, until the hot, dry weather of early summer slows their regrowth, and they no longer satisfy her hunger. Meanwhile, the rest of the field — the light brush, weeds and less tasty grasses — has grown tall, coarse and unpalatable, so she stands at the gate and bawls an unmistakable message: "My Brussels sprouts are cold!"

The husbandman, of course, cannot threaten to withhold dessert from his beef- or milk-producing charge, so he moves her to a fresh pasture, where the process is repeated with the universal result familiar to any midsummer driver of country roads — pale green pastures clipped to a mosslike shortness between numerous stalks and clumps of weeds and tall, coarse grass. Gone is the lush, dark green pasture of spring that held so much promise, the uniformly high carpet of nutrition that once set hooved heels a-flying in grateful exuberance. Now sere and unproductive, a beleaguered grassland struggles to withstand the summer sun until fall rains release another burst of growth.

Across Canada, this is the accepted state of affairs, and if standard agricultural wisdom has moved to counter the status quo, it has done so by eliminating pastures, unreliable and inconsistent as they are, from the farm programme and turning to feedlots and zero-graze schemes, whereby feed is brought to the cows year-round. And yet there exists a pasture-management system that avoids the inefficiencies traditionally associated with the grazing of animals, a system which lengthens the pasturing season, keeps the grass as lush and richly green in midsummer as it is in May, improves the quality of the plants in the field in terms of nutrition and digestibility and can double or even triple the carrying capacity of virtually any pasture immediately.

This system is used successfully with beef and dairy cattle, as well as with sheep, goats and horses, and can be adopted by anyone from the small landholder who milks a couple of goats or fattens a steer or two for the freezer to the largest of commercial cattlemen or dairy farmers. Known as intensive rotational grazing, the system is elegant in its simplicity. Instead of keeping animals in a large pasture for a long time, they are moved through a series of small pastures, or paddocks, spending a short time in each. That, in essence, is all there is to it.

It is enough. Dr. William Murphy, an associate professor with the department of plant and soil science at the University of Vermont, raises replacement dairy heifers on a 25-acre farmstead that he purchased in the Green Hills area of Vermont in 1980. That summer, he kept nine Holstein yearlings on pasture, but the following year, after simply dividing his pastureland into 11 paddocks, it carried the original nine animals, now each a year older and bigger, until he sold them in midsummer and replaced them with 16 new heifers. His land did not grow more grass that year, or at least not much more, but Murphy forced his cows to make better use of what they had.

Cows (or other grazing animals) put into a small paddock will eat the tastiest, most nutritious grasses first, but then, still hungry, they will turn to their second and third choices. As long as these plants — grasses, weeds, even the leaves off small brush — are young, tender and succulent, they will be eaten. In a couple of days, when the cows have cleaned up everything in one paddock, they can be moved to the next and then the next and eventually brought back to the first to repeat the rotation. In contrast to pastures usually seen from the window of the family sedan on a Sunday afternoon drive in the country, a pasture managed under this regimen is a verdant quiltwork of small paddocks at different stages of recovery growth — each composed of plants of the same height and each a uniformly rich, dark green colour even in the midsummer drought.

The initial research in intensive grazing was done in postwar France by André Voisin, who published his findings in *Grass Productivity*. Although translated into English in the 1950s, his work was virtually ignored in North America, the land of plenty, including plenty of free-ranging cattle. Instead, Voisin's theories were tested, adapted and perfected in New Zealand, where the enthusiasm for what they call controlled grazing systems (CGS) has grown to an almost religious fervour. By decreasing its acreage of machine- and energy-intensive crops like corn and by concentrating on its clover-choked natural grasslands, New Zealand has become a moving force in the world agricultural market. On a land base smaller than Labrador, the island country now exports more than half the value of agricultural products that Canada, the breadbasket of the world, does. "Clovers are to New Zealand what oil is to the Arabs," says one proud dairy farmer, and according to G.D. Miller, a regional agricultural advisory officer based in Hamilton, New Zealand, "We are promoting CGS as the key management factor in increasing production and profitability from New Zealand livestock farms." One sheep farmer who switched to

"Productivity has just gone crazy," says University of Vermont forage specialist Dr. William Murphy since stringing enough electric fence to divide his pastureland into 11 paddocks. He intends to divide his land even further in the future.

CGS management expanded from 1,200 ewes with an 80 percent lambing rate to 2,000 ewes and a 105 percent lambing rate in 12 months. Able to take his first overseas vacation within a year of instituting this programme, he likened CGS to democracy: "Not perfect, but a darn sight better than anything else." Another farmer increased his flock from 800 to 3,000 over a five-year period, turning his gross-profit figure from a three-digit number to a six-digit number.

Progressive dairy farmers in New Zealand now move their milking cows to a new paddock every 12 hours — after each milking — although heifers and dry cows are rotated more slowly. One sheep farmer with 10,000 ewes on a 1,000-acre farm has divided his land into one hundred 10-acre plots. In a system that gives real meaning to the term "mob stocking," he moves all 10,000 sheep to a different 10-acre paddock each day.

"North American farmers aren't going to go for something that extreme," admits Murphy, although he cannot resist adding, "at least not at first." He recommends starting with 10 paddocks, confident that as the system proves itself, each farmer will find himself dividing his pastures even further. "More is better," notes Murphy, a claim that he intends to back up this summer by increasing his paddocks to 15. He also plans to expand his herd again, from the 20 pregnant Jersey heifers he kept last year to 30. This on the same land that four years ago supported only nine animals.

"Productivity has just gone crazy," he says.

If the concept of rotational grazing seems simple, the mechanics of it — the underhoof photosynthetic machinery — though commonsensical, can be fairly complex. Plant physiology is based on an interaction between green leaves, which turn sunlight into energy, and roots, which draw moisture and minerals from the soil. In a somewhat oversimplified view of the process, nutrients are passed from the roots to the leaves, processed into a more usable form and returned to the roots for storage. Thus when an animal eats a plant's leaves, slowing or stopping photosynthesis, there is still an energy reserve in the root system that allows that plant to send up fresh leaves and to revive the process; in fact, it will actually speed it up somewhat.

The sole intention of any plant — even a perennial like grass — is to grow, then set seed and either die or go dormant. When that schedule is interrupted, as any Saturday afternoon mower of lawns can attest, plants respond with a period of vigorous growth in an attempt to make up lost time. However, in a "set stocking" situation, where a given number of animals are left in a large pasture for a period of time and some plants are continually eaten back, these favourites have no opportunity to build up root reserves between mealtimes, so their ability to respond to leaf loss with a burst of fresh growth is lost. The reduced leaf area cannot process the amount of nutrients gathered by the roots, which respond by shrinking in size, and the plant is stressed by a continuing cycle of less greenery reducing the root system, which further cuts back green growth. In time, the pasture deteriorates as the best plants are weakened and crowded out.

An intelligent system of pasture management depends as much on resting paddocks between grazing periods as it does on intensive grazing. Even during the time of lush spring growth, paddocks should be rested for 20 days between grazing periods, a figure that should be increased to 35 days or more in the dry, hot days of slow summer growth. This allows the grass to experience the vigorous regrowth it wants to give itself and to build up root reserves so that it can respond to the next grazing period with another vigorous regrowth. As a beneficial side effect, plants expand their root systems instead of reducing them, which furthers growth and results in a thicker, more dense pasture. A given piece of land, then, will carry more animals not only because the animals are eating everything that is there but also because, increasingly, there is more there to eat.

At the same time, there is an improvement in the quality of the plants in the pasture. Legumes, like clover, desirable because they are rich in protein and because they can add valuable nitrogen to the soil, require a lot of sunlight (hence their broad leaves), but they are relatively low-lying plants whose growth is especially hindered by overgrazing, which reduces leaf area, or by being overshadowed by taller plants. Rotational grazing, which keeps all plants shorter than eight inches, encourages legume growth — so much so that Henry Swayze, a Vermont sheep farmer who has studied the New Zealand methods, cites research which demonstrates techniques that control the number of legumes. "The fellow divided a 15-acre field into three 5-acre plots and kept the middle one as a control. Within five years — without seeding, mind you, just by management — the plot on one side was a 90 percent pure stand of clover, and the other was 90 percent grass. Then, just to show that he could do it, he spent another five years and reversed them: grass in the clover plot and clover in the grass plot. Clover is there if you handle your fields properly."

Vaughan Jones, a New Zealand dairy farmer who keeps 220 cows on 200 acres of what he calls "poor land" and ships 660 Imperial gallons of milk a day without feeding any grain, agrees: "Some farmers in Canada tell me that their land won't support clover, but there we are on the chap's front lawn, ankle deep in it. I ask him if he planted his lawn in clover, and he says, 'No, of course not.' But when I ask him how it got there, he's dumbfounded. The plants have been there for years, but because he mows the lawn regularly, they start to flourish."

Of course, too much clover can be as awkward as too little, even causing bloat in livestock. According to Jones, a pasture overgrown with clover can be brought back to a proper balance by letting it grow and by taking a hay crop off the land. Forage specialist Murphy concurs: "Plants respond differently to being cut and being grazed," he says. "I don't know why, but it's true. For instance, red clover in a hayfield will die out in two or three years, but in a proper pasture, it will last almost indefinitely and even spread throughout the field."

A final advantage with intensive pasturing is a reduction in weeds. Annuals, which spread by the yearly setting seeds, never mature to reproduce, and other weeds are gradually choked out by the thickening carpet of nutritious grasses. The exception to this rule is thistle, which cows will not touch, and the only management technique that works, other than herbicides, is to remove the tops as they grow in. Thistles can easily be kicked out of the ground, and a persistent and judicious use of the toe of a rubber boot will eventually win a difficult battle.

The availability of luscious and nutritious green feed throughout the growing season opens some interesting possibilities for innovative management techniques. Farmers in New Zealand, some of whom have been testing the outer limits of this system for a quarter of a century, take advantage of livestock's habit of eating the most nutritious feed first by putting milking animals or growing meat animals in a paddock initially, then rotating them quickly. The paddock is then used for dry or mature stock that cleans up the second-choice plants after the high producers. And in a strategy which leaves North American farmers slack-jawed in disbelief, New Zealand farmers do not provide shade or water in the paddocks, believing that cows will fill

Photographs courtesy Gallagher Power Fencing Systems

Even New Zealand has areas of unproductive scrubland, **top,** *but the same hillside a year later,* **bottom,** *has been transformed into lush pasture by alternating short periods of intensive grazing with long rests. Note the fence dividing the hill into paddocks.*

up unnecessarily on water when the lush, moist grass provides all their needs and that shade reduces production by 20 percent because the animals lie down there when they would otherwise be up and eating. "This business of shade and water is just a craze," says Jones, a mild-mannered man much given to mischievous pronouncements of agricultural sacrilege intended to jolt hidebound farmers into seeing their pastures in a different light.

ROTATIONAL SCHEDULING

Indeed, treating pastureland as an intensive crop is a foreign concept for Canadian farmers, but according to Jones, "Pastures can be your most valuable crop." More sacrilege in this, the land of 150-bushel-per-acre corn crops, but Murphy agrees. "Pasturing is cheap," he says, "but pastures have always been lousy because they're not managed well." High productivity and low input costs can make grassland profitable for livestock operations in any part of Canada.

Farmers who want to adopt the intensive-pasturing techniques, whether they own an acre or a quarter section, can use the same approach. In May, when animals are first turned out on pasture, string a temporary fence around an area that they can clean up in a few days. Electric fencing is the cheapest and easiest. New Zealanders recommend that animals not be left more than three days in any one paddock because they will then start to graze regrowth, but many novices get their feet wet in the new system by aiming for a six-day schedule. Subsequent paddocks, which can be fenced in as needed, do not have to be the same size, as long as adjustments are made in the grazing time to compensate for the different amount of feed available. The important point here is that the rotation schedule be flexible. A calendar is not the proper basis for moving animals to a new paddock; instead, use the condition of the paddocks themselves.

Cattle should be moved into a paddock when the grass is some six to eight inches high; sheep and other animals that graze more closely, when it is four inches high. The sizing of the paddocks is a matter for some experimentation, but essentially, paddocks should be kept to a size that allows them to be completely eaten down in about three days, or whatever schedule is decided on. The smaller the paddocks, the higher the stocking rates; and the faster the rotation, the greater the productivity.

Murphy suggests that animals be moved out when the grass is eaten down to about 1½ inches but cautions against oversimplification of a complex decision. "That's just a guideline," he says, "and it has to be adjusted to suit each farm and even individual fields within each farm. It's a commonsense thing that comes with experience. I find I'm leaving my cows in the paddocks for 12 hours longer than I did when I started." The last grass which cows will eat is that around their droppings, and Murphy uses this knowledge as a measurement tool. "When they start to eat the grass within two feet of a cow platter, I know there isn't much feed left," he says, emphasizing the basic premise of intensive pasturing — that the animals must clean up everything before being moved. If stock is moved out too soon, some plants will start to mature, and the paddock will have to be clipped with a mower, then grazed more intensively in the next rotation.

In the spring, with growth quick and easy, it will be impossible to take the animals through their entire old pasture and still return them in time to catch the first paddock before it matures. Because it is absolutely essential to keep plant growth from getting too tall, New Zealand farmers use this opportunity to take a crop of hay or haylage (grass silage) from land that they cannot get around to pasturing. If hay is not going to be taken off, it is better to mow the grass and let it lie on the ground than to let it grow, for the clover will be stressed by lack of sunlight, and by the time the animals do reach that paddock, much of the coarse growth will be unpalatable.

In the dry months of July and August, when growth is retarded, it will be necessary to add in new fields (ideally, those that were cropped) to allow paddocks sufficient recovery time. During the first few years, paddocks may need 40 days or more between grazings in dry weather, but as the pasture becomes more dense, the grass shades the ground, keeping it cool and moist and improving regrowth. Fall rains mean that animals can go back to their spring rotation schedule, while the former hayfields are allowed to grow again. In milder climates like New Zealand's, this permits a second hay crop, but in most of Canada, these paddocks are put to better use as "fall-saved pasture." Set aside during the late-summer growth spurt, they can be pastured again when cold weather has ended the growing season, and in this way, another month is added to the usual pasturing season, a significant saving in the cost of purchasing or putting up winter feed.

With animals on pasture longer each year, less barnyard manure is accumulated. This represents a twofold benefit for landowners. First, the manure is deposited — with minimal nutrient loss — where it will do the most good, and according to the size of the operation, the savings in labour, time and machinery can be substantial. In fact, one New Zealand farmer refers to his 3,000-ewe flock as a "12,000-foot muck spreader." Traditional North American agriculturists maintain that manure accumulation in a pasture is detrimental to production, pointing out that animals will not eat grass that has been covered with manure. In the sterile biological environments fostered by chemical dependence and laissez-faire management, where two-year-old cow pies litter pastureland like so many organic Frisbees, this argument has some merit. Claiming that the length of time it takes for a cow pie to disappear is an excellent barometer of the health of the soil, Jones says that on his farm, a cow pie vanishes without a trace in only 10 days — an indication of the intensity of the earthworm and microbe activity due to intensive pasturing.

Another reason for such rapid incorporation of manure is the hoof action in mob-stocked paddocks. Ma-

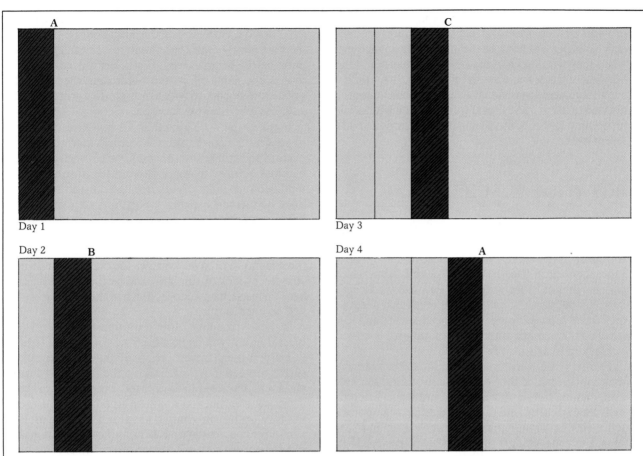

Strip grazing is one method of dividing a permanently fenced pasture into paddocks for intensive management. On Day 1, the animals graze a strip behind a temporary electric fence (A). They are then rotated to a strip between fences A and B on Day 2 and a third on Day 3 between fences B and C. For Day 4 and successive days, new strips are created by moving the unused fence ahead of the others.

nure is trampled into the earth, increasing the soil-to-manure contact; and although in this country hoof action is widely believed to lead to soil compaction and even erosion, the New Zealanders feel that intensive hoof action for short periods is beneficial.

Altogether, then, rotational grazing has the potential to improve the condition of the soil and the quantity and quality of the forage that it supports. By all reports, the increase in production can be expected to double stocking rates immediately and to triple them within five years, while the cost of production plummets due to reduced requirements for hay making and manure spreading. It is hardly mysterious why New Zealanders are so enthusiastic about the system — it is a small wonder that it does not cure the common cold as well. Actually, it does improve animal health by reducing the spread of internal parasites, most of which, released in manure, do not survive the 20- to 40-day rest period between grazings.

Nevertheless, there are some disadvantages to the system. The most obvious is the investment in fences — dividing a five-acre field into 10 paddocks can require, depending on the shape of the field, more than 100 rods of fencing. If using woven fence, the cost of the materials would exceed $1,000, and installation would require a substantial amount of labour. With electric fence, the figure drops to the $250 to $350 range (including a $100 fence charger), and the labour requirement is reduced to an afternoon's work or half

an hour every few evenings if one readies each paddock as it is needed. In New Zealand, rotational grazing has increased in popularity as the appropriate technology has become available. High-powered energizers which can power up to 50 miles of fence and which are not grounded out by weeds have made the large-scale division of land practical and economically feasible.

A more difficult logistical problem is the provision of water in each paddock, for it can safely be assumed that Canadian husbandmen will continue to be committed to the "craze" of watering their animals. Unless the landowner is lucky enough to have a stream meandering through his pastureland, water will have to be reticulated to supply every paddock. Depending on the size of the operation, this can be done with a couple of garden hoses and a few buckets or a watering bowl fitted to a trailer-mounted 200-gallon tank that can be moved to each paddock with the animals.

One tempting solution puts a watering trough in the middle of a pasture that is divided like a pie — wedge-shaped paddocks each offering space at the central waterer. The problem that arises with this design is called nutrient migration — cows have a tendency to eat out by the fence and to relax by the trough, where they urinate and defecate. The eventual result is that the perimeter of the field becomes much less fertile than the central area. According to Swayze, a better solution is a centre aisle: "If you keep it narrow enough, about 12 feet wide, the cows tend not to congregate there. They go back to the paddock to lie down." Another solution is to herd the cows back to the barn twice a day to water them. It may be that, as Jones claims, they will not be particularly thirsty, anyway.

Another drawback to rotational grazing is rooted in the very quality that makes it so attractive: the boost in production. If a given piece of land will carry twice as many animals, those extra animals have to be purchased. Even for a part-time farmer with a handful of beef cattle, that can amount to an additional investment of several thousand dollars. Failure to add enough cows to keep up with the grass growth negates the entire system, so making the extra commitment is an essential, if somewhat burdensome, requirement. A possible way to avoid this situation is to keep the same number of animals on about half the land base, converting some pasture into hayfields and possibly financing the purchase of more stock with the sale of the extra hay.

Lastly, we come to labour and management, represented on the farm not by opposing camps in some dispute but by the members of one family. Traditional set-stocked pastures are as convenient as they are unproductive for one reason: they are largely ignored. Herds or flocks of grazing animals on pasture are moved perhaps a couple of times during the summer, but that is the extent of the labour requirement. At the very least, an intensive rotational grazing system demands that the farmer check the condition of the paddock each day and move his ruminant charges every few days. This last is less of a burden than one might imagine, for the animals learn very quickly that the opening of a gate or the taking down of a portion of fence means a chance to be the first to get at the lush growth of a fresh paddock. Still, pasturing is no longer a respite from the winter schedule of daily chores, a reality that summer-vacation planners must confront. On the other hand, a morning or evening stroll through lush green pastures is not unpleasant and offers an excellent opportunity to keep track of one's expanded herd, watching for early signs of disease, injury or oestrus.

The important thing to note is that intensive rotational grazing is just that — intensive. Like any high-input, high-output system, consistent and committed management is the key to success. The requirements are not that great: a certain amount of faith in the system (yes, the pasture really will support all those cows), a watchful eye, a healthy dollop of common sense and, because for about two-thirds of their time in each paddock the animals are going to wish they were already moved to the next one, some good fences. The knack of it is simple — leave the animals long enough in each paddock, but do not leave any paddock too long without animals in it. However, achieving a balance of pushing your land hard enough without starving your stock is a delicate task that requires careful attention.

As much as intensive grazing increases the productivity of the land, it also increases the drain on the soil's fertility. Two calves, lambs or gallons of milk sent to market instead of one means that twice as much protein, calcium and other nutrients have been drawn out of the earth to be carried off the farm. Manure is a valuable by-product of that process, but as Louis Bromfield points out in *Malabar Farm*, "It is impossible to restore or even to maintain the fertility of a farm by the use *alone* of the barnyard manure it produces." In an intensive high-production system, whether it be a backyard garden or a whole farm, plants use nutrients faster than the natural breakdown of the soil can provide them, so they must be added from an outside source.

The most basic plant food (and the most expensive to purchase commercially) is nitrogen, but fortunately, it can be furnished at no cost by leguminous crops like clover. The catch is that most legumes will not tolerate acidic soil, so in many areas, lime must be added. As well as making it possible for the vigorous growth of legumes, lime offers calcium, another food for grass and one that is removed from the land in large quantities by milk-producing and bone-developing animals. Phosphorus and potassium, promoting the growth of roots and stems, are the other two major plant foods, but trace minerals such as boron, zinc, magnesium, copper and cobalt are equally important. A reliable soil test will reveal the amounts of each that need to be added. The major elements are available from a variety of sources, both organic and synthetic, and the animals' supply of the minor ones can be assured by offering a mineral supplement that will eventually help to increase the soil content of those minerals via bodily excesses deposited in the manure.

Discussion of trace elements and plant foods is nothing new to crop producers; what is unusual is the consideration of pasture as a valuable crop worthy of such talk. Pastures have always been relegated to the back 40, to broken and rocky patches of land too poor to sustain a profitable crop. With agriculture in the 1980s a quagmire of high costs and low prices, keeping the cost of production down is the only chance to keep the farm afloat. Intensive grass farming can make the difference for the homesteader with a few sheep or for the full-time dairy or beef operator.

"Pastures have a lot of potential," says Murphy, "but people tend to think of them as they are and not as they could be." With an intensive-grazing system, pastures could be the backbone of a revitalized animal industry, for although boys will always be boys, cows can be made to eat like grown-ups. ∎

Sources

The following books are both out of print but are available from some libraries:

GRASS PRODUCTIVITY
by André Voisin
Philosophical Library
New York (1959)

PASTURES AND PASTURE PLANTS
R.H.M. Langer et al.
A.H. & A.W. Reed
Wellington, New Zealand (1977)

Live-Wire Grazing

Making good neighbours electrically

Ihad just finished stringing my first electric fence, and with the charger clicking rhythmically, I was ready to test it. I started by touching the wire with a blade of grass, waiting for the mild tingle that would signal a successful installation. When nothing happened, I shortened the blade of grass, then cautiously tapped the wire with my finger and finally, with brave impatience, grabbed the wire firmly in one fist. Still nothing. So there I stood, one hand on the fence, the other holding my chin, head bowed in thought. Of course! I was wearing rubber boots, which insulated me from the ground. With the careless contempt of familiarity, I squatted down, laid a hand on the ground — and promptly let go of fence, ground and some verbal pyrotechnics.

The shock was not serious, really — certainly nothing compared to the time I held my finger in the spark plug connector of a motorcycle while a friend jumped on the kick starter. That knocked me unceremoniously on the seat of my pants, and it is not something I would willingly do again. The sting of the electric fencing is unpleasant enough to breed respect, but it is not really as painful as it is surprising, and that is a fair assessment of an electric fence's operating principle. Like a trip to the dentist, the anticipation is worse than the

reality. "It's a psychological barrier, not a physical barrier, and that is far, far stronger," says Udi Guberman, a shepherd who exchanged a flock of sheep on Israel's Golan Heights for another in the rocky and swampy farmland near Tweed, Ontario. "It's important that what we're talking about with electric fences is not pasture management, which is different for every soil type and climate, but grazing management, which is the same all over the world," he says. "New Zealand developed the idea because they have the biggest need for it — because of the massive amount of pasture they have."

The key that opened the door to intensive grazing in New Zealand was electric fencing. Although it has been around for the last 50 years or so, the past decade has seen tremendous strides in the sophistication of electric fencing equipment. Led by New Zealand companies, manufacturers are now producing low-impedance energizers which put to shame older models barely able to reach around a 20-acre field and which grounded themselves useless every time a weed grew tall enough to touch the wire. The new models are capable of charging 50 miles of fence and continue to work even when buried in wet grass.

How? "Think of the fence charger as a water pump

and the wire as a pipe," suggests Guberman. "If you have a big enough pump, it doesn't matter how leaky your pipe is, you're still going to get water out of the other end." With low-impedance energizers, high voltage (4,000-to-5,000-volt output) and a powerful current make them enormous pumps that can withstand considerable grounding without losing their effect. Such high voltage would be dangerous except that the current is sent out in a brief burst, or pulse, 60 times per minute. "The trick is to make a powerful pulse; but for such a short time, it doesn't cause any damage," says Guberman. High-powered energizers limit each pulse to 300 millionths of a second. In practice, the new fences do not pack much more wallop than the old ones; they just carry it farther.

This degree of sophistication does not come cheaply — such energizers are in the $350 range, six to eight times more expensive than conventional units. And indeed, a small operator should have no need for such a powerful unit, although he may have to spend some time trimming under the fence to keep down weeds; but for pastures requiring more than a mile of wire (a five-acre field divided into 10 paddocks with a perimeter fence uses about half a mile of single-strand fence), the high-powered energizers provide the technology to make intensive grazing practical on a large scale. To complement their energizers, the New Zealand companies offer a full range of special wire, posts, insulators and accessories designed to provide a completely integrated system. In defence of their high cost compared to weaker fences, Guberman says, "Even the most expensive electric fence is peanuts compared to paige-wire."

Guberman, who intensively grazes 120 sheep on 40 acres of steadily improving pasture, rents land to a neighbour who pastures 20 beef cattle (in terms of grazing needs, roughly equivalent to 120 sheep) on 150 acres by putting them out in spring and collecting them in the fall. Noting the difference between his verdant sheep paddocks and the withered area he rents out, Guberman says: "This is the meaning of electric fencing. It makes things turn green."

— *MW*

Sources

Listed below are the Canadian distributors for the two New Zealand fencing systems currently being sold in Canada.

GALLAGHER POWER FENCING SYSTEMS
Box 902
Owen Sound, Ontario N4K 6H6
(519) 371-2141

SPEEDRITE ELECTRIC FENCING SYSTEMS
U.D.I. Farming Inc.
R.R. 1
Springbrook, Ontario K0K 3C0
(613) 395-3535

Abridged

Confessions of an underground engineer

By Alasdair G.B. Wallace

L et it never be said that we set out deliberately to break or even bend the law. Let it rather be said that the law appeared only as a nebulous, ill-defined obstacle which, for the morning, required circumvention. Our usually reliable source had suggested that between noon and one o'clock would be the most propitious time to move our legally dubious load along Her Majesty's Highway, the guardians of the law being between shifts at that hour. He may have been right; we will never know.

And so it was that a bright morning in April saw our freshly felled 50-foot pine logs loaded and chained atop the expandable bed of Allan's newly licensed farm trailer, securely hitched behind Allan's bright red three-quarter-ton pickup. With us, we carried ropes, cant hooks, building jacks and three spare wheels (solely as insurance, of course).

How smoothly those 10,000 pounds rode behind the truck at 30 miles per hour. The slow-moving-vehicle sign, the brake lights shining distinctly on the back of the truck, the $25 trailer licence plate clearly spiked to the end of one log, the scarlet flag — all bespoke the providence, the careful planning, the exemplary nature of the endeavour.

Even the blowout required only half an hour to change, the building jacks worked so well. We were sure that the policeman must have admired the industry and the aura of cleanliness and respectability so evident as he drove by. Why else would he have chosen to inspect our labour so meticulously as he waved us over to the shoulder a scant 200 yards from our destination?

"No mudguards."

"But there's not a cloud in the sky, officer."

"No rear lights."

"But the truck lights are clearly visible."

"Driver's licence, insurance."

"They're in my jacket behind the stove, officer. We left in a hurry. Really."

"Expired trailer licence."

"The sticker's with the insurance. We forgot to affix it."

"Coat hangers don't qualify as safety chains."

"Oh."

"Load length?"

"About 60 feet."

The click of the steel tape and an unidentified "oh, shit!" confirmed the 77 feet of truck, trailer tongue and load. Seventeen feet over length.

Visions of headlines in the local paper flashed before me: ENGLISH TEACHER JAILED. CHURCH ELDER DEFIES LAW. COUNCIL DEMANDS RESIGNATION. An obese ticket pad emerged.

"Failure to provide adequate safety chain: $28 fine, no demerit points. Don't let me see you again."

We unloaded the logs beside a sandy track that disappeared into a formidable 50-foot-wide riverbed, where only two ragged rock piles and a few rotten cedar poles remained as proof of there ever having been a bridge across the gap. The rest had been washed away by the high-water conditions of 1976, leaving us to rely on a rather disreputable canoe for access to our 80-acre retreat. The summer of '77, therefore, became the Year of the Bridge. If Alec Guinness could do it in the tropical heat of mosquito-infested Burma, then surely a couple of high-school teachers and their two very independent young daughters could do no less in the black-fly-infested country south of Bancroft, Ontario.

HISTORIC DESIGN

The terrain in which we were to build is characteristic of much of the Canadian Shield — rocky outcroppings and sandy loam. The water level of our river is controlled by a man-made dam several miles upstream. In summer, two feet of peaty water wash over rippled sand bars, and trout haunt its leafy pools. In winter, deer travel its ice-bound surface. But each spring, the river becomes a raging, ice-grinding torrent between 10 and (we have since discovered) 15 feet in depth.

The location of our site had been decided a hundred years before by men experienced in building logging roads who had chosen to span a relatively narrow stretch of the river bounded by high banks. We were not inclined to challenge their judgement, for in the intervening century, only two bridges had spanned the gap, both of them constructed of two cedar cribs supporting a bed of pole stringers, or beams.

Other materials have been used locally, however, and one fellow, an inveterate scavenger, managed to locate three massive laminated roof trusses, each four feet deep at the centre, for his bridge. Of course, he had a friend with an equally massive flatbed tractor-trailer fitted with a built-in crane to help him set them in place, and he does not object to the resulting hump-backed design, guaranteed to hang up all but the shortest of vehicles, or the thrilling ascent, not unlike that of a 747.

Another neighbour scrounged two 40' x 15" steel I-beams, which he perched atop a thousand dollars worth of railway ties. But then, he drives a Mercedes. Not that we are envious — the old Volvo suits our image and our pocketbook. We like to think in terms of reverse snob appeal: conserver society, airtight stoves, recycling, that sort of thing. Also, aesthetics were important to us, and the woodworker in me rebelled at the prospect of so alien a structure in our remote corner of the wilderness.

Since we needed to build a bridge substantial enough to support a loaded two-ton truck, while staying within a very tight budget, we decided to use available resources whenever possible and to copy the original structure — that first bridge had survived for 60 years. The design called for the 50-foot-long bridge bed to be supported at each end by a cedar pole crib measuring 11 feet on each side, dug back into the bank and partially filled with rocks. Although a rocky outcropping on the east bank provided effective protection for one crib, the site for the west crib was exposed to the full brunt of the current. Consequently, we decided, as our predecessors had, to build this crib into the bank and protect it with rock retaining walls. The

Previous page: Illustration by John Bianchi

Framed by a stringer and a milk-crate chair lift, the weekend work crew struggles to set a cedar log on the second crib.

upstream wall would deflect water around the crib, while the downstream wall would provide lateral support against the current.

Building the cribs 11 feet high would place the bottom of the stringers an apparently adequate 14 feet above midstream bedrock, and having the cribs protrude 11 feet from each bank reduced the 50-foot crossing to a more manageable 28-foot span. When the truck was at mid-span, its wheels would be only eight feet from the nearest crib support. In addition, we implemented two significant modifications: the west crib would extend farther into the bank, and the rock retaining walls would be more massive. Our bridge, we decided, would last 75 years.

April greened into May. The obscene orange of our new workboots mellowed to a more respectable grey. The chain saw lost its showroom shine as we sweated each evening in the cedar swamp to fell, limb and peel the 40 cedars required for the cribs.

"Don't worry. We'll cut it out tomorrow with Rick's chain saw."

"What's a smudge, Daddy?"

"Maybe the wind'll blow it down before next weekend."

Side by side, we grunted the 11-foot, sap-heavy cedar logs to the creek bank upstream of the bridge site. Side by side, tormented by the black flies that revelled in the smoke-thick air, blinded by repellent-laden rivulets of sweat, we persuaded each other that this was really living. Day by day, the brush piles grew — mute testimony to our determination to have both cribs finished by the end of July.

Rather than build atop the apparently sound poles, which still remained in the bottom portion of each crib, we decided to excavate to bedrock and begin anew. That set us back a week. The poles, effectively toenailed together with eight-inch spikes, were embedded in six feet of compacted sand and rock and considered themselves an integral part of the geological strata. By the time the excavations were completed, the stream had acquired a substantial island of rocks, which awaited location in the cribs. Early in July, we floated cedar poles downstream to the bridge site. Construction of the first crib, once begun, progressed rapidly. The bottom round of four outer logs and one central cross brace was shaped to conform to the bedrock. Taking advantage of proven log-building techniques, each side log was shallowly notched with the chain saw to cup over the front and back logs. As the entire weight of the crib and bed is borne by the corners, fitting needed to be precise.

Extending up through each corner was a four-foot length of plated ⅝" threaded rod securely anchored by a nut and large washer beneath the bottom log. The holes for them were drilled with an antique auger which had been purchased at a farm auction for a dollar and which worked like a charm when, two files later, we learned how to sharpen it correctly. A brace and bit would have worked equally well, but we felt that somehow it would not have been in keeping.

To further strengthen the crib, bearing in mind the tremendous forces of the high-water conditions that had carried away the last bridge, every second round incorporated an extra log as a centre brace. The centre braces alternated in direction across the crib's midpoint and transmitted the considerable weight of the rock ballast within each crib to the peripheral logs, in addition to tying the unit more firmly together. These logs were notched and then spiked in place.

As construction progressed, the crib was rock-filled, the larger boulders being manhandled into place. Flat rocks were so arranged that they protruded over the logs, thus effectively transmitting the weight of subsequent rocks to the logs. Since the weight of the entire bridge bed is borne by the extra-heavy top front and back crib logs, these were themselves supported at their midpoints by crossbraces beneath.

On each trip to the bridge site, children, wife, dog and assorted bridge-building paraphernalia vied for car space with rocks pried from highway embankments. The venerable Volvo, belly sagging, tailpipe dragging — it could support six other Volvos on its roof, remember — never faltered.

The luxuriantly glossy growth of June threatened to engulf Wendy's bare arms and legs as she knelt astride the pine logs, stripping away the bark which, seemingly overnight, had acquired an unreasonable tenacity.

"Why do porcupines eat shovel handles, Daddy?"

"The doctor says poison ivy caused these blisters on my arms and legs."

"What do you mean you can't get down? You got up, didn't you?"

"The dog ate *all* the steaks?"

LOGGING BEES

As high-water conditions are relatively short-lived — maybe seven days a year — and as the cribs' function is not to hold back the water and in so doing combat a tremendous lateral force, the exposed west crib was rock-filled only to a height of seven feet, leaving the top four feet open to permit the larger volume of water unobstructed passage. The interstices between the rocks in both cribs and retaining walls filled with compacted waterborne sand the following spring, further strengthening the whole.

By the end of July, the first crib had been completed, and we were justifiably proud when the old man — former logger, Hydro chief, trapper, woodsman and owner of the property — passed his judgment: "That's a good crib." But we had by this time depleted our stock of 11-foot cedar logs, and our entire supply of rocks reposed in the one completed crib. We needed help.

Logging bees were once commonplace in our neck of the woods, as any student of Susanna Moodie will attest, and our decision to emulate the custom would, we believed, attract a similar number of would-be loggers. However, rather than issue a carte blanche invitation to all and sundry, we decided, in light of Susanna's experience, to be more selective. We, too, would be exemplary hosts by providing both food and beverage, thus, we felt, imposing a subtle moral obligation on our guests.

As the great day dawned, cars, trucks and vans disgorged ropes, chain saws, Molsons (just in case), gas, oil, tents, Labatts (in a case), canoes, pulleys, Carlings (by the case), barbecues, cant hooks, children and dogs. Our wilderness retreat resembled Labour Day weekend at Mosport Raceway, and directing and controlling the considerable energy of such a motley crew afforded a stimulating challenge. Cut and peel 20 cedars, excavate the bank, haul rocks, raft logs, build a crib: the work gangs were equipped and assigned to their respective tasks.

Drawknife in hand, the author smooths the tops of the pine stringers before nailing on the deck planks.

"Is this a cedar?"

"Where's the opener?"

"Come on. They'll think you've gone back to help get lunch."

With all the available manpower, it seemed reasonable, at this point, that we position the two initial stringers across the face of the first crib in preparation for winching them tip-first across the 28-foot span. Since the balance point of the logs was appreciably closer to the butt end, there would be less of a tendency for them to tip into the river as they awaited construction of the far crib.

An elevated snatch block, attached to a conveniently located maple on the far side of the river, in conjunction with Pete's truck and 200 feet of three-quarter-inch polypropylene rope offered a simple, logical means to an end. Since the approach to the bridge is a slight downhill curve, the driver of the truck would be unable to watch the log's progress in his mirror. Therefore, a system of signals was devised and a semaphore man strategically located where he could see both log and truck.

Moving the truck 10 feet up the track took up the slack, and another 10 feet stretched the rope. The log remained totally unimpressed by the ominous creakings. From behind the safety of a tree, crib or relative, we watched. "Gun it!" shouted someone who obviously had no vested interest in block, rope or crib.

Dual wheels churned. A dust cloud enveloped the semaphore man. The coefficient of static friction was suddenly overcome by 450 cubic inches of V-8 power straining in bull low. The truck shot forward. The log careened down the track, bounced over the crib edge and came to rest with its tip halfway across the river, exactly where required, if not quite as planned.

Invention flourished; ingenuity rampaged. A chair lift suddenly appeared, designed to leave its occupant perilously suspended midstream. Middle-aged Tom Sawyers discovered the joys of log rafting: log-rolling and jousting competitons were improvised. A ⅝" hole bored with the aid of an industrial drill and portable generator proved indistinguishable, even by a purist, from one produced 50 times more slowly by the pioneer's auger. It was discovered that the combination of industrial drill and clogged bit can throw the uninitiated into the river.

Rhythms evolved. Side by side, strangers discovered the joys of working together for a common, visible end. Friendships were struck. Two men notched the logs; one man drilled them. The same men effortlessly lifted the logs over the threaded rods which were themselves guided into the holes by two other men. A team of men raised the logs from the river as effortlessly as the crib itself rose from the river bed. By nine o'clock that night, it lacked only two rounds to bring it level with the first crib.

"Help! We've run out of beer."
"Anybody seen Gord?"
"Would the generator run the drill and floodlight?"
"The hell with that. Let's eat."
The clear coolness of the river soothed toil-worn bodies. High-cholesterol barbecued steaks appeased honest appetites. Messrs. Molson, Labatt and Carling lubricated parched throats. Off in the distance, an owl hooted. Weary bodies slept.

Noon the following day saw the completion of the second crib. Rather than risk demolition of the cribs by using the block-and-truck technique to move the stringers into their final positions, a rented two-ton "come-along," while agonizingly slow, enabled one man to position the logs in a sane, predictable manner with literal single-handedness.

A balanced bridge, one that is equally strong at either end, requires that the stringers be laid with their butt ends pointing in alternating directions. Each of our cribs, then, supported two butt ends and two tip ends, with the natural result that the 16-inch butts loomed over the adjacent 10-inch tips. Removing wood from the cross members, on which the stringers rested, would encourage rot by providing a water-retaining pocket; conversely, removing wood from the butt ends and cupping them over the cross members would weaken the stringers. We chose to raise the tip ends by shimming underneath them.

STRINGER PLACEMENT

The final spacing of the stringers across the crib face depends upon the number and size of the stringers and the wheelbase of the vehicles which will use the bridge. In our case, two stringers are approximately one foot inside the Volvo's wheeltrack, the other pair approximately one foot outside. Rather than bolting the shimmed stringers in place, we toenailed them lightly to the cribs and lag-bolted shaped locating blocks on either side of them. In the event of ice jamming against the bed during run-off, we would prefer to lose the bed and retain the cribs intact. We were surprised when, in 1981, the river flowing *over* the bridge failed to float the bed free of its blocks. Had there been a simultaneous ice jam, nothing could have withstood it.

In order to encourage air circulation around the ends of the stringers, the location at which rot was most likely to begin, and to allow regular applications of creosote, our bridge design incorporated the construction of low cedar-pole retaining walls between the bank tops and the ends of the stringers.

Our original intent was to have a 10-foot-wide bridge — hence the 11-foot-wide cribs; however, since the price of a sufficient quantity of 10-foot planks exceeded the cost of a first-class chain-saw mill, we made the obvious decision and arranged a trial. So convinced was the distributor of the efficacy of his mill, that he was readily persuaded to part with his demonstration model for the weekend in the light of what both he and we considered a certain sale.

After felling a large, conveniently located spruce, we attached the cutting guide and settled in to save ourselves a medium-sized fortune. Half an hour and two tanks of gas later, we had completed the first of many cuts. A trained beaver could have outchewed this contraption. We must be doing something wrong. Little daunted, we returned the equipment to the distributor and explained our difficulties. He would be pleased to demonstrate. A log was set up, and the chain saw started.

"The first cut's always the most difficult."
"Let's try a new chain."
"We'll check it out and call you."
We never did hear from him. As a compromise, we followed up an ad in the local paper offering used 2 x 8s. They were only eight feet long, but there was a sufficient quantity, and the price was reasonable. After all, the Volvo's 54-inch track width would leave an adequate, comfortable 21 inches on either side of the wheels.

Before attaching the 2 x 8s, we had to prepare the stringers by levelling their top surface. Standing on

Author's family and Volvo pause above the temporarily idyllic stream to celebrate the completion of the bridge.

one of the planks, we used a chalkline and builder's level to mark the stringers and then did the work with an old-fashioned adze. Had it not been for our steel-toed boots, we would have found out too literally why the old man referred to it as the "toenail trimmer." Once levelled, the stringers and the 2 x 8s were thoroughly creosoted. We wondered, as the oily black globs rainbowed the river beneath, whether our downstream neighbours were enjoying their afternoon swim.

Since we anticipated some flexing of the bridge deck under load, we used a dozen six-inch galvanized ardox nails to affix each plank to the four stringers, leaving a one-inch space between the planks to facilitate water run-off and encourage air circulation around the stringers.

In all our dreams of the bridge, the hours at night we had lain awake thinking through the entire process, anticipating every minor detail and mentally solving every problem, we had never anticipated the actual trauma of having the bridge completed. We had envisioned the utility it would afford — the accessibility of firewood and building supplies — but we had not prepared ourselves for the experience of that first crossing.

Part of the trepidation was undoubtedly linked to our relationship with the Volvo. Well into her second time around, just like Grandpa, she was very much a member of the family. She had couched our amorous bodies; she had carried us to the hospital; she had cradled our children. Like Grandpa, she had never refused our requests, unreasonable though they had often been.

"It's getting late."

"You're not going to drive across today, are you?"

"It looks awfully narrow."

"We'll watch."

And watch they did as the Volvo was ceremoniously parked mid-span. The Mommesin — we were really flying — was uncorked, and we toasted ourselves, our friends and our bridge.

Today, six years later, we trundle across in the two-ton with a cord and a half of logs. The lumbering five-ton bulldozer, which, this summer, pushed a road through the swamp, posed midspan for a photo. We're proud. We've come to our bridge, and we've crossed it. ■

Alasdair G.B. Wallace is a high school teacher who lives near Lakefield, Ontario.

Calculated Crossings

One case where common sense may not be enough

Would-be bridge builders, as they amend various sketches in an effort to bridge their own particular gap, might care to consider more than just cost and appearance. Preservation of life and limb must at all times be paramount, but few novice bridge builders have the engineering skills to calculate the stresses that will be imposed upon their structures. Driving across a home-built bridge, the Force is indeed with you, but how much force and how much is too much?

Dr. Karl Van Dalen, a civil engineering professor at Queen's University who has conducted research on wooden bridges, points to three aspects of bridge design that may interest potential builders: "One is to ensure that the deflection, or sag, isn't excessive. Assuming the bridge is sufficiently strong, deflections are not too serious, although it tends to cause some trepidation on the part of the driver of the vehicle.

"The other two are to ensure that the bending stresses and shear stresses do not exceed permissible levels. These are interrelated quantities, but since the maximum values don't occur at the same time or in the same place, one has to imagine a vehicle in two different positions. Bending stress is the result of bending of the beams, or logs: the top of the member goes into compression, and the bottom goes into tension. One good thing about bending stresses is that they are usually accompanied by large vertical deformations, so you have some warning that the stresses are reaching a critical level. Hopefully, the driver will realize the danger and will back off the bridge before a failure occurs."

Oddly, the maximum bending stress does not occur when the vehicle is exactly in the middle of the bridge; rather, the critical position is when a point halfway between the vehicle's centre of gravity (somewhere between the axles, depending on what portion of the load each axle carries) and its heaviest axle is at the midpoint of the bridge. Then, the bridge is most likely to break under the heaviest axle.

Unlike bending stress, maximum shear stress occurs near the support as the vehicle first drives onto the bridge. "Generally speaking," Van Dalen says, "wood is quite weak in shear because of the way it grows, and for most timber structures, that's the more critical stress." As anyone who has spent an afternoon with a splitting axe knows, tree growth consists of long vertical fibres, and it takes much less force to separate the fibres longitudinally than it does to break the log crosswise. Shear stress can be demonstrated by bending a telephone book — as it bends, the pages slice apart. In a wooden bridge, shear stress could cause a log to split down its length, and the resulting two half-logs may not be strong enough to support the vehicle. Van Dalen stresses that he is not talking about the normal splits and checks of the drying process. "If you get a bit of splitting, there's no long-term effect, but if the log is underdesigned, you get a vehicle driving across causing the shear stress to be larger than the capacity of the wood, and then you get a splitting failure. This generally happens without very much warning, and collapse can occur almost instantaneously.

"For a member of a given size, maximum shear stress is not related to the span of the bridge but rather to the load imposed by the axle as it comes onto the bridge; bending stresses increase proportionately to the span. In general, for short spans, the shear stresses will get you; for longer spans, the bending stresses come into play."

Calculating the strengths and load-bearing capacities of various structures requires some fairly advanced mathematics, the sort of thing, says Van Dalen, that requires an extensive background in theory that "has to be drummed into you for a couple of years" and which most nonengineers "would probably find as dull as dishwater." Common sense in bridge design is not always enough, he says, pointing out that the bending strength of a log varies according to the cube of its diameter — an eight-inch diameter log is only half as strong as a ten-inch diameter log.

His advice is to the point: "Most of the time, people are lucky: they throw a few logs across and nail on a deck and there's no problem, but for whatever a professional engineer would charge, I think it's money well spent to have him or her take a look at your design. Spend a few dollars and get a professional opinion."
— *Michael Webster*

Coppice Comeback

A centuries-old technique
revolutionizes the home woodlot

By Michael Webster with photography by Stephen Errington

"**A** little more . . . a little more . . . *Okay!*" While air brakes shudder and sigh, gears growl softly as the hoist engages, and the 16-yard box on the tandem-axle dump truck begins to rise. The driver trips the tailgate, and tons of moist green wood chips flow into what was once the coal bin at the physical plant of Grenville Christian College, a private boarding school near the St. Lawrence River in Brockville, Ontario.

Here, the chips will be dried, then burned, to heat the 70-year-old complex of limestone buildings that house a staff and student body numbering 420. The first institution of its size in this country to convert to wood chips for its heating needs, Grenville has replaced its $100,000-a-year dependence on oil with bark waste and chips — in very large quantities.

To keep Grenville's new Swedish-built central furnace roaring requires a constant supply of wood that comes, in part, from an ancient method of tree culture known as coppicing, which is now being rediscovered by experimental foresters and home-woodlot owners alike.

Simply put, a coppice is a grove or plantation of multitrunked trees that have sprung from the stumps of previously harvested trees. When cut at the right time of year, certain species of trees show a strong inclination to send up new sprouts or suckers. Coppicing seeks to take full advantage of this bit of genetic design. Such new shoots easily outstrip the growth of seedlings started at the same time and under the same conditions, since the coppice draws on the vast underground strength of the root system of the cut tree to spur new growth. Properly nurtured, a coppice can be cut time and again — in theory, providing an unending supply of wood for fuel, pulp, light construction or fence building.

Coppicing works not only in theory, however, but also in practice. Coppices appear in early Egyptian hieroglyphics and can be traced to the Roman Empire. The Romans spread the technique throughout Europe, where it was carried on by mediaeval and modern societies. Some British coppices still in production today are hundreds of years old.

Indeed, it is assumed that cavemen practised a form of coppice management. Their stone tools were far better suited to chopping down trees of small diameter, and it is highly likely that they returned to the same area to fell the new growth that followed previous visits. As communities became established, coppices were cared for in a more purposeful way, and according to Dr. Geoffrey Stanford, an expatriot British researcher now working with short-rotation forestry techniques in Texas, "From that time until around 1850, when coal became freely available, coppice wood was the only fuel available for homes as well as for industry."

When Columbus first set foot in the Americas, there were "lawes" in England to provide for the continued harvesting of forested areas, strictly enforced rules that prevented clear-cutting or pasturing animals on logged-

Showing typical coppice growth, this clump of mature sprouts grew unbidden from the stump of a harvested basswood tree.

over areas. A century later, in 1598, Thomas Marr-wood gave this definition of a forest: "A certen territorie of wooddy grounds and fruitfull pastures, priviledged for wild beasts and foules of forrest, chase and warren, to rest and abide in, in the safe protection of the king, for his princely delight and pleasure."

UBIQUITOUS WOODLOT

Prior to the Industrial Revolution in England, that princely delight included allowing peasants to care for coppiced forestland as part of a village "common," where villages harvested coppice wood for fences, furniture and numerous other uses. At that time, sawn lumber was not widely available, and construction was accomplished with round wood as much as possible. Coppices supplied uniformly sized poles for this purpose, and the staves for innumerable barrels, tubs and pails were riven from the same coppice growth. Coppices also provided the small stems to weave baskets and, in the absence of wire, to make hurdles, portable woven livestock fences. The smallest branches were gathered for fuel, and the fruit from the dozen or so large trees (standards) per acre that were left uncut fattened free-ranging geese and pigs. In short, coppices were almost as essential to the life style of a British peasant as the caribou herds were to the Inuit.

Coppices also provided the bulk of the wood that was made into charcoal, vast quantities of which were burned for iron smelting and foundry work. "In England," says John Seymour in his book, *The Country-side Explained*, "there are hardly any wild, self-sown indigenous trees which are not deformed by coppicing or pollarding." (Pollarding is a variation of coppicing in which the trees are cut off at a height of some six feet to keep the tender growing shoots out of reach of grazing animals, thus lessening the output of wood but adding to available pastureland.) Oak, beech, willow, hazel, hornbeam, sweet chestnut, birch, alder and ash were all cultivated by one of these two methods.

By the 1600s, coppices with standards were an unfailing presence in Britain and other European countries. Seymour described one as a "sweet chestnut coppice with oak trees towering above it at intervals." The coppice was cut for fences, furniture and fuel every dozen years in a planned rotation, and the oak standards were harvested once a century for shipbuilding material. Oaks grown in this manner had room to spread out, and they developed many twisty, curved branches — "crooks" that were needed for the frames of a ship's ribbing.

This happy cohabitation continued until the middle of the last century, when several factors combined to force coppicing out of the marketplace: The wide-scale adoption of coal eliminated the need for large amounts of charcoal; the development of high-quality steel cutting blades made lumber making popular; and the newly developed steam engines to power sawmills made lumbering practical on a large scale. The emphasis in forestry shifted to the long, straight, large-diameter boles, or trunks, needed for lumber production,

thus making both coppices and standards obsolete. Interest in coppicing as a desirable forestry practice lay fallow for a century and never found widespread acceptance in North America, with its seemingly everlasting virgin-timber resources.

Today, however, Domtar Paper is experimenting with coppiced poplars in Ontario; Scott Paper is planting poplars on islands and floodplains in British Columbia's Fraser Valley, and in the largest hardwood plantation in North America, Crown-Zellerbach now has 18,000 acres of Mississippi Delta planted to cottonwood. The U.S. pulp-and-paper giant was one of the first to recognize that the inexhaustible forests were tiring at an alarming rate, and their cottonwoods are now coppiced on a 10-to-12-year rotation and processed into paper, some of which fills the needs of the magazine industry.

Some farmers and small woodlot owners have also embraced the concept of coppicing, and the early results appear highly encouraging, especially to those with limited acreage or with a desire to concentrate their woodlot activities. Because of the productivity of a coppice, some experts say that individual landowners should be able to meet their fuelwood needs by gardening relatively small plots. Based on his experiments at the Greenhills Center in Cedar Hill, Texas, just south of Dallas, Stanford says that a family of four can do all of its cooking — forever — with the wood cut from a well-managed coppice measuring less than 70 feet on a side, a scant one-tenth of an acre.

Figures like that, indicating a production level 5 to 10 times greater than that from seedling growth, are considered normal for coppices and can be attributed to three factors: use of the established rootstock, the wounding syndrome, and juvenile vigour. Shoots growing from a freshly cut coppice do not have to expend energy in creating a root system — it is already there. Furthermore, when cuttings are made during the winter dormant period (as they should be for successful coppicing), most of the tree's nutrients are being held in storage by the root system in preparation for spring growth. That growth appears as suckers in the absence of the tree trunk.

Added to that jump start is the spurt given by something called the wounding syndrome, a phenomenon that spurs growth in plants that have been cut back in some way. Finally, with its continued harvesting of fast-growing young trees, coppicing is a form of eternal youth, repeatedly taking advantage of the vigorous growth in the early years of a tree's development. Coppicing, then, is more than just automatic reforestation; it is a way to increase the production of a woodlot dramatically, giving new meaning to the concept of wood heat as a renewable resource.

Certainly, it is a concept that has been accepted at the Grenville Christian College. Built in 1914, the large three-storey limestone main building was heated with a coal-fired boiler until 1971, when the system was changed to oil. As energy prices rose during the late 1970s, the school's administration looked for a cheaper fuel, hoping for one that would give them a degree of self-sufficiency. They chose a system centred on a

Coppice management is based on the ability of hardwood trees to send up sprouts from dormant buds lying hidden underneath the bark. This poplar stump, now in its third two-year cycle, bears both the promise of a future harvest and the scars of previous cuttings.

Swedish furnace that burns wood chips, and in the first year, their energy costs dropped from more than $100,000 to $45,000. Spokesman Dan Ortolani expects the figure to fall to the $30,000-to-$35,000 range in the second year, explaining that they rarely hit peak efficiency last winter. Although highly automated, with auger feeds and ash removal, the furnace is basically an overgrown wood stove and, as such, requires some care. "You have to get a feel for it," says Ortolani. "It's not like an oil furnace that you can just stick in the basement and leave alone. But when you're saving $70,000 or $80,000 a year, you don't mind spending

a few hours a week with the thing."

The school's furnace is currently burning bark wastes that have been put through a hogger, or chipper, at the end of the production line at a local lumber mill. Three or four times a week during the winter, a truckload of chips is dumped into the converted coal bin, truckloads that the school pays for at the rate of $30 per tonne — furnace oil to provide the equivalent in Btus would cost $100. In hopes of increasing its savings even further, the school has purchased a 350-acre farm on which it intends to produce its own wood chips. While the administration plans to continue renting out the prime agricultural land to a local farmer, some 200 acres of bush and wetland will be dedicated to coppices of fast-growing hybrid poplar. Intending to harvest the trees on a seven-year rotation, the school planted the first of its seven plots in the spring of 1984 and will make its first cutting in 1991. Meanwhile, they will continue buying chipped-bark wastes from lumber mills, as well as 250 cords a year from the Ministry of Natural Resources (MNR) experimental poplar coppices.

Brian Barkley, a forestry specialist involved with MNR's breeding and production experiments, is clearly a man who loves trees. When walking through one of his poplar plantations, he holds out a hand against the trees — not pushing the branches out of the way but just touching them, letting his fingers run through the leaves the way a small boy drags his hand in the water behind a rowboat.

Barkley works almost exclusively with hybrid poplars and willows, species that conventional foresters (and many wood burners) think of as weed trees. "Hybrid poplars produce seven times the Btus per acre that hard maple does," says Barkley in their defence, pointing out that an acre of carefully managed weed trees will replace seven acres of hardwood. "If you started with an acre of mature hard maple trees, any age you want," he challenges, "and I started with nothing but a bare field, I could heat my house for seven times as long as you could each and every year — including the first year." On the other hand, poplar is a fast-burning wood, requiring two cords to equal the heat output of one cord of a hardwood like maple.

"Sure, I'd burn hardwood too," says Barkley, pausing to make his point, "if it was available." To harvest a modest five cords of firewood per year, the wood cutter must own or have access to between 10 and 20 acres of valuable hardwood forest. The 10 cords of poplar required to produce the same amount of heat can be harvested from a coppice less than two acres in size and situated on land that might otherwise go to waste.

With poplar coppice management, wood-stove owners lucky enough to have a substantial woodlot would be freed to manage it for profitable timber production. Those who groan at the thought of handling twice as much wood for the same heat value can console themselves with the knowledge that although they would handle twice the volume, the weight would be the same. "Pound for pound," says Ken Kern in *Masonry Heaters*, "all wood contains the same amount of heat energy. The tree's rate of growth is more significant than the density of its wood."

The beginning coppice manager is certainly not restricted to poplar or willow. All hardwoods, with the exception of hickory, will coppice naturally, although hard maple and oak do so poorly. Soft maple, birch, cherry and basswood sprout readily. "Ash coppices well," says New England horse logger Toby Bashaw, "and the second growth is good for making axe handles." Of the so-called desirable woods, perhaps ash coppices the best, giving an average annual growth of three feet in height and up to half an inch in diameter. Still, as in any garden, it is the weeds that grow fastest. "Generalities are dangerous," observes Barkley, "but it's pretty safe to say that the closer a species is to being a shrub, the better its coppicing ability." Hence the emphasis on poplar, cottonwood, alder, box elder (Manitoba maple) and locust. The only conifer to show any inclination toward coppicing is the redwood, but little or no work has been done with this species.

In fact, almost all the North American research involves poplars, partly because research dollars are kept flowing by the speedy and dramatic results — the MNR achieved a remarkable 400 percent increase in tree growth in less than a decade by simply selecting nursery stock for fast growth and taking advantage of hybrid vigour. While the most spectacular results can be seen with the weed trees, Stanford lists ongoing research projects on the coppicing ability of 91 species of trees worldwide, ranging from exotics like eucalyptus and teak to familiars like alder and birch.

Of course, if one chooses to convert an existing woodlot to coppice management, there is no choice of species to be made — one simply uses what is there. Be forewarned, however, that woodlot conversions are often not as successful as new plantings because older trees, those beyond about 30 years of age, do not sprout readily. Nevertheless, if a woodlot is still young, it can be turned into a coppice by simply chopping part of it down each year. "Cut the young growth when it is six inches in diameter, and you're off," says Stanford.

To convert a five-acre lot of young ash trees to a coppice managed for stovewood on a 10-year rotation, one should cut the trees in a half-acre area every year. Each stump will produce two or three sprouts, and the spaces between them will be taken up by the natural growth of young seedlings — all of which can be cut again a decade later, when the rotation returns to that section. Although the harvesting must be done in blocks to provide the young shoots with the sunlight that they need, clear-cutting is not necessary or even desirable. Stanford believes that a coppice with standards is successful partly because the taller trees cause a gentle air turbulence which provides a warmer climate for the coppice. However, no more than 10 or 12 trees per acre should be left standing.

Still, with the development of fast-growing hybrids, it may make more sense to start a plantation from scratch. For most noncommercial uses, primarily fuel for home heating, this puts silviculture in the realm of agriculture — or even horticulture — and the problems associated with establishing a stand are those already familiar to farmers and gardeners: site selection, seedbed preparation, spacing and weed control.

Immersed in his work, forestry specialist Brian Barkley makes a midsummer examination of the lush first-year growth of coppiced willows at MNR's Kemptville, Ontario, nursery.

Traditional hardwood species prefer well-drained locations, especially hillsides, but the faster-growing trees can be planted on land too wet for other uses, in low areas or along the edges of swamps, where drainage is too poor for field crops. Soil acidity is another factor to consider, but generally speaking, local species can be relied on to do well in a coppice. Specific advice on species suitability for individual sites can be obtained from provincial forestry experts.

"With a fresh planting," says Stanford, "you're going to have a problem with weeds." Barkley agrees: "The most important thing is to get rid of the vegetation," he says, strongly recommending a year of summer fallow before planting — that is, ploughing the site in early summer and cultivating it regularly throughout the growing season to prevent weed growth. Although this will help prepare the site, the regimen of weed control must be carried on for the first two years of the plantation's life. "It's like planting a garden crop in sod," says Barkley. "You don't just plant it and walk away. You weed it and weed it again and again — whenever it needs it." While sod plantings of a conifer like white pine can have success rates of 60 percent, Barkley says that the figure falls to 5 percent with hardwood species intended for coppicing.

WEED CONTROL

Until the young trees have established root systems which go beyond the depth of the roots of grasses and trunks that reach above their stalks, the trees are apt to be choked out by other vegetation. The MNR's programme, which encompasses some 5,000 acres of widely scattered plots, uses herbicides for weed control, principally Roundup to deal with a persistent quack grass problem, but Barkley is quick to point out that it is more a matter of scale than of preference. "It doesn't matter how you get rid of the weeds," he says. "If you're a private landowner, you've probably got the equipment and are willing to put in the time to control the weeds mechanically." Tractor cultivator, horse-drawn disc, rototiller, hoe or mulch, whatever the choice, it is absolutely essential to keep weeds down in the first two years — after that, especially in the narrow spacings where canopies close over rapidly, the trees will turn the tables and begin to force out the weeds.

As for proper spacing, it depends on the intended use of the trees. Coppices planted for veneer logs, harvested in cycles ranging from 25 to 75 years, are traditionally planted every 20 feet in rows 40 feet apart. Pulpwood, grown on a 10-or-12-year rotation, however, needs a 10' x 10' spacing. It is possible, though, to plant as for pulpwood, remove every second row at 10 years and then cut back to the 20' x 40' spacing at 20 years. Alternatively, row crops may be cultivated between the widely spaced trees until they become large enough to allow pasturing or hay cropping.

Wood for fuel can, of course, be harvested at any age, although the fastest growth occurs in the first few years of the tree's life, and young trees, lacking the resins and oils that accumulate in mature heartwood, burn more cleanly than older trees. Barkley is experimenting with two rotations for fuelwood: a five-to-seven-year cycle with 4' x 4' spacing and a two-year cycle, which crowds the trees into a 1-foot spacing in rows 3 feet apart. With his fast-growing hybrids, the former, at six to eight inches in diameter, are worthy of a chain saw; the latter, only an inch or two thick, can be harvested with an axe, a brush saw or even a farm forage harvester, which, fitted with a corn head, slices the young trees into chips and blows them into a wagon.

Regardless of the implement used, coppices should be cut while the trees are dormant, preferably during the early winter. As a tree prepares itself for winter, it builds a store of nutrients in the root system, and cutting before this accumulation is complete hinders spring growth — not a consideration in normal tree harvesting but vitally important for successful coppicing.

Nevertheless, spring growth from the cut stumps is somewhat late, and Barkley recalls the first time they harvested a plantation: "We cut in the fall, and in the spring, nothing happened. We thought, 'My God, we've killed all these stumps. What are we going to do?' " The coppice showed no signs of life until about a month after other spring growth had begun, a normal delay for a coppice, which can be traced to the nature of the sucker growth. Hardwood trees have many dormant buds just under the bark surface. "When trees are stressed and aren't photosynthesizing enough," Toby Bashaw explains, "these buds come to life." In a coppice, the dormant buds form new branches that grow from the stump or even from the upper part of the rootstock. Despite a somewhat late start, these fresh sprouts, with the advantage of an established root system, soon equal and surpass seedling growth.

In many cases, each stump will only send up two or three shoots, an ideal situation. Other trees, notably box elder and alder, produce a thick clump of sprouts, and although the larger sprouts will eventually dominate and incorporate the smaller ones as branches, the process is inefficient and should be helped along by some judicious trimming of the small sprouts, much as one would thin a row of carrots. Unlike the pruning of orchard trees, this thinning can be done in the summer, thus discouraging regrowth of the trimmed branches. At the end of its second rotation, the trees will begin growing suckers on the suckers and can be expected to support four or five sprouts.

At the end of their first rotation, when the trees still have only one stem, or trunk, they should be cut off an inch or two above ground level. Stanford says that the initial cut, whether by axe or by saw, must be kept very close to the ground and must be made cleanly, without tearing the bark. He recommends making the cut on a slight angle so that water will not collect on the fresh wood, which would increase the chances of fungal rot and thereby weaken the rootstock. In subsequent rotations, when several stems are being cut from one stump, each successive generation must be lopped off close to the trunk. "After a number of cycles," says Stanford, "the enlarged rim of the stump will be knotted and gnarled; it must then be trimmed back evenly almost to ground level."

Barkley's poplars have been harvested mostly with chain saws or power brush saws, with little regard for height or cleanness of cut, and he feels that there has been no detrimental effect on the next growth cycle. He will begin experiments this winter with a machine made especially for the harvesting of coppices for fuelwood. "It's designed to fit on the three-point hitch of an ordinary farm tractor," Barkley says. "The operator will drive beside a row of trees, and the machine will cut them off close to ground level, gather several stems

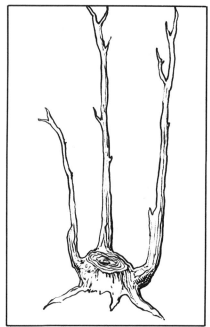
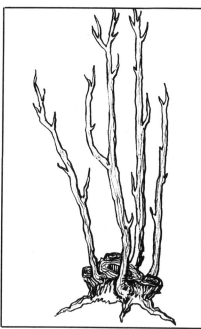

After the original trunk is cut, second-cycle growth emerges from the stump. A midsummer pruning restricts the number of sprouts to two or three.

In the third cycle, the enlarged stump is capable of supporting a ring of four or five sprouts, but the unprotected wood in the centre begins to decay.

The stump becomes bigger and more gnarled in later cycles, until it is finally overtaken by the enlarging centre rot.

into a bundle, tie them together and deposit the bundle on the other side of the tractor — sort of like an old-fashioned grain binder." Without hazarding a guess at its cost, he says that the harvester, which is capable of cutting trees up to eight inches in diameter, is intended for farm use by individual landowners.

Whether bundled or not, the fallen stems are gathered and stored to dry. The wood from rotations of 10 years or more can be treated like any other cordwood, but wood from the short rotations, even with hybrid trees, is just kindling size and is only suitable for burning as chips. In some parts of the country, especially the Maritimes, chip burning is already becoming popular as wood burners take advantage of the slash left from pulping operations and as special stoves and furnaces are making their way onto the market. Wood chippers can be rented from big-city rental outfits, although forage harvesters are probably cheaper and more common. Farmers may be reluctant to put their machinery to such use, but Barkley says that the farmer whose harvester he rented was surprised to find that the cutting blades needed sharpening less often for trees than for cornstalks, even when chopping two-inch-thick saplings that had been allowed to dry for nearly a year.

Like any other fuelwood, the chips should be stored under cover for the best results, and Barkley recommends that the saplings be dried before chipping, lest the pile of green chips begin to ferment.

But can this cycle of repeated cutting continue indefinitely? "For all practical purposes," says Stanford, "a tree is a new structure each year, thinly spread over and around last year's tree. In this view of the model, a tree is more analogous to a coral reef than it is to an animal; so long as the coral reef continues to receive nutrients, and other factors are suitable, it will continue

to grow. Juvenile vigour may be able to continue indefinitely." At least that is the theory. In practice, as the stump becomes larger with every rotation and its centre succumbs to rot, it becomes weaker — less "wind firm" and more likely to split, allowing the tree to blow over. "Every time you harvest a coppice," says Barkley, "you trick the tree into thinking that it's young again." As the tree ages, it becomes harder to fool it into thinking it is still young — a phenomenon most of us can empathize with — and usually, the stumps will not last beyond five or six cycles.

Still, with most cycles in the 10-to-30-year range, senescence is not an everyday problem. "Some species will coppice for 150 to 200 years quite easily," says Barkley, although he points out that the high-producing hybrids in minirotations of two or three years may only last a decade. But with each newly developed hybrid offering dramatic increase in growth, Barkley speculates that woodsmen using the short rotations will probably want to switch to a different tree stock every 10 years or so anyway.

With this sort of intensive silviculture being practised constantly on the same piece of ground, conscientious cultivators may worry about the loss of soil nutrients, but surprisingly, coppicing can actually increase the productivity of the soil. "Rainfall leaches nutrients out of the topsoil down into lower areas of the soil profile fairly quickly," says Barkley. Tree roots go beyond the depth of grasses and draw these lost elements up to the leaves, where they are used in photosynthesis. "Thirty percent of the biomass of a tree is in its foliage," Barkley adds. "Most of the nutrients are in the leaves — that's where all the action is." With the autumn leaf loss, these nutrients are released at the top of the soil profile, ready to repeat the cycle. As the trees grow, they deposit more layers of leaves and form a closed canopy that shades the ground. A substantial leaf litter accumulates, and the quality of the ground vegetation improves — the traditional, though accelerated, transition from open pasture to forestland. At the same time, the roots loosen and aerate the soil, thus improving drainage and attracting populations of earthworms and soil bacteria. "What we find on most of these farm sites," says Barkley, "is that although they have a nice stand of grass on them, the organic matter is about two percent, which is almost the minimum amount you can afford to have for growth. By the time we're finished a 10-year rotation, the amount of organic matter is up to about 15 percent. You end up with a site that's much better than when you originally got it."

Another benefit is a reduction in the water table, a phenomenon that allows low-lying abandoned pastures to be put back into production. Trees transport enormous quantities of water from their root systems to their leaves, where it is released into the atmosphere. Barkley describes the leaves as "huge wicks flapping in the breeze." Oak trees use 10 pounds of water to produce 1 pound of biomass, and other species are even less efficient, with some poplars operating on a 40-to-1 ratio. The result is a drier soil in the forested area, meaning that coppices can be planted on marginal land, leaving the valuable well-drained sites for agricultural purposes. Depending on the ability of a particular soil structure to transmit water laterally, it is even possible to improve adjacent fields, perhaps allowing earlier spring planting or later ploughing in the fall.

Despite gains in humus and drainage, there is an unquestioned loss of some nutrients as the trees are harvested. If the harvest is for fuelwood, simply sprinkling the ashes in the coppice will replace all the phosphorus and potassium drawn from the site. Nitrogen is lost during the burning process, but with the wider spacings, a cover crop of some leguminous plant like clover can supply nitrogen from the air, or failing that, fertilizer applications can be made. Grenville Christian College plans to use liquid chicken manure obtained from the farmer who rents their land, and Barkley's group has done some work with sewage sludge. The primary concern there is the presence of toxic heavy metals, but with the trees' low nutrient requirements, Barkley finds that "we end up having too much nitrogen on the site before we have any heavy-metal accumulation, although it's something we're very conscious about." He feels that another promising advantage to intensive silviculture is the filtering out of heavy metals in sewage wastes. "Something like cadmium, for example, only accumulates in the foliage. It's tied up in the tissue there, and that can be a benefit because it gives you a way of cleaning out the material. You could harvest the area and still use the tree, then travel through the area with some sort of a vacuuming apparatus to collect all the material and have the heavy metals pretty much concentrated." Other metals remain in the wood but are not released to the air during burning. "Instead of having several thousand tons [of contaminated sludge] over a year, you end up with one ton of ashes, or something like that. We've only done some preliminary work — tissue analysis of the trees, finding out where the metals go, trying to answer some of the questions."

If coppices can serve as a biological sieve for pathogen-laden sludge, so much the better, but for the moment, their function as a source of large quantities of pulp or fuelwood grown on marginal land will suffice. With thousands of acres of plantations already feeding the voracious appetite of our pulp industry, coppicing is no fairy-tale scheme for the future. Barkley hopes to see the technique used extensively by private landowners as a source of fuelwood and suggests that the first place to begin is with the farmers who grow grain crops. Standard agricultural practice, particularly with grain corn, is to dry the crops in huge forced-air drying bins fired by oil or gas, but Barkley would like to see the farmers set aside a small piece of wetland to grow their own fuel to dry crops. "The farmer who is growing corn now has the need and the equipment," he says, anticipating that as coppice management moves out of the hands of foresters and into those of farmers and gardeners, it will once again become the commonplace source of fuelwood that it has been in nearly every recorded civilization.

Gautama Buddha once said: "The forest is a peculiar organism of unlimited kindness and benevolence that makes no demands for its sustenance and extends generously the products of its life activity; it affords protection to all beings, offering shade even to the axeman who destroys it." Now, perhaps, the axeman toiling in the leafy shade can work with the knowledge that he is not destroying the forest but is helping to rejuvenate it. ∎

The Elementary Chandler

Shedding new light on the old alchemy of home candle making

A Harrowsmith Staff Report with photography by Ernie Sparks

B.H. we might call it, Before Hydro, that time when the threat of one's being abandoned to freeze in the dark was curiously less threatening than it is now. Cold was so familiar then that many rooms were closed off in winter; darkness was a simple fact of night. Along 18th-century European streets, candles were lit only on moonless or overcast nights and, even so, were snuffed out before midnight, after which time, all but the most spendthrift of insomniacs huddled under blankets in the dark. For all but the wealthy, most reading was done by daylight or firelight in an era when the other choices of illumination were often dim, smoky and vaguely fragrant of resin or animal fat.

Now that candles burn more dependably and brightly, ironically, they are burned much less frequently. But it is still the candle we reach for when the hydro fails or the flashlight dies. If it is properly made, the candle remains a simple, reliable and elegant piece of equipment, both fuel and support for the flame it provides. Fifteen years ago, candles shaped like Buddhas, toadstools, frogs and bad dreams sputtered and died in legions as overtaxed wicks drowned in neon-coloured wax. The candle market is only now recovering, as once-burned buyers search for plain, attractive candles that produce a clean, steady flame.

Such candles can be made at home quite easily, too, and for about a tenth of the cost of dollar-and-a-half commercial tapers. And, as Catharine Parr Traill wrote in mid-19th-century Upper Canada: "There is no mystery and not much skill required in making candles." The simplest type, rolled beeswax, requires only wax and wicking, while the best quality moulded candles demand those two basics as well as a few pieces of equipment available in most kitchens.

Most of Traill's candles were made of tallow, the rendered (melted and strained) fat of cattle or sheep. The fat from bear, moose, deer and elk was preferred to the fat from pigs, which was too soft for good candles. Cheap and usually available in the country home, tallow produced relatively soft, slightly sticky candles that bent in hot weather, produced a smoky, intermittent flame and might turn rancid or be eaten by mice if improperly stored. Traill also referred to "the strong smell which newly made candles, especially if not made of pure tallow, are apt to emit." Nevertheless, tallow candles were considerably superior to the pioneer's most inexpensive lighting alternatives, among them what one settler termed "such candles as the Indians commonly use," splinters of pine fixed into holders or chinks in the wall and lit to then drip pitch while providing a few minutes of odorous, smoky glow. More capable of utilizing pig fat was the Dutch, grease, or betty lamp, a metal dish filled with animal fat with a bit of rag for a wick. A Pennsylvania pioneer wrote that in 1841, such a lamp "smoked and gave a dismal light, yet women cooked, spun and sewed, and men read the few books they had as best they could. The aroma from this refuse grease was simply horrible." The eulachon, or candlefish, of the west coast, so rich in oil it could simply be stuffed with a wick and lit, must

The Bettmann Archive, Inc.

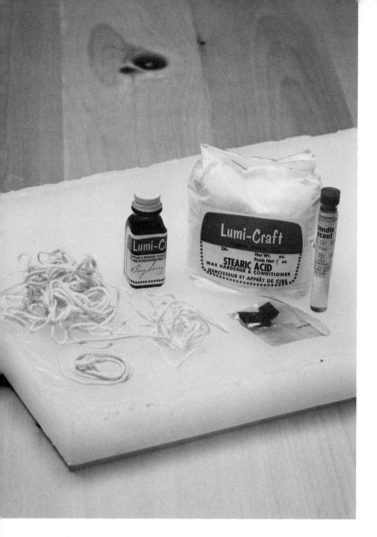

have been similarly pungent.

But not all early candles were so flawed. Bayberry was a sweet-smelling alternative to animal fat but was only locally available (see "Burning Bushes"). Beeswax, which produced beautiful, sweet-smelling candles, was available wherever bee hives were plundered or tended, but the wax was a precious commodity, to be bartered or sold for articles beekeepers needed more urgently than quality candles. While Roman Catholic churches burned beeswax, the common householder was more likely to opt for simple rushlights, common rushes peeled and dipped in animal fat, then set on an angle in special holders and burned.

Until the 18th century, almost all candlelight was provided by tallow and beeswax. At that time, a new use was found for the already beleaguered sperm whale. From the head of the whale came an oil which excited chandlers such as the one in Boston who said that spermaceti candles exceeded "all others for Beauty; Sweetness of Scent when extinguished; Duration, being more than double Tallow Candles of equal size; Dimension of Flame, nearly four Times more, emitting a fast easy expanding Light. . . ." In the 1830s, stearic acid further improved candles. A purified form of tallow that acts primarily as a hardener of other materials, stearic acid, or stearine, is still commonly used today, its main drawbacks being that it will eventually yellow, that it produces a chalky, cloudy finish and must be used in quantities as large as one part stearic acid to two parts paraffin. Commercial candle

producers now usually use plastic hardeners such as lustre crystals, only a teaspoon of which will treat two pounds of wax without the danger of future yellowing.

Paraffin, a petroleum product, was introduced in the 1860s. Though the first paraffin had a very low melting point, about 120 degrees F, several grades with differing melting points were soon available. Today, the hardest will melt at about 162 degrees. Cheap, translucent, clean burning, odourless and easy to work with, paraffin is still the material of choice for most candle makers — though it is very seldom used without some sort of hardening additive and dye.

BEESWAX

Beeswax, too, is seldom used alone, although for different reasons. At about three to ten times the price of paraffin, it is expensive. Also it will not take to being moulded unless mixed with other ingredients. This is the reason that high-proportion beeswax candles are usually dipped or rolled. One Ontario candle maker, William Nelson, maintains that the perfect candle consists of 51 percent beeswax, 10 percent stearic acid — less than 10 percent can produce a mottled candle — and 39 percent paraffin. Hobby chandlers Joanna and Ankaret Dean find that 10 percent beeswax is enough to give a candle its characteristic sweet smell without costing too much, while more than 51 percent produces a candle that is tacky and therefore difficult to remove from a mould.

Most of the beeswax available for candles comes from cappings that beekeepers must scrape off the comb before its honey can be extracted, though a darker wax can be obtained from inside the combs. John Craighead of F.W. Jones & Sons beekeeping supplies in Bedford, Quebec, points out that cappings wax is light because it is renewed every year, while "wax from the comb can be quite dark because the same wax is used year after year — the honey is extracted, and then the comb is put back into the hive." Comb wax can vary from dark brown to butterscotch coloured, while cappings wax is usually white or pale yellow. Either can be made into candles, although dark wax is more likely to contain wick-clogging impurities, and as a result, often produces a lower quality candle. In any case, all adhering honey must be removed from the wax before it can be used.

Small-scale beekeepers who wish to save their wax can uncap the comb over a tub that drains at one end. In a warm room, most of the honey will have drained off the wax in about 24 hours. The result is crude wax, for which a beekeeper usually receives about two dollars a pound. More efficient honey removal methods call for pressing the cappings or processing them in a centrifuge. The cappings are then rendered in a stain-less steel, aluminum or ceramic pot — copper, iron, zinc or brass may discolour the wax — to remove any remaining impurities. Small amounts of wax can be rendered on the stove in a pot about a quarter full of water. As the wax melts, the honey and solids will dissolve or sink to the bottom of the floating wax layer. The melted wax is then decanted off, ladled into containers or left to cool and harden in the pot, after which the bottom of the wax is scraped clean before it is processed further. Often, the wax for candles is chemically bleached. Beekeepers usually receive about four dollars a pound for rendered wax. Because purified bleached beeswax sells for about one dollar an ounce in hobby supply shops, it can be well worth the chandler's trouble to try to buy crude or rendered wax directly from a beekeeper.

Beeswax is also sold in sheets that are basically the same as the foundations used by beekeepers. They are simply rolled up for candles. Rolled beeswax candles are elegant and unusual, yet very easily made at home. Purchase sheets of white or coloured wax from a hobby shop or bee supplier. One sheet of about 8" x 16" will produce four tapers 8 inches tall at a cost of about 75 cents from a bee supplier or three dollars from a hobby shop. Cut the sheet of wax crosswise into two equal pieces by putting it on a breadboard, placing a ruler against the line to be cut and pressing along the line with a sharp knife. Now cut each half diagonally. 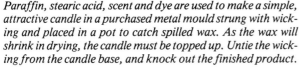 Place a piece of 9-inch-long, square braided wick (we used size 40) on one triangle a quarter inch from the

*Left, sheets of beeswax can be left whole or cut into triangles and rolled into straight or tapered candles. **Right**, a juice can in boiling water holds a beeswax mixture for dipped tapers. The candle pair in the foreground has been dipped 45 times.*

longest edge of the L and parallel to it so that the wick meets the bottom corner (the right angle) and extends beyond the top. The wick now looks like a flagpole, with the piece of wax a pennant. Using the warmth of your hands to soften the wax, and to prevent it from cracking, work very gradually and gently up and down the edge of the pennant, pushing the wax up against the length of the wick and over it, then slowly and carefully rolling the wax around the wick, always moving back and forth. The tighter the candle is rolled, the better it will burn. As the candle becomes fatter and the wax pennant narrower, it will become easier to roll. Finally, press the spiralled wax edges in toward the candle, or flute them slightly outward.

Many other candle shapes are possible with rolled beeswax. Depending upon the dimensions of the triangle and the way it is rolled, tapers may be tall and thin or short and fat. Rolled candles can also be straight — simply roll a square or rectangle of wax from one end to the other.

The wick size in a rolled taper is of necessity a compromise — the top of the candle is very thin, the bottom thick, and yet the wick is the same size at both ends. The candle will then likely burn slightly better at one point than another, because, in general, larger candles take fatter wicking than more slender candles.

To understand why, one must have some understanding of the workings of a candle. Once lit, it first burns the wick alone, but then the wax beneath the flame melts and is drawn up the wick by capillary action. The melted wax evaporates at the tip, producing vapour, the fuel for the flame that melts the wax, thus continuing the process. A properly sized wick will burn all the melted wax as quickly as it accumulates. As Martha Henniger, owner of Cascade Candles of Inverary, Ontario, says, "What has to happen is that there has to be a balance between wick size, hardness of wax and size of candle."

WICKING POSSIBILITIES

The wick provides one point of that three-cornered balance. Early home chandlers used almost any available material for wicking, including yarn or flax, but anyone who could purchase cotton wicking did so. It is treated for proper burning and costs little — only about 10 to 15 cents a yard for a minimum order of plain, braided wick. However, in a pinch, cotton yarn can be used, but it should first be soaked overnight in a solution of two tablespoons of borax and one teaspoon of salt in a cup of water, then dried. Commercial wicking is now available in three basic types; flat braided, square braided and with a core of metal or paper.

Flat-braided and metal-cored wicks are graded by the number of strands of cotton in the three-strand braid, with a higher number indicating a thicker wick. Flat-braided wicking bends to one side as it burns, producing an off-centre flame that is advantageous in some candles as it makes the burning process more efficient. Flat-braided wicking is, then, used in the majority of candles. Use a small size of wick (less than 30 ply) in candles between 1 and 2 inches, medium (about 30) in candles of 2 to 4 inches and large in those of 4 inches or more. However, all the tapers, egg-sized and teardrop-shaped models produced by Cascade Candles use number 36 flat wicking. Paper-cored and metal-cored wicking is used in container candles (including sand candles), unevenly shaped moulded candles or very large candles, where it can hold the flame upright should there be a pool of wax.

Square-braided wicking, whose sizing is complex — the smaller sizes receive a double number — does not bend as it burns, an advantage in very slender candles where an off-centre flame would burn away one side of the candle. Most candle suppliers simply label wicking as small, medium and large.

There are no rigid rules about candle size and wick size because, as Henniger says, there is a third factor involved, wax hardness. Harder wax makes the total fuel supply disappear more slowly, as would also happen if the candle were larger. Thus smoking, often a symptom of too large a wick for the size of candle, can also be caused by wax that is too soft. Either a smaller wick or a harder wax or a larger candle or a combination of all three should stop the smoking in later efforts. Dripping, or a very small flame, on the other hand, can be caused by wicking that is too small or wax that is too hard (i.e. too much stearic acid in the wax). An undersized wick melts the wax only in the candle centre. Dripping, if it is not intentional, is most common with large candles because most wicking is not large enough to burn all the wax produced by a candle more than a couple of inches across. Guttering, uneven burning, and dripping can be produced by an off-centre wick or the use of a flat-braided wick in a very slender candle. Henniger says, "The burning can be affected even by the air current in a room — it can burn perfectly in one room and smoke and drip in another."

A sputtering flame may be caused by impurities in the wick or wax, or by a wet wick. Wicking should either be stored dry until it is used or, better yet, prewaxed in a little melted paraffin before it is used. Lay it on wax paper to dry.

In preparing wicking, and indeed at almost all times, wax should be melted over water, as it is a flammable material that ignites at a temperature of about 400 degrees F and must never be poured over an open flame or stove. Over boiling water, however, it cannot heat beyond 212 degrees, hot enough for almost all uses (although one exception is described later). Candle wax is, in fact, usually poured within a temperature range of 160 to 195 degrees F, which can be measured with a candy thermometer. Alternatively, it should be at about the right temperature when, after first melting, it has heated for an additional 10 minutes over boiling water.

Caution is needed in other respects, too. Joanna and Ankaret Dean report that they melt their wax in a can over water and keep a box of baking soda handy should it catch fire. And, they note, "In one foolish moment, we poured hot beeswax into a plastic container in the sink. The container melted, and the beeswax wended its way from the sink through almost the entire plumbing system, where it cooled and hardened. We spent a terrible afternoon pulling it out of the pipes."

Because wax adheres to most surfaces and can be difficult to remove, it is best to use old or discardable pots for melting it — tin cans or aluminum frozen dessert containers work well in most instances. Press one edge into a spout for easy pouring. Wear old clothing, keep a potholder and baking soda handy, and if the wax does splatter, scrape it off cloth or hard surfaces with a knife. Waxy cloth can then be placed between two sheets of paper towel and pressed with a hot iron, after which a few washings should remove any remaining stain. Send unwashable fabric to be dry-cleaned. If hot wax splashes on the skin, harden it under cold water, scrape off the wax and wash with warm, soapy water. Good pots or thermometers can be cleaned by being heated just until the wax melts, wiped with paper towelling and then washed in hot water.

Wax is sold in blocks, chunks, flakes or, in the case of some beeswax, in sheets, usually by the pound, costing about a dollar a pound for paraffin. A candle three inches wide and six inches tall will require about a pound and a half of wax; a taper eight inches tall only about two ounces — so the latter can be made with about 12 cents worth of paraffin and a few cents worth of wicking and additives. Break up the wax with a hammer before placing it in the pot or can with any hardening additives that will be used. Use only those dyes (liquid, solid or powder) made for candles, not crayons, lipstick or food colourings that contain wick-clogging substances. Dyes and oil-based scents are added to the wax just before it is poured.

SAND-CAST CANDLES

Although sand candles are a good project for the beginner, who then need not worry about kitchen messes or preparing and cleaning moulds, they are among the easiest candles to make poorly and the most difficult to make well. However, the result can be an attractive, rustic candle that is well suited to picnics and porches. Sand candles are made directly in sand — in a bucket, at a quiet beach or in a sandpile. Plan for the entire operation to take several hours. Use a hot plate for the backyard sandpile, a Coleman stove or a small fire at the beach, and bring a candy thermometer, an old pot (not a can), a supply of large wire-cored wicking (we used size 60), a small trowel or spoon and the wax mix of your choice — perhaps the stearic acid, beeswax and paraffin mixture, favoured by William Nelson or perhaps a pound of paraffin and three tablespoons of stearic acid.

Because the best sand candles require wax heated above the boiling point of water, a double boiler will not be necessary. The hotter the wax, the thicker the sand coating on the candle will be, with 250 degrees F the hottest that one will need, producing a heavy crust

While sand candles are a good project for the beginner, they are among the easiest candles to make poorly and the most difficult to make well.

that resembles ceramic. At 150 degrees, there would be little or no sand adhering to the candle, and temperatures between 150 and 250 degrees produce varying thicknesses of coating. Place the wax mixture in the pot on the fire, hook the thermometer over the pot side, and begin stirring and melting the wax. Keeping an eye on the thermometer, prepare the moulds as the wax melts.

Use damp sand for the mould; dry sand cannot be shaped and also absorbs a good deal of wax. There are two ways to make sand candles: upside down or right side up. The former produces something of a mound-shaped candle with sand on the top, while the latter, whose preparation is described, can produce a more attractive candle that burns better because it is sandy only on the base and sides.

With a spoon or trowel, dig a hole — the mould — in the damp sand. The challenge here is to produce a flat bottom and sides that are relatively straight, rather than sloping outward toward the top. With a little practice, using a tin can or drinking cup as a press, a fairly flat bottom can be made, and the base can always be pared down later if necessary. The formation of three or four legs with fingertip or stick produces an attractive base that, again with the help of a little trimming after removing the candle, can be quite stable.

Once the mould is made, cut a piece of wicking a couple of inches longer than the depth of the mould,

and insert it into the sand at the centre of the base of the mould so that it stands upright. If it tends to fall to one side, support it with a stick laid over the mould top. Fill the mould with hot wax, and allow it to set. Stand back while pouring, as the hot wax will spatter as it contacts the wet, cooler sand. The candle will set more quickly if it is shaded from the sun but may, nevertheless, take several hours to harden. When it is ready for removal, the candle will have shrunk considerably around the wick — paraffin shrinks as much as 10 percent in cooling. Rather than topping it up now, carefully remove the candle by digging down beside it, prying it out and brushing off as much loose sand as possible. Snip or burn off any wick that extends from the base. At home, trim the bottom of the candle so that it stands level, melt a little wax over a pot of water on the stove, top up the candle and let it stand until set. Add more wax if necessary. When the surface is level and cool, snip off the wick to within a half inch of the wax.

Sand candle moulds have two big advantages: economy and flexibility. Every candle will look different from every other at no cost to the chandler. But this can also be a disadvantage should one want an even, symmetrical candle or a set of matching candles. Virtually all commercial candles are now made in moulds, the hardened wax removed by a piston arrangement that presses out the candle. Early candle moulds made of tin or pewter were often sold in clusters so that a matching set of candles could be poured all at once. Now, there are commerical moulds of plastic, glass or metal to fashion almost every imaginable shape of candle. They are fairly expensive, about two to ten dollars apiece, and once you have bought a mould, you will be able to make only one shape of candle with it. But commercial moulds produce a shiny finish and are easy to work with, and you will still be able to experiment with materials, colours and scents.

However, there are many containers in the home that can be used as candle moulds: muffin tins, mailing tubes, milk cartons, plastic dairy containers and cans. Whatever the mould, first wash it thoroughly, and coat the inside with vegetable oil. If practical, punch a small hole in the centre of the base of the mould. Thread a piece of wicking up through the bottom of the mould, and tie it to a pencil that rests across the top of the mould. To hold the wick securely at the base, insert a nail or screw into the base hole, and wrap the wick around the nail, then secure both wick and nail in place with masking tape or mould sealer to prevent wax leakage. Alternatively, the wick can be attached without a hole. Metal-core wicking can be fashioned into a spiral at one end and placed in the centre of the inside base. A soft wick can be tied to and held down with a wick weight or washer. In either case, the wick is attached to the centre of the base with a little wax and held at the top by a pencil. If using a cardboard mould, cover all seams with masking tape, and wind tape around the top, middle and bottom as reinforcement. Do not pour wax hotter than 160 degrees F into cardboard or plastic containers. In other moulds, the wax can be poured at 180 to 200 degrees.

Place the mould on some newspapers and then pour the wax in slowly so that no air bubbles form. Allow the wax to cool at room temperature, which will take several hours. When a well begins to form around the wick, poke deeply into the top of the wax with a wire or stick to release any air bubbles. Without allowing it to overflow the edges of the original pouring, pour more wax into the depression, and allow it to harden. Repeat as many times as necessary to produce a flat surface.

When the candle is cold — leave it overnight to be sure — remove it by untying the wick from the outside of the mould base and turning it upside down. If the candle does not drop out readily, tap the mould gently or place it in the refrigerator for a half-hour before trying to remove it. A mould that still will not release the candle can be doused with hot water, which will loosen the candle but will also soften it and mar the finish.

DIPPED TAPERS

Some of the most elegant candles today are those that have been dipped, a process that, by its nature, produces a candle that tapers outward toward the bottom. Tapers have been in use for a very long time and were the most common candles of pioneers who could not afford moulds. Though basically easy to make, they are time consuming and require the use of a pot at least an inch deeper than the desired length of the candle and plenty of wax — the supply has to be kept topped up even as the candles increase in size.

Virtually any wax can be used, even pure beeswax. Barbara Singleton, who demonstrates candle dipping at Allan Macpherson House in Napanee, Ontario, uses a mixture of 2½ pounds of tallow, a cake of camphor (to ward off mice), a tablespoon of alum (a hardener) and an egg-sized lump of beeswax.

To make dipped tapers, loop lengths of small-sized wicking about a foot longer than the length of two candles over a board wide enough to keep the candles separated by two or three inches, with each pair separated by two inches along the length of the board. Heat the wax as usual, and dip the hanging lengths of wick in the wax to the depth of the desired length of candle for about five seconds. The board is then suspended between two chairs for the adhering wax to cool, while excess wax drips onto newspapers (or, for the pioneers, pieces of kindling). When the wax layer is cool, the process is repeated. Dipping time and wax temperature are critical, with the best temperature usually in the range of 160 to 170 degrees F. If the wax is too hot, previously accumulated layers will melt away; if too cool, the new layers will be lumpy. Expect about 40 dips to produce a candle something less than an inch across at the base.

An alternative way to make tapers, also practised by the pioneers, circumvents the need for a very deep pot and large supply of wax. Hot wax is poured from a pitcher over the wicks into a waiting pot, the wax again accumulating in layers. This method makes the production of a fairly even candle more difficult. With either process, after the first few layers have collected, the candles are straightened by hand, and when finished, their bases are snipped off straight. These candles will, however, always be slightly uneven, one of the charms, to the modern eye, of these rustic reminders of the rigours and pleasures of life Before Hydro. ∎

Sources

LEWISCRAFT
40 Commander Blvd.
Scarborough, Ontario M1S 3S2
Lewiscraft operates retail stores from Alberta to Ontario, as well as a mail-order service selling a full line of craft supplies. Candle-making equipment includes chunk, slab and shredded wax, books, stearic acid, lustre crystals, dyes, scents, six sizes of wicking and two pages of moulds. Minimum order $10. Catalogue free.

F.W. JONES & SONS LTD.
44 Dutch St.
Bedford, Quebec J0J 1A0
As well as a full range of beekeeping supplies, Jones sells beeswax sheets for rolled candles, 24-ply and 30-ply wicking and two books on candle making. Catalogue free.

POURETTE MANUFACTURING CO.
6910 Roosevelt Way N.E.
Box 15220
Seattle, Washington 98115
An extensive, 60-page listing of moulds and other equipment, including 13 sizes of wicking, beeswax sheets, waxes by the pound. Catalogue $1.00 (U.S.) refundable on the first order over $5.00.

BENSON BEE SUPPLIES
Box 9
Metcalfe, Ontario K0A 2P0
(613) 821-2797
Source of beeswax for rolled candles. Also an extensive line of other beekeeping supplies.

HODGSON BEE SUPPLIES LTD.
Box 297
New Westminster, British Columbia V3L 4Y6
(604) 521-2606
Has been giving excellent service to B.C. apiarists for over 45 years. Beeswax for rolled candles in a wide range of colours. Catalogue free.

LUMI-CRAFT
Box 666
Kingston, Ontario
Wholesale and retail manufacturers and distributors of craft and candle supplies, including 26 pages of moulds. Catalogue $2.00.

WESTERN HANDICRAFT SUPPLIES
292 Vaughan St.
Winnipeg, Manitoba R3B 2N8
Craft and candle supplies including wax, stearic acid, wicking, dyes and moulds. Catalogue $4.00.

For Wholesalers:

FRANK B. ROSS CO., INC.
Jersey City, New Jersey 07304
Canadian warehouse and agent:
HARRISONS AND CROSFIELD (CANADA) LTD.
Toronto, Ontario M4H 1G1
Natural and synthetic waxes, ten pounds or more. Includes paraffins in five melting temperatures, stearic acid, wax whitener, bayberry wax. Catalogue free.

Burning Bushes

Botanical candle wax and ornamental bonuses from bayberry

Moulded from petroleum-based waxes and plastics, synthetically perfumed and dyed, what passes for a bayberry candle today bears scarcely a glimmer of resemblance to its historical namesake — a candle made from the clean-burning, pale green, fragrant wax of berries that still grow throughout parts of North America. Moreover, the bayberry or wax myrtle family includes sweet-smelling plants that grow continent-wide and have medicinal, culinary and decorative uses as well. It was so versatile that in 1861, the bayberry (now almost forgotten) was called "one of the most valuable [plants] of this or any other country" by American physician John D. Gunn.

However, just two North American species were used in pioneer candlemaking. The task required a waxlike, fatty substance found only on the berries of the northern bayberry, *Myrica pensylvanica* (or *M. carolinensis*), and the southern bayberry, *Myrica cerifera*. The wax includes a high proportion of palmitic acid, also found in the oil of palm trees and sperm whales. When bayberries are boiled, this wax rises to the surface of the water. The 18th-century Jesuit missionary Sébastien Rale sent bayberries and their wax from the Atlantic coast to Quebec, where, he stated, the wax "was pronounced excellent." He wrote further: "I have no need to economize in wax, for this country furnishes me with abundance. The islands of the sea are bordered with wild laurel, which in autumn bears berries closely resembling those of the juniper-tree. Large kettles are filled with them and they are boiled

in water; as the water boils, the green wax rises and remains on the surface of the water . . . it is very pure and very fine, but is neither soft nor pliable. After a few experiments, I have found that by mixing it with equal quantities of tallow — either beef, mutton or elk — the mixture makes beautiful, solid and very serviceable candles."

Wyman's Garden Encyclopedia estimates that 1½ quarts of berries will produce a single, eight-inch candle, while Maude Grieve noted in *A Modern Herbal* that four pounds of berries produced about a third of a pound of wax. What Rale did not mention was that pioneers gathered the berries about the time of the first fall frost, when their wax content was highest and their colour was greyish-white. The dark, opaque wax that rose to the surface of the water was skimmed off and reboiled so that the impurities settled out, leaving a transparent green wax that might be kept melted in a pot by the fireside, ready for dipping; or poured into moulds by housewives fortunate enough to have had the time-saving devices.

Bayberry wax must have seemed a godsend. It could be used in soapmaking, where it was substituted for the animal fats normally used and produced a soap one traveller judged "the best for shaving." It was not only free for the taking, but also made candles that did not melt as quickly as tallow and were, moreover, more attractive and better smelling. But its candles produced only a small flame and were very brittle, so it was often combined with softer materials such as tallow, as Rale noted, or beeswax. One 18th-century journalist noted that *M. pensylvanica* wax was "not so valuable as beeswax being of a more brittle nature, but mixed with it makes a good candle which as it burns sends forth an agreeable scent." Virginia's Robert Beverley said of such mixed candles: "If an accident puts a candle out, it yields a pleasant fragrancy to all that are in the room; insomuch that nice people often put them out on purpose to have the incense of the expiring snuff."

But wax was not the bayberry's only attribute. As well, the leaves and berries of bayberry and the leaves and twigs of *Myrica gale* can be used in dyeing. Karen Leigh Casselman's *Craft of the Dyer* (University of Toronto Press, 1980) includes excellent instructions for the use of *M. pensylvanica* and *M. gale* in dyeing. Powdered bayberry root bark from *M. cerifera* or *pensylvanica* had many medicinal uses: externally applied as a poultice on skin ulcers and wounds, used as a snuff for nasal congestion or prepared as a tea for dysentery and for gargling. A scientific study published in 1976, however, indicated that tannins of *M. cerifera* root bark extracts injected into rats over a period of 78 weeks "produced a significant amount of tumours." Root bark medicines are, then, best left to the history books.

However, no danger has been ascribed to bayberry leaves, which are high in vitamin C and can be steeped into a tea or used as a substitute for bay laurel leaves in cooking. In *Stalking the Faraway Places*, Euell Gibbons said that the fresh leaves were especially good steamed with seafood, "and they make a fragrant, delicious tea that can perk up a meal no end."

The northern bayberry, *M. pensylvanica*, is the most northerly of the berry producers and attains a height of about five feet in thickets along the seashore from southern Newfoundland to Texas. Because it is a very attractive landscaping plant, however, with shiny green leaves, greyish bark and clusters of grey fruit, its range has spread somewhat. It has been found to be hardy as far north as U.S. zone 4, which extends as far as the northern shores of the Great Lakes and to southeastern British Columbia and southern Alberta. But, says Leon C. Snyder of the University of Winnipeg, in zone 4, "some dieback can occur after a severe winter."

Liles Bellam of Ontario's John Connor Nurseries says that bayberry is a fairly recent introduction to Canada as an ornamental but that it is considered to be "extremely hardy" and disease free. It grows even in heavy, clay soils, although it will produce suckers and form a thicket only in the light, sandy soil of its seashore habitats. It should be treated like a blueberry, says Bellam, as it requires acidic soil. Alkaline or neutral soils should be spot treated with sulphur compounds (available in garden supply stores) to lower the pH to between 5 and 6. The plants are sold when they are about a foot tall and are already fruiting. Like most Myricaceae, they are dioecious, with male and female flowers on separate plants, so anyone who wishes to collect berries from cultivated plants must purchase at least two plants, a male and a female, only the latter of which will produce berries.

The wax myrtle or southern bayberry, *M. cerifera* (which means wax bearing), is taller, at 10 to 30 feet,

E.J. Revell/From 'and some brought flowers': Plants in a New World, by Mary Alice Downie and Mary Hamilton, by permission of University of Toronto Press, 1980.

Producing a high quality, sweetly scented wax that can be used to make candles and soaps, the fruit of the bayberry, Myrica pensylvanica, *contains palmitic acid, a constituent also of palm oil and sperm whale oil.*

and inhabits a more southerly region, from New Jersey and Michigan to Florida and Texas, while the California bayberry or Pacific wax myrtle, *M. californica*, grows from California to Vancouver Island. Sunset Magazine's *Western Garden Book* of 1954 recommends *M. californica* in coastal landscaping, calling it "a very clean, striking plant of upright, naturally bushy growth." Tall and evergreen, it produces purple berries covered with grey wax. The non-wax-bearing sweet gale, *M. gale*, inhabits tidal flats, swamps and bogs from Alaska to Newfoundland, where it is often one of spring's earliest blooming plants, its flowers appearing before the foliage, both of which are fragrant. Catharine Parr Traill, observer and recorder of human and plant life in 19th-century Upper Canada, wrote that sweet gale "sends out its sweetness on the desert air — just for itself and God."

But its sweetness, like that of the other Myricaceae, has also been appreciated by mankind. If the leaves, twigs or berries of any of the family members are pressed, a distinctive smell that Traill described as "evanescent" and "somewhat like the flavour of freshly-ground nutmeg" is released. That scent, quite distinctive and memorable, is the easiest way to identify members of the bayberry family.

Sweet gale has been used to scent clothes closets and to flavour beer. And, in *Edible Wild Plants of Eastern North America* (Idlewide, 1943), authors Fernand and Kinsey wrote that "the nutlets of sweet gale have been used in France and certainly should be used elsewhere as an aromatic spice, having a delicious fragrance suggestive of sage. The leaves, when cured, make a delicate and palatable tea and are much in repute in country districts in northern Maine (under the name 'Meadow fern') as a cure for colds and catarrh, popular with the children if not always efficacious."

Catharine Parr Traill also praised sweet gale in her 1885 book, *Studies of Plant Life in Canada*. The bush was, she said, "not quite overlooked by the native Indians, and by some of the old inhabitants of the back country, who use the leaves in some of their home-made diet drinks and in infusions for purifying the blood. As the luxuries of civilization sweep in among the settlers," she added disapprovingly, "they abandon the uses of many of the medicinal herbs that formerly supplied the place of drugs from stores."

Indeed, scientific sophistication invaded the uses of the bayberry family on all fronts. It was not the brittleness of bayberry wax, but the sheer amount of labour involved in gathering masses of berries and boiling the wax twice that ended the use of bayberry candles as soon as cheap, plentiful, brighter-burning materials such as spermaceti and paraffin became available. Bayberry was even less desirable when candle making moved from the kitchen, where inefficient production was permissible, to the factory, where it was unprofitable. The coastal habitat of the bayberry, too, was increasingly cleared and developed, decreasing the berry supply.

Now, those few bayberry candles that do include bayberry wax almost exclusively employ the product of South American plants, whose berries have a higher proportion of wax and are therefore more profitable to use. Colonial Candle of Cape Cod, one of the United States' largest candle manufacturers whose original product was a bayberry candle from local Massachusetts berries, has recently begun making real bayberry candles again, this time exclusively for Colonial Williamsburg, a pioneer showplace in Virginia. But the wax is imported from Colombia where, according to Mary Theobold of Colonial Williamsburg, changing markets are again shouldering out the bayberry. "It's more profitable to grow illegal drugs than to grow bayberries," says Theobold, "so we had some trouble getting hold of it."

— *JB*

Sources

While there are no Canadian mail-order sources of bayberry bushes, plants are available through some retail and wholesale outlets, and a local nursery may be willing to order plants from them for a customer. Both Sheridan Nurseries of Etobicoke, Ontario, and John Connor Nurseries of Waterdown, Ontario, ship plants to nurseries throughout Ontario and Quebec; Milligan Brothers Ltd. of Waverley, Nova Scotia, also operates outlets in Dartmouth and Halifax.

DUTCH MOUNTAIN NURSERY
7984 North 48th Street, Rt. 1
Augusta, Michigan 49012
Myrica pensylvanica to U.S. addresses or to Canadian customers who have an importation permit from Agriculture Canada. Catalogue 50 cents.

MELLINGER'S
2310 West South Range Road
North Lima, Ohio 44452
(216) 549-9861
Myrica cerifera and *M. pensylvanica* plants to U.S. addresses only. Catalogue free.

A WORLD SEED SERVICE
Box 1058
Redwood City, California 94064
Myrica pensylvanica. Catalogue $1.00.

RICHTERS
Goodwood, Ontario L0C 1A0
(416) 640-6677
Myrica pensylvanica. Catalogue $2.00.

The Harvest Cellar

Putting down roots: A guide to building and stocking the winter larder

By Michael Webster

Robert Kaufman

"We visited, some time ago, the residence of a friend who had given as much attention to the finishing and arranging of his cellar as to that of any other part of his house. It was more worthy of a visit than the finest drawing-rooms with rosewood furniture and Wilton carpets. In the first place, the walls were built in the smoothest and most substantial manner; the floors were covered with the best water-lime cement, now as hard as flagging, and as smooth as planed boards; the cellar was divided into apartments, one for vegetables, another for fruit, another still for provisions, a fourth for the dairy, and a fifth for coal and furnace — for the cellar extended under the whole house, kitchen and all. In the vegetable apartment, bins were made in the middle, so as to have a passage around them, and in these bins, the vegetables were placed, some with only a cover, and others packed in sand, or in moss. Nearly dry and fine moss was preferred to anything else for packing beets, turnips, parsnips and cabbages. The bins were not made of rough boards, as generally seen, but were planed and painted, and the whole presented the neatest appearance. The fruit shelves were, in a similar manner, made of planed and painted material, with a passage all around them, both for ventilation and to allow the attendant to assort them frequently.

The partitions between the different apartments were brick walls, and each one was easily accessible, both from the outside large door and from the kitchen."

— J.J. Thomas
Illustrated Annual Register of Rural Affairs
1861-1863

In contrast, most rural homes of a century ago sat over cellars that were dank and forbidding, little more than rudimentary holes in the ground, with thick stone walls, earthen floors and a permanently damp atmosphere. They were unheated — cool in summer, but cold in winter — and dark and draughty in all seasons. In short, they were ideal for their primary use, the storage of root crops. The word cellar, in fact, derives from the Latin *cellarium*, meaning "storehouse," and Thoreau, with his keen eye for ostentation, took obvious pleasure in noting that "under the most splendid house in the city is still to be found the cellar where they store their roots as of old."

Things have changed today, and the modern basement is seldom built with harvest storage in mind. Well-lit, relatively dry and comfortably warm in winter, it has a basement recreation area and the overall environment is better suited to the needs of a Silicon Valley Apple than a peck of *Granny Smiths*. Nevertheless, those gardeners willing to set aside a corner of their basements to serve as a vegetable larder can, with relatively little effort or expenditure, recreate the conditions of the old-fashioned cellar that did the job so well.

Cellars, of course, were not always under the house; historically, outdoor root cellars were more common. "I dug my cellar in the side of a hill sloping to the south," reports Thoreau, "where a woodchuck had formerly dug his burrow, down through sumac and blackberry roots and the lowest stain of vegetation to a fine sand where potatoes would not freeze in any weather." The most elementary outside storage facility is a clamp — a pyramidal mound of roots covered with straw and then earth, with an insulated vent created by leaving a shock of straw poking through the dirt. Poor insulation renders clamps ineffective throughout most of Canada, but other outdoor facilities including boxes, crates, barrels, refrigerators and even old delivery-van bodies, buried or half buried in well-drained locations and fitted with double doors separated by a layer of insulation, have been used successfully. The major drawback to any outdoor cellar is simply that — it is outdoors, and fetching vegetables for the dinner table can involve getting bundled up like an Arctic explorer, wading through drifted snow and shovelling out the entrance to the buried storehouse before trudging back to the house with an armload of vegies. Convenience, if not history, dictates a cellar in the basement.

OPTIMUM CONDITIONS

Regardless of location or type of shelter, the most vital factor in the preservation of root crops is temperature. A root cellar should be kept as close to 32 degrees F as possible without going lower. The best way to accomplish this, excluding expensive refrigeration units, is by using the natural cooling of the earth and outside winter air. Hence there is a further emphasis on the importance of delaying harvest as long as possible, until air temperatures have dropped sufficiently to allow effective cooling of the storage area.

Nearly as important as temperature control is humidity. Even in storage, vegetables are living things, and as such, they continue to respire and age despite the retarding effect of cold temperatures. In the process, they lose moisture; in dry air, this is exaggerated so that the vegetables quickly become shrivelled and unappealing. Humidity can be provided by pouring water directly on the floor or into a large, shallow tray — a pail does not offer enough surface area — and should be kept at a constant level throughout the storage period.

Working against this ideal is yet another factor: ventilation. Good air circulation is important for removing odours, volatiles (like ethylene gas) and airborne bacteria as well as preventing the formation of mould. However, ventilation works at loggerheads with humidity control because the incoming cold air holds less moisture than that in the room, necessitating a constant infusion of moisture to hold the humidity steady. Furthermore, ventilation must be coordinated with temperature control — excessive fresh air in the dead of winter can freeze the vegetables, and in other seasons, it can raise temperatures beyond the limits of reasonable storage requirements.

A basement storage room should be situated to enclose one of the basement windows which can be converted to provide ventilation. Also a corner location (requiring the construction of only two walls instead of three) will cut costs substantially. The ideal site is a north-east corner, the juncture of the two coldest walls of the foundation. Although in some pioneer homes, the root cellar was a full-sized room, modern gardeners with freezer space available need not be so expansive. The harvest from even an ambitious and productive garden will fit in a modest storeroom — a 5' x 8' enclosure can easily hold 30 bushels of produce.

Construction begins with a curb at least four inches high under the proposed walls of the room to allow water to be kept on the storage-room floor without rotting the studwall or seeping into other parts of the basement. Materials include concrete poured in forms or bricks or blocks mortared in place; regardless, two anchor bolts should be installed in each curb to tie down the studwalls. For added strength, drill holes in the floor and cement the anchor bolts into the existing floor.

A wall of 2 x 4 studs is sufficient in all but the warmest of basements, where the extra insulation space afforded by 2 x 6s would be effective. Since the walls are not load-bearing, further savings can be achieved by placing the studs on 2-foot centres.

Particularly in fall and spring, temperature losses are hard to come by in a cool storage room, and they should be jealously protected. Walls need to be insulated against the invading warmth of the rest of the basement, using batt-type insulation. Similarly, the ceiling should be covered with batts or rigid board insulation, as much to protect the floor above from becoming cold as to prevent heat intrusion.

As well as retaining humidity within the storage room, a vapour barrier protects insulation from the condensation that forms where a cold surface meets warm air. Construction-grade polyethylene can be used, but do-it-yourselfers accustomed to stapling up plastic on the inside of buildings must prepare themselves for the shock of putting it on the *outside* of the room's insulation — above the ceiling insulation and on the basement side of the walls. Vapour barriers are intended to be on the warm side of insulation; it may help to think of the storage room as part of the outside environment.

Both sides of the walls should be sheathed with any of an assortment of materials, ranging from panelling or drywall through plywood to rough-cut lumber. In choosing a material, it is wise to bear convenience in mind as well as expense — difficult-to-clean cracks and joints can harbour decay-causing bacteria and should be kept at a minimum on the inside. Protect the vegetables and the insulation from each other by sheathing the ceiling as well.

Pioneer root cellars were entered, as they are still in many northern cabins, by a trapdoor in the kitchen floor, a method few owners of split-level bungalows will want to imitate. An insulated, conventional walk-through door is easily constructed by sandwiching a framework of 2 x 2s and rigid board insulation between two sheets of light plywood or other sheeting. Obviously, the door should be tight fitting and latched snugly. The room's window must be covered to prevent light from causing the produce to sprout.

With the room closed in and sealed against heat and

moisture losses, it is time to turn one's attention to a ventilation system. Ideally, cold air should be introduced near floor level, preventing the vegetables from being subjected to blasts of damaging below-freezing air. Furthermore, a low inlet provides a handy layering of temperatures, with cold-loving keepers like apples at floor level and potatoes, which prefer somewhat warmer temperatures, basking in the relative warmth of a top shelf. Incoming cold air may be routed to the floor through a pipe or a duct made of metal or wood and fitted with an adjustable closure.

The outlet duct should draw air from the ceiling area, thus setting up a circular flow pattern that will feed itself — cold air falls through the inlet duct, emerging at floor level and, drawing warmth from the contents of the room, rises slowly and then is pushed through the outlet by more incoming cold air, a sort of vegetarian thermosyphon. The two air ducts should total at least a square foot in cross section, and be tightly screened to prevent entry by marauding insects or rodents. The weakness in this system is in its regulation: the process may reverse itself when outside temperatures exceed those in the root cellar, warming the room instead of cooling it, or it may continue unabated in the bitterly cold weather of midwinter until the vegetables are frozen.

Measures to control the flow must be taken, ranging in complexity from the occasional stuffing of insulation in the ductwork to the installation of a louvred fan run by a dual-control differential thermostat. The

For best results, pears should be taken out of cold storage and held for several days before they are eaten.

choice is usually based on how much one is willing to pay for convenience, since without some form of automatic regulator, proper temperature control requires faithful manual operation. During fall and spring, it is often necessary to open the ducts every evening to let in the cool night air and close them in the morning as the outside temperature rises. Winter operation involves preventing the harvest from freezing in cold spells while still providing adequate ventilation. It may be necessary to open the storeroom door on occasion to warm the room enough to permit the addition of extremely cold ventilating air.

Many experts recommend installing a small (600 watt) electric heater wired through a thermostat to come on when the air temperature reaches about 33 degrees F, and certainly a thermostat connected to a warning light or buzzer in the kitchen is invaluable. There are few chores as heart-breaking as emptying a storeroom of the results of months of hard work turned to mush by a few days' forgetfulness. Whether manual or automatic controls are used, the goal of each is to maintain air temperature in the root cellar between 32 and 40 degrees.

Finally, proper ventilation relies on fresh air circulating around vegetables, not just in a narrow pattern near the vents. Slatted shelves and bins are effective aids in improving circulation, as is keeping the bottom

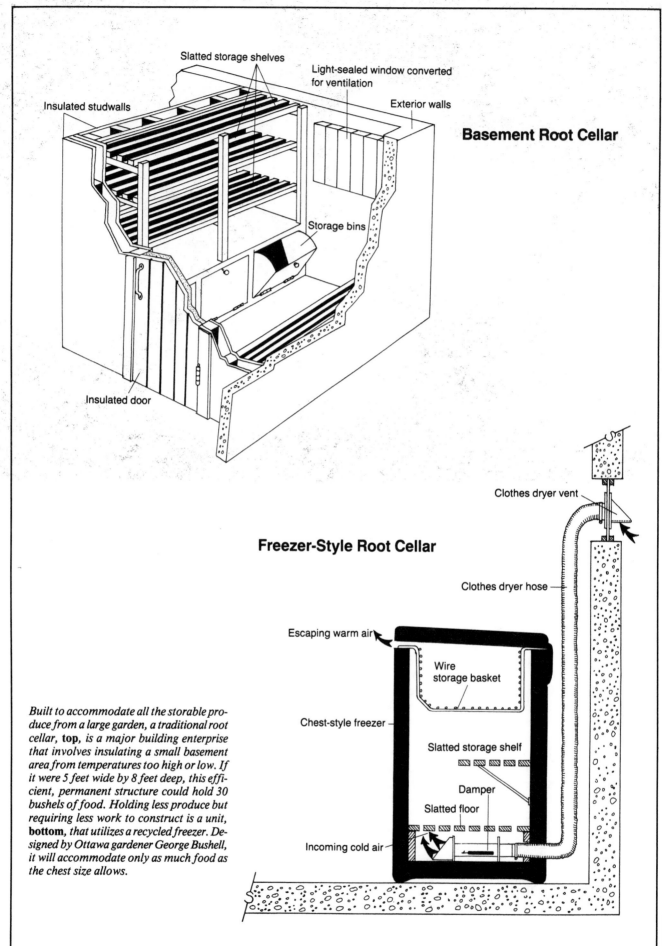

Slatted storage shelves

Light-sealed window converted
for ventilation

Exterior walls

Insulated studwalls

Basement Root Cellar

Storage bins

Insulated door

Clothes dryer vent

Freezer-Style Root Cellar

Clothes dryer hose

Escaping warm air

Wire
storage basket

Chest-style freezer

Slatted storage shelf

Damper

Slatted floor

Incoming cold air

*Built to accommodate all the storable pro-
duce from a large garden, a traditional root
cellar,* **top,** *is a major building enterprise
that involves insulating a small basement
area from temperatures too high or low. If
it were 5 feet wide by 8 feet deep, this efficient, permanent structure could hold 30
bushels of food. Holding less produce but
requiring less work to construct is a unit,*
bottom, *that utilizes a recycled freezer. Designed by Ottawa gardener George Bushell,
it will accommodate only as much food as
the chest size allows.*

David Stone

bin or shelf a good four inches off the ground — a technique that will also ease spring clean-up.

For all the simplicity of building a basement root cellar, one must still purchase a variety of lumber, insulation and other materials and have the time and skill to build the room and equip it with shelves, vents and a properly insulated door. "Faced with mounting fall harvest, unsatisfactory storage conditions and the unpleasant task of building a storage room," says George Bushell, an active Ottawa-area urban gardener, "I actively searched for a better approach, finally hitting upon the idea of using a discarded chest-type home freezer. They are well insulated, can be installed in a basement easily and are very inexpensive, if not free."

FREEZER VENTING

Indeed, appliance dealers often take freezers on trade, remove the compressors and discard the boxes, which are available for the hauling. Bushell brought home a 15-cubic-foot model in the back of his station wagon and, with the help of a neighbour, lugged it into his basement. "Without the heavy motor and compressor, two people can easily handle even a large home freezer," he says. "But, of course, the inside of a freezer, sitting in a corner of a warm basement is no better for storing produce than the basement itself — it must be cooled by outside air just as any cold room."

Opting to vent the chest with a flexible 4-inch clothes-dryer hose, Bushell cut a hole through the double wall of the freezer. "Making this hole turned out to be fairly awkward — the greatest difficulty, in fact, in the whole operation, though it took me only half an hour," he says. "I cut a hole in the outer wall first, using a jigsaw and steel blade and then, still from the outside, drilled ⅜" holes in the inner wall around the circumference of the 4-inch hole. It was then a simple matter to cut between the holes with a hacksaw, leaving a hole through both walls of the freezer." The vent hose was inserted in the hole and vented outside as if for a clothes dryer.

As with a root cellar, it is important to keep the vegetables above the level of the too-cold incoming air, so Bushell installed his vent as low as possible and improvised a slatted floor just above it. "Any small pieces of scrap lumber would do," he says, "but I used broken hockey sticks." He rescues them from the local arena, using them for garden stakes and in other projects requiring slender, sturdy lengths of hardwood. The wire baskets that came with the freezer were retained as second-storey storage units.

To achieve flow-through ventilation, Bushell left the top of the freezer open about an inch, allowing the relatively warm air at the top of the freezer to escape and be replaced by cooler air from the bottom. The humidity level was maintained by packing the root crops in moist peat moss in perforated plastic bags, but temperature control was another matter. "That first winter, I was kept very busy stuffing the vent pipe on cold days and opening it on milder ones," says Bushell, "and in spite of my best intentions, I forgot

to close the vent pipe on a few occasions when the weather turned rapidly colder, with the result that some of my fruits and vegetables were frozen."

By spring, he was searching for some form of automatic airflow control, an energy-free system that did not rely on thermostats or expensive fans. "During the summer, while visiting a friend's greenhouse," he says, "I noticed that the vents in the roof were opened and closed by a cylinder filled with a special heat-sensitive material. This got me thinking that perhaps something similar could be developed for my freezer." Getting together with some associates, Bushell produced a damper that would automatically stop the flow of air when the temperature in the bottom of the freezer fell to the freezing point. Two years of use have convinced him of the merit of his device, two years of completely automatic operation and not one frozen vegetable. Bushell, who says the device can be used in any cold room, has applied for a patent and began marketing in late 1983.

One of Bushell's concerns about his root chest was the steady flow of cool air into the basement from the propped-open lid of the freezer. Although necessary for proper ventilation, he worried that it might cool the house as well as the vegetables. "However," he says, "I was pleasantly surprised," explaining that all furnaces and stoves require fresh air to support combustion and normally draw this air from around main-floor doors and windows. With a fresh air source in the basement, Bushell noted that draughts were reduced in the upstairs living area. "Contrary to intuition," he says, "an air intake source in the basement usually improves a home's energy efficiency, air freshness and personal comfort." Notwithstanding, the benefits from this arrangement are tempered by the fact that, during the coldest weather, when furnaces or stoves are working hardest, the freezer damper is likely to be closed.

Whether one wants to build a permanent basement structure or reincarnate a dead freezer into a new life as a cold storage chest, the effective shelf life of fruits and vegetables can be extended significantly by understanding their requirements and providing the proper conditions for their winter survival.

Fruits and vegetables fall into five distinct categories of storage conditions: warm and dry, cool and dry, cool and moist, cold and moist and, lastly, cold and very moist. The more closely one adheres to the requirements of each crop, the longer one can expect it to keep and the more pleasure there is in serving a crisp, fresh vegetable that "took care of itself."

Green tomatoes, pumpkins and squash are the three fruits that require a warm, dry storage spot, although tomatoes like more humidity than the others and would benefit from storage in a corner of the basement where the temperature is between 50 and 60 degrees F. Tomatoes picked for such storage should be mature but still green, free from imperfections and picked before the first frost. Specimens from young, vigorous plants are reported to store better than those from older vines; regardless, they should have the stems removed and be placed so they do not touch each

Fruit And Vegetable Storage Chart

	Temperature (degrees F)	% Relative Humidity	Life Expectancy in Storage
Apples	31	85-90	3-8 months
Beets	32-35	90-95	1-5 months
Cabbage	32-35	90-95	3-4 months
Carrots	32-35	90-95	4-5 months
Celery	32-35	90-95	3 months
Citrus Fruits	32-35	90-95	up to 10 weeks
Garlic	32-35	50-70	6-8 months
Grapes	32-35	80-90	1-2 months
Horseradish	31	90-95	10-12 months
Kohlrabi	32-35	90-95	2-4 months
Onions	32-35	50-70	5-9 months
Parsnips	32-35	90-95	2-4 months
Pears	31	85-90	2-5 months
Potatoes	35-40	80-90	4-6 months
Pumpkins	50-60	70-75	4-6 months
Radishes	32-35	90-95	2-4 months
Rutabagas (Swedes)	32-35	90-95	6 months
Squash	50-60	60-70	6 months
Tomatoes (Green)	50-60	85-90	2-6 weeks
Turnips	32-35	90-95	6 months

other. It is neither harmful nor helpful to keep them in the dark. Tomatoes that have been exposed to temperatures consistently less than 50 degrees for more than a few days may refuse to ripen. The process can be hurried by introducing a few apples among them. The apples give off ethylene gas which encourages ripening. This fact has not gone unnoticed in the agribiz world, where tomatoes are picked green and hard so they can be shipped and stored with less damage, and then are gassed with ethylene for instant ripening. Tomatoes should be sorted weekly to pick out those that are ripening or rotting.

Both pumpkins and squash can stand a few light frosts, protected as they are by their leafy canopies, but, when picked, they should retain their stems to prevent spoilage starting in the stem scar. If a stem does get pulled off, the scar can be painted with wax to delay spoilage, although the treated individuals should be used first. Despite their tough-looking skins, both pumpkins and squash will bruise easily, the bruises rotting first. After harvest, they should be held for a week or two in warm temperatures (between 70 and 80 degrees F, perhaps beside a furnace), allowing the skin to dehydrate somewhat and form a hard rind.

The warm and dry conditions (warm is a relative term, meaning warm in comparison to a cold storage room; see the accompanying chart for specifications) that will sustain pumpkins and squash through many months of storage can be found in an unused bedroom, a closet that faces an outside wall, or any other cool corner of the house where the vegetables can be easily reached. Any house that is largely heated by wood will likely have several such corners. Theoretically, pumpkins need more humidity than squash do, but in practice they can be stored together. Although both will suffer damage in temperatures below 50 degrees F, they will also become dry and stringy if kept above 60 degrees.

The only vegetables that demand cool, dry storage are the tangy pair: onions and garlic. Perhaps this is just as well, for they must be stored away from most other fruits and vegetables anyway — the strong odour that makes them welcome as bug-deterring companion plants will transfer to their neighbours in storage. John Seymour, in *The Complete Food Gardener*, suggests breaking the necks of onions by bending them over "when the tips of the leaves start going yellow." This encourages the ripening process, and the bulbs can be gently dug out of the ground a week later. Leave them to dry in the sun, preferably off the ground, for a few days or a week and then let them cure in a warm, shady spot for another week or two, or until the papery outer skins are dry enough to rustle. Bulbs with thick necks do not store well.

Garlic should be left in the ground until the tops have died back, then dug, dried for a few days and put directly in storage. The tops can either be left or removed, but roots should be trimmed as closely as possible. Both garlic and onions prefer dry, airy conditions and temperatures as cold as possible without freezing. "Onions," advises an anonymous 19th-century gardener, "are often injured in winter by keeping them in too warm a place." They can be braided, hung in net bags or stuffed into old pantyhose (by putting two or three bulbs in the toe, then tying a knot and repeating the process; small groups of bulbs can be retrieved with a pair of scissors, starting at the bottom and working up) and hung in the coldest part of the house, perhaps the top of the basement stairs or against a north-facing wall in a seldom-used room.

SPROUTING TIME

The group of vegetables that should be kept in a cool, moist area is small; in fact, it is a group of one. If the weather is dry, late potatoes can be left in the ground as long as six weeks after the tops have died. They should not, however, be dug until the tops are completely dead because the growing plants retain their carbohydrates as sugar, whereas the dead plants have converted the sugar to starch, "which," says John Seymour, "is really what potatoes are."

Freshly dug potatoes should be dried briefly in the sun and then held in the shade in warm, moist air for a curing period of one to two weeks. During this time, the skins will thicken, and if the temperature is above 50 degrees F, small cracks or skinned areas will actually heal themselves as the vegetables prepare for winter. Although curing helps to retain moisture and thus prevent shrivelling, some gardeners minimize this step for fear the skins will become unpleasantly tough.

Sort out damaged potatoes before packing the keepers in bins, crates or double burlap bags and place them in a dark, cool, moist corner of the basement. Potato tubers are especially sensitive to light, even artificial light, and any prolonged exposure will cause them to turn green. The green portions are mildly toxic, but their bitter taste precludes any danger of poisoning. Although freshly dug tubers enter a dormant period of two to three months when almost nothing will induce them to sprout, late winter and spring sprouting can be caused by either light or warm temperatures. The measure of one's potato storage facilities is taken by the length of storage before sprouts appear.

"Our potatoes stay firm and sproutless in a pit under the cabin floor till the end of June," says Yukon homesteader Mickey Lammers. "During the following month, small sprouts show, but the potato is quite edible yet. What they taste like in August, only my rabbits know — we rob the new plants." An expert from the 1880s, quoted in Jean Cross's *In Grandmother's Day*, promises that "good potatoes the year around, without hard strings and watery ends caused by growing" can be had by briefly dousing the potatoes in boiling water before putting them in storage.

Ideal potato storage temperatures are between 35 and 40 degrees F, but it is not often practical to provide separate storage for them, and they are usually kept in a root cellar at a temperature less than optimal. This results in the tubers converting some of their starches back into sugar, and potatoes stored this way can take on an unpleasantly sweet flavour. Happily, this can be undone by holding small groups of spuds at room temperature for several weeks prior to use.

Cold and moist conditions are the domain of fruits such as apples, pears and grapes, whose freezing point is in the 28- to 29-degree F range. Generally speaking, these fruits should be kept as cold as possible without freezing; ideally, their storage space is too cold to be shared with vegetables, and good spots around the house include under a bay window or concrete porch or just outside the basement door in a covered stairwell.

A further reason to store fruits separately is that they are not compatible with some vegetables. They can absorb odours from potatoes and other root crops, giving the fruit an unpleasant flavour often described as "earthy," although unfairly so, for it is the vegetables, not dirt, that produce the flavour. Also, as one might expect, incompatibility is a two-way street: apples and pears in particular give off ethylene gas in their natural respiration, and while this phenomenon can be used to good effect with slow-ripening tomatoes, it can cause a loss of colour in green vegetables like cabbages and an intense bitterness in carrots. Though it is often impractical to provide two separate storage facilities, compromises should be tempered by common sense. Store apples in the coldest part of a cold room and keep them away from root crops. Good ventilation is essential to protect fruit and root crops from each other, and while it would be foolish to store a basket of carrots in a room full of apples, the home gardener, with a more eclectic selection of crops for storage, can get away with keeping a couple of bushels of each in a well-ventilated storeroom.

"The apple is the queen of storage fruits," says Nancy Bubel, author of *Root Cellaring*, but to achieve their full potential, the fruits should be picked when they are at their peak of ripeness, handled carefully so they do not bruise and stored with the stem left on so that rot-causing bacteria are denied easy access to the interior of the apple. Cold temperatures are essential for storage — apples will ripen twice as fast at 40 degrees F as they will at 32 degrees, four times as fast at 50 degrees and eight times as fast at 70. Leaving apples at 70 degrees for one day would reduce their effective storage time at near-freezing temperatures by more than a week. The trick is to pick the fruit after it is ripe but before it starts to soften, cool it as quickly as possible and then retard the natural ageing (ripening) process with continued cool surroundings.

As with all home storage crops, humidity is nearly as important a factor as temperature. Overly high humidity will encourage rot, especially at temperatures above 35 degrees F, and inadequate levels of humidity will cause the fruit to shrivel. Apples can be stored in slatted crates, in perforated plastic bags or nestled in dry maple leaves in a traditional apple barrel.

Christina Bates quotes Dr. Alvin Wood Chase recommending, in 1867, that "fruit be rubbed over with chalk and dipped into a solution of rosin, tallow and beeswax; cooled to set; and packed away." In the same era, she writes, "apples were punched through from stem to eye with a goose quill. The puncture was filled with sugar and the apples were then stored in a tight cask."

REDUCED OXYGEN

Modern commercial apple growers, no doubt suffering from a dearth of goose quills, rely on a technique known as Controlled Atmosphere (CA) storage that puts apples on supermarket shelves year-round. Apples are stored in bulk bins in airtight refrigerated buildings, where, in addition to temperature and humidity, levels of oxygen and carbon dioxide are monitored and controlled. For example, both red and yellow *Delicious* apples are held at 32 degrees F, 3 percent oxygen (reduced from about 21 percent) and 2.5 to 3 percent carbon dioxide (increased from almost nil), a condition that effectively puts the apples to sleep and extends their storage life to six months.

Home gardeners will have to settle for reduced storage periods, depending on conditions, and also on the variety of apple chosen for storage. *Newton* and *Winesap* apples will store for very long periods, up to seven months; *Stayman, York Imperial, Northern Spy* and *Rome Beauty* for up to five months; *McIntosh, Cortland, Spartan, Rhode Island Greening* and both colours of *Delicious* for four months, although Macs prefer a warmer storage temperature of about 38 degrees F; *Jonathan* and *Grimes Golden* for only two to three months.

Pears should be picked before ripening because those allowed to ripen on the tree will turn gritty in storage. Wait until they are fully mature, then pick them as they change from a dark to a light green and separate from the tree easily. Pears should be stored under the same conditions as apples, although they will not keep as long. If held for too long, the fruit will rot instead of ripening, and it should be brought into a warmer room, about 60 to 65 degrees F, for several days before eating to let it ripen properly. *Winter Nelis* and *Anjou* are excellent keeping varieties, lasting in storage until Christmas; *Bosc, Bartlett* and *Kieffer* (a cooking variety) do not keep as long. *Clapp's Favourite* do not keep well and should not be stored.

Bates says that, in the 1800s, grapes were wrapped "in soft paper to set in a jar, covered in layers with bran. The lid of the jar was cemented closed with the curd of skim milk and lime." Contemporary viniculturists may content themselves with keeping their produce in shallow crates with apples and pears.

The last and largest group of vegetables requires cold and very moist conditions and includes those that most properly belong in a root cellar — root crops, as well as leafy vegetables like celery and cabbage. "In my view," says John Seymour, "celery should be eaten only in winter. During the rest of the year, it is tasteless and insipid, because it has not had the benefit of frost." He recommends leaving it in the ground as long as possible, protecting the plants with mulch or cloches when the heavy frosts begin. Celery should be dug before freeze-up, taking care to keep the roots intact in a clump of soil. Store upright on the root-cellar floor with the root clumps tightly packed. By keeping the soil moist without getting water on the tops, home-grown celery will keep long enough to help stuff the Christmas bird.

As with celery, a few light frosts will improve the taste of cabbage, although neither should be allowed to freeze. Cabbages should be harvested by pulling up the root and all, choosing only firm, heavy heads for storage. Hang the heads upside down by the root or remove the root and the outer leaves and place bottom up on shelves in a well-ventilated basement storage. Cabbages have a strong odour, an odour that can pervade a house until the whole place smells like the back door of a sauerkraut factory, but the effect may be lessened by wrapping the heads in burlap or newspaper.

Because of their odour, cabbages, like garlic and onions, are often stored separately for they can taint other vegetables. Both cabbages and celery can be stored in two-foot-deep trenches in the garden. For cabbages, place the heads, complete with roots, upside down on a layer of hay or straw in the bottom of the trench and then pack with loose hay to ground level. Covering the trench with whole bales should protect the heads through all but the most severe winters. Although covered the same way, celery should be placed in a trench, standing upright with the root clumps packed tightly in moist soil. Both vegetables will rot if they are placed in trenches with moisture on the leaves or stalks.

Root crops, as the name implies, grow in the ground and are used to a cool, dark, moist environment. When exposed to dry conditions, they lose moisture rapidly, becoming shrivelled and unappetizing; warmth causes them to turn soft and then woody; light causes bitterness. Ideal storage conditions for these crops would approximate their growing medium, and therefore, they are usually packed in moist sand or peat moss and kept in a cold corner of the basement.

Because root crops are resistant to frost, it is a good idea to leave them in the ground as long as possible, reducing out-of-ground storage time and enabling the root cellar to become chilled before it is loaded. In fact, carrots and parsnips can be left in the ground for all or part of the winter. Just before the ground freezes, cover a row or bed of roots with bales of hay or straw, stuffing all the crevices with loose hay, and then pack dirt around the bottom of the bales. One of the first gardening pleasures of spring is pulling off the weathered bales to harvest a crop of crunchy fresh carrots or parsnips. Of course, if the mice have gotten there before you, you may find nothing but carrot-shaped holes; this calamity can be prevented with a layer of hardware cloth. This spring harvest must be gathered before the plants start to sprout, or else the roots will turn woody.

Carrots, usually the backbone of any home storage plan, are the standard against which other root crops are measured. They should be dug when the soil is dry, after which their tops can be cut or twisted off close to the crown. Although carrots are 88 percent water and are susceptible to shrivelling, they will remain pleasantly edible until spring if given proper treatment. Store them in boxes or bins, in layers of moist sand arranged so they do not touch each other in case rot does begin. Periodically, moisten the sand to maintain a high humidity. Another method is to line the bins with a sheet of heavy polyethylene loosely tucked in around the top. Finally, one can simply place them in perforated polyethylene bags. Each of these methods, when accompanied by humid atmospheric conditions, helps to maintain the moisture level in the carrots, but do not try to trap moisture in airtight bags — without ventilation, the roots will acquire a musty flavour.

Although few will keep as long, all other root crops, including beets, horseradish, kohlrabi, parsnips, winter radishes, rutabagas and turnips are stored like carrots. They may be washed before being stored, when the dirt will come off more readily than it will after months of storage. This makes them more pleasant to handle and, by improving air circulation and reducing the bacteria present, may reduce the chance of spoilage, especially for those stored in polyethylene bags. Washing, as with all handling of storage vegetables, must be done gently to prevent bruising or skinning. Soak the roots in a washtub for 15 or 20 minutes, then drain and spray with a garden hose, avoiding vigorous scrubbing which might damage the tender skins.

Finally, when all the onions are braided and hung, when the upstairs hallway is lined with squash, when bushels of apples are tucked under the basement stairs and the last of the parsnips are bedded down in the root cellar, the gardener, content that the harvest is complete, can turn his attention to other pre-winter chores. Or he can take a well-deserved and long-awaited vacation.

"Even so long as till the New shall incite you to quit the Old," wrote John Evelyn in 1675, "you will taste your Fruit with infinite more gust and contentment than in the Summer itself, when their great abundance and variety rather cloy you." Either from the backyard garden or purchased in bulk when prices are low, the contemporary gardener may also enjoy out-of-season vegetables with "gust and contentment." He simply has to incorporate a few 19th-century ideas into some 20th-century architecture. ∎

Sources

GEORGE BUSHELL
Freeze Control Damper
Box 534
Orleans, Ontario
K1C 1S9

Publications

ROOT CELLARING
By Mike and Nancy Bubel
Rodale Press
297 pages
136B — hardcover, $14.95
Available from Harrowsmith Books, Camden East, Ontario K0K 1J0.

STOCKING UP
Edited by Carol Hupping Stoner
Rodale Press
532 pages
1B — hardcover, $23.95
Available from Harrowsmith Books, Camden East, Ontario K0K 1J0.

THE SELF-SUFFICIENT GARDENER
By John Seymour
Dolphin Books

PUTTING FOOD BY
By Ruth Hertzberg et al.
The Stephen Green Press

Fungal Exotica

Adventures in a kingdom of delectable home-grown mushrooms

By Adrian Forsyth

Humankind may be the ultimate weed. We have invaded and established ourselves in even the bleakest and most remote habitats on Earth, an expansion that is usually explained as the product of our intellectual advances. As a biologist, I am inclined to credit this great dispersion more to our growling stomachs than our superior minds. Humans, along with other ubiquitous animals such as swine, dogs and some cockroaches, have an adaptable palate: we eat everything from algae to the brains of our fellow humans. We have a willingness to domesticate other species, to cultivate, bake, breed and ferment them. Still, we have failed to understand or make use of most of the species that surround us. Despite our omnivorous nature and our burgeoning populations, we have largely ignored the world's greatest renewable food resource — plant cellulose, the woody, fibrous material that acts as the support system of plants.

Unfortunately, only a few microorganisms — fungi and insects — have the digestive enzymes needed to turn cellulose into food. Cows and other ruminants provide the living quarters and gather the raw materials for the microorganisms in exchange for the nutrients they provide. This system requires multiple and cavernous stomachs, along with much belching and venting of the gaseous by-products of fermentation. Rather than go this route, humans have traditionally tapped the cellulosic treasure trove by milking the cow or eating it, an indirect and inefficient method, considering that there is much plant material that neither cow nor even goat can stomach.

The alternative is to harness the chemical jaws of fungi. With fungus, dead elms can be transmogrified into racks of firm, white oyster mushrooms, and oak shavings can be converted into exotic and expensive-to-buy Shiitake.

This is a time-tested and proved method first developed by ants and termites, which have been growing mushrooms on leaves and woody debris for eons. About 3,000 years ago, humans began emulating these insects by cultivating padi straw mushrooms (*Volvariella volvacea*) on rice straw in southeast Asia. Since then, Asians have domesticated more than a half-dozen different mushrooms, which feed not only on straw but also on sawdust and cordwood. Of these, spawn (mushroom "seed") is now available in North America for oyster mushrooms, Shiitake (Chinese black mushrooms), winter or velvet stem mushrooms and padi straw or Chinese mushrooms.

Unlike the common button mushroom, *Agaricus*, which requires carefully made compost and a cool,

Mushroom harvester plucks a clump of oyster mushrooms from the growing racks at Toronto's Royal Mushroom Company, which cannot keep up with North American demand for their fresh gourmet fungi.

dark basement, many of the mushrooms that feed on cellulosic materials can be grown indoors, in natural light and at room temperature. For those interested in attempting this relatively little-known form of gardening, the raw materials are readily available inasmuch as the cellulose substrate or growing medium can be made up of sawdust, wood shavings, rotting logs, old hay, straw and even newspaper.

Whatever the type of cellulose-consuming mushroom selected, the grower will follow the same general steps to cultivate it. First, the spawn used to start a culture must be obtained. This is readily procured from mail-order sources at prices of approximately $8 to $10 per quart, enough to inoculate roughly 20 pounds of growing medium. Mushroom supplier Ralph Kurtzman of California says, "If you like a sure thing, try using a little more spawn; if you are a gambler, try using less. The amount of spawn affects the certainty of success. The amount of straw or other substrate determines the amount of mushrooms." Yield will depend on the skill of the grower and on the species being grown. The smallest harvest, about 5 pounds of mush-

rooms from 20 pounds of straw, comes from padi straw; the largest, about 20 pounds of mushrooms on 20 pounds of straw, from oyster mushrooms.

Next, the gardener must gather the appropriate substrate, which varies with the type of mushroom being grown. To make it easier for the mycelia to spread and penetrate, the substrate should be chopped into pieces with a shredder or cleaver. In most cases, the substrate must be wetted and heated, sometimes under pressure, to kill competing fungi and other microorganisms. Third, the prepared substrate is inoculated with the spawn. Fourth, the inoculated substrate is kept in a protected environment within a specified temperature range, allowing the spawn to grow through the substrate as mycelia, masses of thin, whitish threads. Eventually, the entire mass of substrate will be colonized. Step five involves a shift in environmental conditions that causes the mycelia to form pinlike primordia, which rise up into mushrooms. Several flushes of mushrooms then occur at intervals until the substrate is depleted.

Home mushroom growing offers pesticide-free, fresh mushrooms in varieties that are often unobtainable commercially. And there is something inherently interesting in the process of growing them. Unlike a garden plant, a mushroom erupts overnight. Out of a chaotic, amorphous clump of mycelia, a precise sophisticated structure is suddenly created. But still, the how and why of this process are little understood. The precise growing requirements and life histories of most edible mushrooms remain unknown. In fact, it was only in the last decade that a consensus was achieved among biologists as to whether fungi merit taxonomic status as their own kingdom separate from plants and animals. (They do.) Here, then, is a chance for gardeners to add to their repertoire not just a new variety of vegetable species but the members of a little-known kingdom.

OYSTER FARMING

Oyster mushrooms are generally acknowledged to be the easiest to cultivate; they are fast-growing and accept a wide variety of substrates — hardwood logs, wood shavings, sawdust, corn cobs and stalks, paper, hay and straw, and at least one Canadian company is growing them on pulp-and-paper wastes.

With a shelflike shape and small stem, oyster mushrooms bear little resemblance to the common button mushroom. Nor do they taste the same. Articulating a taste is always difficult; the only flavour I can think of which is close to that of oyster mushrooms is that of fried Yucca blossoms. They are mild and agreeable to most mushroom eaters.

Oyster mushrooms have cultural demands similar to those of houseplants: a source of indirect sun or fluorescent light (incandescent is of no use), high humidity, good ventilation and the appropriate growing and fruiting temperatures. For the native North American species, *Pleurotus ostreatus*, the ideal temperature range during incubation — the growth of the mycelia — is 59 to 68 degrees F. There are, however, several other strains and varieties with different temperature requirements, so the gardener can practically choose the mushroom best suited to his environment. For instance, the variety *Florida* and species *P. cornicopiae* have a higher growth optimum temperature (68 to 77 degrees and 66 to 77 degrees, respectively), while *P. sajor-caju*, an Indian species, prefers an even warmer environment, 77 to 86 degrees. The species *P. sapidus* has similar temperature requirements to those of *P. ostreatus* and is considered easier to grow, but I find its flavour inferior. In each case, the optimum temperature for fruiting is close to the low end of the range.

Oyster mushrooms can be grown indoors, or, provided the growing conditions are suitable, outdoors. In my first outdoor experiment with *Pleurotus ostreatus*, I used hay as a substrate. If using hay or straw, be sure that it is clean, free from moulds and not at all spoiled. The substrate has to be soaked in hot water, around 160 to 170 degrees F, for at least an hour. This not only adds moisture but also pasteurizes the substrate and reduces the risk of its suffering contamination by other fungi and microorganisms. It also leaches out soluble compounds in hay and straw that could impede the growth of the mycelia. It is wise to remember that the soaking will greatly increase the weight of the substrate. I found that the 60-pound bale I soaked in the bathtub turned into a sodden 200-pound mass, which was cumbersome and messy to drag outdoors.

Kurtzman has a more practical soaking method. He recommends that the gardener set a 45-gallon drum, half filled with water, over a burner outdoors, chop the straw into pieces about an inch or two long (though I did not chop mine, and it still worked well) and stuff it into a wire basket that easily fits inside the drum. Heat the water to 160 to 170 degrees F, submerge the basket and cover the straw with a weight to keep it underwater. After it has soaked for about 45 minutes, lift the basket and let the straw drain until it stops dripping. Now, wash your hands and arms, spread the wet straw out on a clean surface and leave it to cool to about 80 degrees. Mix crumbly oatmeal-like spawn as evenly as possible through the substrate, then pack it into containers or, as I did, simply pile it out of doors in a shady spot and cover the pile with a sheet of black plastic.

Quebec mycologist Gyorgy-M. Ola'h has published another method for growing *Pleurotus* mushrooms outdoors. His book, *A New Way to Grow Edible Mushrooms*, advises that in late spring, the home grower use freshly cut deciduous logs about a foot long and 10 to 14 inches in diameter and saw an inch-thick layer off one end. About an inch of spawn is spread over the cut end of the log, and the removed layer is nailed lightly back in place, creating a spawn "sandwich." The log is then put in a garbage bag containing five inches of wet sand or vermiculite, and the bag is tied shut and stored in a cool place for four or five weeks, or until the mycelia have spread over the log. Then the bag is removed, and the log is set outdoors in four or five inches of damp soil in a shady, sheltered place. The culture and the surrounding soil should be dampened during dry weather. Harvesting, writes Ola'h, should begin about mid-July and continue until the first frost. New flushes will erupt in summer for the next four or five years.

For indoor use, a good substrate commonly used by Japanese commercial growers consists of four parts sawdust and one part bran. The sawdust from deciduous trees is best and may be aged as long as a year. Very fine sawdust, such as that produced by sanding and circular saws, should be avoided because it compacts and becomes waterlogged. The authors of *The Mushroom Cultivator* note that if the sawdust is presoaked and then mixed with dry bran, the mixture will approximate the optimum 60 percent moisture. "A firm squeeze of the mixture should produce only a few drops of water between the fingers." Such a loose medium can be autoclaved — pressure-cooked and sterilized — at 15 psi for 20 minutes. I have a 22-quart All-America cooker, a widely available, good-quality pressure cooker that has sufficient capacity to be practical.

I have had and heard of few problems with contamination in oyster mushroom culture, and insects are rarely a bother, but pressure-cooking and other rigours are necessary to produce the massive and predictable yields demanded by competition in the commercial

A small rack of oyster mushrooms grown on an artificial substrate consisting of three parts sawdust and one part bran.

Gail Harvey

market. The Royal Mushroom Company in Toronto, for example, churns out some six or seven thousand pounds of oyster and Shiitake mushrooms every week. (Incidentally, they report that demand greatly exceeds supply; as well as serving a busy local retail market, they export as far south as Florida.)

After heating, cool the substrate to about 80 degrees F, inoculate it with spawn and pack it into Mason jars or plastic bags. Whatever the substrate or container used, cover it and place it where the temperature is stable and as close to the recommended optimum as possible. Avoid areas near radiators that suddenly give off bursts of heat, since any temperature above 95 degrees may prove fatal. Light is neither necessary nor desirable at this stage.

During the next 30 to 40 days, the mycelia will grow through the substrate until it has become a solid mass, at which time it is ready for fruit induction. Mushroom formation is usually triggered by exposure to light and by a drop in temperature of about 5 to 15 degrees, which can usually be effected by moving the culture to a cooler room or from a high place to the floor. The cover should be removed to allow light penetration and ventilation. If the culture has been grown in a plastic bag, removing the bag will now reveal a self-supporting mass the shape of the container. Too little light or air will produce long, stringy stalks and fewer palatable mushrooms, but since these mushrooms normally grow in shady forests, the amount of light required is low; if it is bright enough to read by, it is bright enough

for *Pleurotus*. A north window is ideal, since direct sunlight will kill mycelia. To achieve adequate ventilation and to allow venting of the carbon dioxide that the mycelia give off in great quantities, while retaining high humidity, most growers cover the open top of the culture with a clean plastic bag in which holes have been made with a nail or a paper punch. Since carbon dioxide is heavier than air, it sinks, so do not seal the bottom rim of the covering bag.

Plan to mist the culture about once a day. Commercial operations achieve the preferred humidity level of about 80 to 90 percent by keeping the floor wet. When I grew these mushrooms in Arizona, misting three or four times a day was not excessive, but someone in the Pacific rain forest or in any other cool, foggy region might not need to mist at all. The culture should never appear dry.

After the culture has been moved to a cooler, brighter location, pinlike primordia will form on its surface. In a week or two, these will grow into mushrooms. Once they are picked, there will be another period of primordia formation and a second flush of mushrooms about two weeks after the first. Normally, this exhausts the culture, but really large cultures may keep fruiting after this. One can gauge the possibility of future flushes by the progressive reduction in yield. The culture should yield about one pound of mushrooms for every pound of dry substrate, an alchemy made possible by the addition of water to the system. When fruiting finishes, about 20 percent of the substrate will remain. This is a mineral- and humus-rich crumbly mix that makes a valuable soil amendment and also has a feed value equal to hay for livestock such as cattle.

Their high-humidity requirement and voluminous carbon dioxide production would seem to suit *Pleurotus* culture to shady sites in greenhouses. However, those who grow them indoors should be aware that as they emerge, these mushrooms give off great quantities of airborne spores that have caused respiratory allergies and sickness in some workers in high-volume commercial operations.

The Shiitake, Chinese black, Black Forest mushroom, or Dunku (*Lentinus edodes*), is one of the best-flavoured and most expensive mushrooms. It has a typical mushroom form, a dark velvet-brown colour and a quality comparable to that of *Boletus edulis*, a mushroom fondly called *porcini*, "piglets" in Italian, indicating the almost meatlike flavour of the species. Shiitake are common in Chinese and Japanese cooking. And the species has medical as well as gastronomical interest, since it contains several anti-tumour compounds.

Unfortunately, Shiitake mushrooms are also difficult to cultivate, their fundamental problem being slowness of growth. While an indoor *Pleurotus* culture might produce a harvest in six weeks, *Lentinus edodes* will not do so for about five months — and even that is fast. Like *Pleurotus*, Shiitake can also be grown outdoors, but this traditional method is very slow — it can take two years to produce a crop — and is subject to changes in the weather. Outdoors, Shiitake mushrooms are normally grown on the same trees that host wild members of the species, dead wood of trees in the beech family, Fagaceae, which includes oaks, beeches, chinkapins and chestnuts. United States Department of Agriculture research has also found black willow, alder and birch to be suitable, and Maryland grower Byong Yoo reports that maple produces a quick, if short-lived, crop. Oaks, however, are the favoured host species of most growers.

I have not grown mushrooms on cordwood, but this is the dominant and traditional method of mushroom culture in southeast Asia, where some 200,000 growers produce about 140,000 tons of cellulose-digesting mushrooms annually. Shiitake culture involves cutting live wood of one of the preferred host-tree species, ideally in fall and winter, when the sugar content of the wood is highest. Logs three or four feet long and three to six inches in diameter are used, a size that is a compromise: larger logs are too difficult to move, smaller ones become exhausted quickly. And the larger the log, the longer the colonization time for the mycelia, which not only delays the time of first harvest but also gives contaminants more time to invade.

Although logs may be used when freshly cut, commercial growers allow the logs to dry somewhat, stacking them in the shade for a month or more, after which hairline cracks appear in the ends. In temperate regions, logs should be cut in late winter or spring to be ready for inoculation at the start of summer, when temperatures have risen high enough to promote rapid mycelial growth.

Inoculation is done by drilling holes roughly a half-

Adrian Forsyth

Cold-hardy and productive outdoors when all other mushrooms have disappeared, the winter mushroom, or velvet stem, parasitizes elm logs or can be grown in a culture medium.

inch in diameter and an inch deep every 4 to 10 inches along and around the log. The greater the density of inoculation, the more quickly the log will be colonized. The spawn is available either as sawdust or as solid wood plugs, which are pushed snugly into the holes and sealed with wax to prevent drying and contamination.

Inoculated logs are placed in a shady spot with good air circulation, usually in stacks with each course of logs set at right angles to the next to allow air movement. Some growers claim that stacking logs at a 45-degree angle increases the rate of mycelial spread, while others rotate the logs every few months to encourage an even growth of the mycelia away from the inoculation holes. In dry climates or during droughts, logs are lightly watered to prevent their drying — the fine cracks in the log ends should not increase in size. Direct sunlight, excessive dryness and temperatures above 95 degrees F can kill the mycelia.

It takes a year or two for mycelial colonization to be completed and for fruiting to begin. Fruiting is associated with the low temperatures and rain of spring and fall, when the harvest continues for several weeks. New flushes may occur each spring and fall for as long as five years. During this time, a cord of oak may produce up to 500 pounds of mushrooms, which retail for $7 to $20 a pound.

Because Shiitake culture has not been widely tested in this country, it is not clear if outdoor culture is viable in Canada. Kurtzman claims that there are Shiitake strains which should be winter-hardy throughout southern Canada, and a cottage Shiitake industry does exist in British Columbia. The Horticultural Research Institute of Ontario (HRIO) and the University of Toronto Botany Department report that neither the oyster mushroom nor the Shiitake mushroom strain tested "appears to be able to survive outdoors over the winter since attempts to reisolate them from the dead areas [of wood] were unsuccessful." But they inoculated live trees, which do not support Shiitake growth. It remains to be seen if cordwood culture can weather northern winters beyond warm coastal regions.

Besides the possible disadvantage of winter tenderness, the shortcomings of outdoor culture include its use of live wood and its slowness. The indoor culture of Shiitake, on the other hand, utilizes already existing cellulose wastes and by-products and produces more rapid results, although it is more labour-intensive and involves fuel consumption. Indoor growing offers the advantage of speed and predictable yields at the cost of its need for daily attention. Outdoors, Shiitake mushrooms can be grown in large volumes with less labour and without pasteurization.

The researchers at the University of Toronto Botany Department and HRIO recently published a recipe for indoor Shiitake culture. Such recipes have previously been trade secrets protected by various patents. Their formula for substrate (which can be packed into plastic bags such as milk or freezer bags) consists of 80 percent hardwood sawdust, 17 percent wheat bran, 1 percent molasses, 1.5 percent yeast extract, 0.2 percent calcium carbonate (limestone) and enough water to produce a 60 to 65 percent moisture content by weight. They kept the sterilized and inoculated bags at 75 to 79 degrees F for 15 weeks, after which the permeated substrate resembled a solid log of mycelia. They submerged these logs in 59-to-60-degree water for 24 hours and then kept them at 50 to 59 degrees. Mushrooms appeared within 10 to 12 days. Thus the production time was reduced from two years for outdoor culture to less than five months. The bran, molasses, calcium carbonate and yeast extract are not essential but possibly accelerate growth by providing extra nutrients. It should be pointed out that this recipe, like all substrate recipes, is adjustable, and many other variations work.

Some growers remove the bag after incubation to lower the humidity, but I have grown the mushrooms simply by opening the end of the bag, which provides a fruiting surface while reducing the area exposed to drying.

KIT CULTURE

Mail-order kits are available for the production of both oyster and Shiitake mushrooms. Usually, they consist of a plastic bag packed with a cellulosic material that has already been spawned and run through with mycelia. The buyer needs only to soak the "log" in cold water and then place it in the perforated plastic bag in a suitable spot, as described previously. Regular misting is required. The advantage of these kits is that they produce mushrooms in a short time, 7 to 10 days for oyster mushrooms and a month for Shiitake. Kits, then, may be a convenient introduction to these mushrooms for gardeners who do not have access to mature ones and who want a small quantity quickly. They may be worthwhile for those who are reluctant to become involved with a more elaborate, if economical, method of growing without ever having tasted an oyster or Shiitake mushroom. In addition, the kit can be used to spawn a larger culture after it has finished fruiting.

The disadvantage of kits is their cost: about $7.50 for a kit that produces two pounds of oyster mushrooms. The yield of mushrooms is roughly one-quarter of the weight of the kit, and since that weight must be moved by mail, the resulting mushrooms cost as much as they sell for at a retail market. One mycologist has pointed out that the Shiitake kit can be purchased for about $25, while for only a few dollars more and some work with a drill and logs, a gardener could inoculate about 60 logs and produce hundreds of pounds of mushrooms (based on the price of chip Shiitake spawn from the Dr. Yoo Farm).

Kurtzman says, "Buying such products is like buying a tomato plant by mail and expecting to get your money's worth by setting it, in the original container, on the windowsill and watering it." I have grown oyster mushrooms using one of the mail-order kits sold by Gourmet Gardens and have been satisfied with its production. It fruited twice; then I put it on the compost pile where it fruited again, probably triggered by the change in temperature. My experience growing Shiitake with a mail-order kit was less successful. It only produced two mushrooms, and Kurtzman claims that this is typical. Poor yields with such a kit may simply attest to the buyer's not having bothered to strictly control the growing conditions of such a small endeavour, rather than point out any defect in the product, since the procedure recommended with the kit is sound and is used commercially.

The winter or velvet stem mushroom (*Flammulina velutipes*) is, like the oyster mushroom, a native species. It is cold-hardy and grows at temperatures between 50 and 55 degrees F. Often sold under its Japanese name, *Yenoki-take*, it has a long, thin, brittle stalk densely covered with short blackish brown hairs. Under natural light, it grows in dense clusters and has a pleasant, if not particularly exciting, flavour. Most remarkable to beginners is the colour of the small cap, which is yellowish orange to reddish orange.

The standard commercial substrate used for winter mushrooms is similar to that used for oyster mushrooms, sometimes consisting of four parts hardwood sawdust to one part bran and is sterilized in the same way. Packed into plastic bags or quart Mason jars, the inoculated substrate is held in the dark at 72 to 77 degrees F for about three weeks, after which the containers are moved into the light at cooler temperatures of 50 to 55 degrees. The containers should produce two to three flushes of mushrooms at intervals of about 10 days.

MUSHROOM FORAGING

The padi straw or Chinese mushroom (*Volvariella volvacea*) is a pale tan tropical species that thrives at 85 to 95 degrees and is thus well suited for growing during the steamy dog days of summer. Even the spawn is susceptible to damage by chilling and is therefore shipped only in summer. The only ones I have eaten tasted like the tin can they came in, but padi straw mushrooms are popular throughout southeast Asia. Picked when immature, they do not compare favourably in yield with other mushrooms grown on straw.

As their name might imply, padi straw mushrooms are traditionally grown on rice straw, although experiments with cotton wastes and wheat bran have proved successful. In one procedure, the substrate is pasteurized for 2 hours at 140 degrees F, then conditioned for a further 8 hours at 125 degrees and finally lowered to 77 degrees for 8 to 12 hours. Inoculated, the substrate is kept in total darkness at 88 to 95 degrees for about a week. The containers are then moved to diffuse natural light and temperatures between 82 and 88 degrees, where they should begin to produce in about a week and continue flushing about once a week for a month or two.

Wood ears or tree ears (*Auricularia auricula*), for which spawn is occasionally available, are gelatinous, tasteless fungi that resemble a piece of rusty cartilage. The Chinese like their slippery, crunchy texture and use them in classic dishes such as hot and sour soup. Wood ears do well under conditions similar to those enjoyed by oyster mushrooms.

Every spring and fall in the northern forests, prime cellulosic mushrooms erupt from dead elms, tree stumps and logs and then gradually wither or rot, ignored by virtually everything but fungus gnats and beetles. The unappreciated abundance of Canadian mushrooms often mystifies mushroom-loving Europeans who come to this country. My wife, who grew up in Germany, pointed this out when she introduced me to mushroom foraging. Our first harvest — pounds of golden chanterelles — was growing in a busy east coast campground and was being trampled beneath the feet of other campers. Aghast at the sight of such waste, she recalled how, in Germany, her family would rush to the woods at dawn in furious mushroom-for-

aging competition with the neighbours. But in Canada, on hundreds of forays on private and public land, we have never encountered another mushroom hunter. And on occasion, we have filled garbage sacks full of prime edibles, many of which are cellulose-digesters.

Even a small woodlot will produce more varieties of edible cellulosic mushrooms than anyone can cultivate. Many of these species have a large fruiting mass, are easily identified and fruit year after year from the same spot. In the deciduous woods of eastern Canada, whenever there is cool, wet spring or autumn weather, one can commonly find various oyster mushrooms, tooth fungi (*Hericium*), sulphur brackets (*Polyporos sulphureus*), beefsteak fungi (*Fistulina hepatica*), winter mushrooms (*Flammulina velutipes*), various puffballs (*Lycoperdon*), *Pholiota*, tree ears (*Auricula*) and Jelly fungi (*Tremella mesenterica*).

Of course, many inedible and poisonous mushrooms also grow on cellulose, so foragers must learn to identify the species. This can be entertainment, rather than a chore, and it can be inexpensive, too, now that excellent field guides are widely available. *Toxic and Hallucinogenic Mushroom Poisoning* by Lincoff and Mitchell should, I believe, be required reading for all those who go this route.

Although it is seldom done here in North America, Europeans have long worked to encourage mushroom growth in their woodlots, even going so far as to water highly productive stumps. There is nothing to prevent us from doing the same, bringing mycelium-rich sections of logs home from the forest and attempting to inoculate stacks of wood that we are willing to sacrifice to mushrooms.

In the end, one comes to realize that this is a form of gardening which requires a special fascination with the way things grow. I am not about to argue that we should all be turning our waste cellulose into mushrooms on a large scale, and there is no pressing need for us to eat more cellulosic mushrooms. However, there is a great satisfaction in coming to appreciate some of the biological diversity and culinary values of our own woodlot. We will grow and eat more kinds of mushrooms not just to make full use of dead elms and old bales of straw but because of our fundamental human urge for a diverse diet — full of the minerals, vitamins, trace elements and, yes, the succulent, rare flavours upon which we thrive. ∎

Sources

KURTZMAN'S MUSHROOM SPECIALTIES
815 South Harbor Way
Richmond, California 94804
or
c/o Lloyd Armstrong and Kurtzman Mushroom Co.
9451 Canora Road
Sidney, British Columbia V8L 1P3
(604) 656-5704
Kurtzman's Mushroom Specialties offers perhaps the largest selection of cellulosic mushroom spawn, along

with equipment and literature and a newsletter. Kurtzman, who has years of technical experience growing cellulosic fungi, answers the queries of his customers, provides complete instructions with all spawn and is a valuable source of information and supplies. He is also willing to ship spawn to Canada, although customers who wish to import spawn must apply to Agriculture Canada for a permit to do so. His Canadian dealership is designed to eliminate importation problems. Price list free.

WESTERN BIOLOGICALS LTD.
Box 1253, Station A
Vancouver, British Columbia
V6C 2T1
Culture, kits, supplies for exotic mushrooms. Catalogue $1.00.

MUSHROOMPEOPLE
Box 158H
Inverness, California 94937
I have received prompt service from these people on the several occasions I have dealt with them. In addition, Bob Harris of Mushroompeople has published a couple of inexpensive books, such as *Growing Wild Mushrooms*, which discuss how to collect plugs of wild mushrooms for starting spawn and how to grow spawn from scratch using spore prints. I have followed his procedures and found them successful. He has recently produced a book on growing Shiitake on small logs indoors. Price list free.

DR. YOO FARM
Box 290
College Park, Maryland 20740
(301) 854-6088
As well as seeds for Oriental vegetables, Dr. Byong Yoo sells Shiitake plug spawn and a pamphlet on the traditional Oriental method of cordwood culture. He is planning to offer oyster, Enokitake and Nameko spawn (sawdust and plug-spawn form) in the next catalogue. Note that he and most other plug-spawn suppliers require weeks to months advance notice for Shiitake spawn orders. Price list free.

W.H. PERRON
515 Labelle Blvd.
City of Laval, Quebec H7V 2T3
Vegetable and flower seeds as well as *Pleurotus* spawn and instructions for growing oyster mushrooms outdoors. Catalogue $1.00.

FUNGI PERFECTI
Box 7634
Olympia, Washington 98507
(206) 426-9292
A small, family-run mail-order business offering high-quality equipment, selected for home cultivators. Spawn for *Coprinus comatus* (shaggy mane), *Flammulina velutipes, Lentinus edodes, Pleurotus ostreatus, Stropharia rugoso-annulata*. Owner Paul Stamets is one of the authors of *The Mushroom Cultivator*. Catalogue $2.50 (U.S.).

THE KINOKO COMPANY
8139 Capwell Drive, Box 6425
Oakland, California 94621
(415) 562-3671
Kits for growing Shiitake and oyster mushrooms; also compost, spawn and other equipment. Price list free.

Books

Most of the suppliers provide growing instructions with their spawn. However, gardeners serious about growing cellulosic fungi would do well to buy or to consult *The Biology and Cultivation of Edible Mushrooms*, edited by S. Chang and W. Hayes. Published in 1978 by Academic Press, this is a technical and massive tome that costs about $100, but that is little more than the cost of half a dozen pounds of fresh Shiitake.

Many field guides are available. Most foragers will find that two books are needed, as there is a trade-off between the quantity of colour photos and text. The Audubon field guides or Simon and Shuster's guide contain more than twice as many photos as Orson Miller's *Mushrooms of North America*, but the latter contains identification keys that the lavishly illustrated guides do not. An important book for all mushroom foragers is *Toxic and Hallucinogenic Mushroom Poisoning* by Gary Lincoff and D.H. Mitchell, published in 1977 by Van Nostrand Reinhold, though now out of print.

THE MUSHROOM CULTIVATOR
By Paul Stamets & J.S. Chilton
415 pages
384A — paperback, $27.95
Available from Harrowsmith Books, Camden East, Ontario K0K 1J0. This illustrated guide includes instructions for growing all popular and many unusual mushroom species for which spawn can be purchased.

MUSHROOMS OF NORTH AMERICA
By Orson K. Miller, Jr.
368 pages
55A — vinyl field guide, $15.95
Available from Harrowsmith Books, Camden East, Ontario K0K 1J0.

THE MUSHROOM HUNTER'S FIELD GUIDE
By Alexander H. Smith & Nancy Smith Weber
316 pages
221B — hardcover, $21.50
Available from Harrowsmith Books, Camden East, Ontario K0K 1J0.

GROWING YOUR OWN MUSHROOMS
Cultivating, Cooking and Preserving
By Jo Mueller
174 pages
73A — paperback, $7.75
Available from Harrowsmith Books, Camden East, Ontario K0K 1J0.

Untamed Turkey

A wild gobbler in every pot

By Michael Webster

Ah, the Christmas turkey! Lovingly placed on an outsized platter, it highlights an already overloaded sideboard. Its graceful curves of plump meatiness, the golden brown of its crisp, crackling skin (perhaps brushed with a touch of garlic), its open maw of exposed stuffing — all bespeak the hidden white and dark delights awaiting the carver's knife. Inside, the grain of the meat exudes the tasty juices of butter, or perhaps coconut oil, injected into the carcass before freezing. "Know why they do that?" asks Dick Jones, his voice rising in ill-suppressed indignation. "Because all the flavour and texture has been bred out of these birds — they're just chewy fluffballs. These highly bred birds are so dry and tasteless, we had to end up with something like the Butterball."

Jones, an expatriate Englishman now settled on a 100-acre farm near Chatsworth, Ontario, where he raises game birds, explains: "Basically, what's happened in the poultry industry is that the producer has line-bred and genetically engineered hybrids that have done tremendous things for the producer. The rate of gain and the [feed-to-meat] conversion ratio have been improved tremendously, but for everything gained, there's something lost. Over the years, I think what we've lost is the texture and flavour of the original bird. The industry has taken care of its own interests in terms of economics. Consumers are getting a cheaper food basket, but they've lost on the culinary qualities of the bird."

Not surprisingly, the energetic and outspoken Jones offers an alternative: the American wild turkey, genetic ancestor of today's overbred domestic hybrids. "I still get excited every time I sit down to a meal of wild turkey," says Jones. "They're that good. I took one of the birds to a party in Toronto once, and a friend of mine barbecued it. The partygoers were a young and middle-aged crowd of sophisticated people — well dressed and, you know, 'socially mobile' — but when he set that bird down, it was like a school of piranha: the thing turned to nothing but bone right in front of my eyes. They just tore it to shreds. It was embarrassing to watch."

The difference, according to Jones, is breeding. "These birds are pure-strain American wild turkey. They haven't been messed with genetically. With domestic hybrids, that genetic potential has all gone into deposition of breast meat and rate of conversion. The birds' ability to give a good, textured, flavourful meat has been sacrificed for rate of gain and feed conversion. That hasn't been done with wild turkeys. These are the same birds that the Pilgrims ate."

Every school child in Canada and the United States knows the story of the first Thanksgiving turkey, that gift of friendship from a plague-ravaged band of Indians to an equally vulnerable society of Pilgrim settlers at the time of the first celebration of a bountiful harvest in the fall of 1621. It was a gift they could afford to part with. At that time, the wild-turkey population

Once an endangered species, the American wild turkey is now reestablished throughout much of its original territory.

in North America, although never accurately calculated, must have numbered many millions of birds, in a range that extended from southwestern Ontario through at least 36 of the as-yet-unestablished states and down into Mexico.

However, the wild turkey is a shy bird that prefers a habitat of large expanses of untouched forest, particularly hemlock and beech. As the land-clearing pioneers moved west, the wild turkey retreated before them, and any that remained fell victim to greedy and unrestricted hunting. Two hundred years after the first Thanksgiving feast, the wild turkey had disappeared from most of New England, and this trend continued until the 1920s, when the turkey population consisted of a scant 20,000 or 30,000 birds scattered across only 18 states — an endangered species by anyone's definition.

This tale holds true for Canada as well, where wild turkeys inhabited the moist and forested bottomland in 15 counties of southwestern Ontario. Writing in 1902, naturalist Edwyn Sandys noted that "30 years ago, one could drive in almost any direction through the woods of western Ontario and reasonably expect to see either the birds themselves or their tracks crossing the snowy roads. Today, there is perhaps a single narrow strip where one might strike a trail and possibly catch a glimpse of a fleeing survivor of the old-time hosts." A narrow strip, indeed, for although a turkey-hunting season was maintained until 1910, it is generally accepted that the winter of 1902-03 was the one in which the last Canadian wild turkey perished. Like their American counterparts, they had fallen victim to the unceasing transformation of forest to farmland. "The curtain came down simultaneously on turkey and forest," said naturalist C.H.D. Clarke in a 1948 report for an Ontario Ministry of Natural Resources publication. "The last bird may have been shot, but if he was, it was the axe and not the gun that made him the last."

Massive releases of pen-raised birds during the 1930s and 1940s failed to halt the downward trend in the United States. The Canadian population was considered gone forever. "Bring it back?" Clarke asked. "It would be just as reasonable to reintroduce the bison to the prairie wheat belt." The postwar situation on both sides of the border seemed bleak, but during the 1950s, two trends emerged that helped reverse the downward spiral: A good deal of second-growth hardwood forest gained enough maturity to support a wild-turkey population, and a new breed of wildlife biologists began live-trapping and transplanting native birds into the newly inhabitable areas. The result is one of the most successful wildlife programmes ever initiated. Today, there are two million wild turkeys in North America, and in addition to repopulating all their ancestral range, these birds have spread into every state (except Alaska) and into each of the western provinces. Hunting groups, many of whom worked diligently for the return of the wild turkey, now reap the benefit of its comeback under a strictly controlled hunting programme that sees approximately 10 percent of the population harvested each year.

Turkey hunters are a dedicated and enthusiastic lot, and an examination of their quarry reveals the cause. The wild turkey is a large bird — adult toms sometimes exceed four feet in length and 25 pounds in weight, although the hens are considerably smaller, usually around three feet long. "A day's bag of lesser game birds could be used as stuffing for one ordinary wild turkey," wrote Clarke, adding that "some of the game birds would certainly gain flavour in the process." In addition to its twin inducements of size and taste, the turkey must be hunted under the difficult shooting conditions presented by its thick forest habitats and the fact that it is a strong runner and a fast flier over short distances. Its legendary wariness has earned it the reputation of a game bird without equal in the world.

TURKEY CALLING

Virtually impossible to approach within shooting distance, turkeys are hunted by positioning oneself in a likely spot, "calling" a bird with any of an astonishing variety of ingenious devices made of boxes, tubes, slats or diaphragms, then, dressed in full camouflage gear, sitting absolutely still until a turkey arrives. The bird's stealth and its seemingly supernatural ability to take advantage of minimal cover, set against the hunter's knowledge of the area, talent at calling and ability to conceal himself from his sharp-eyed, cautious prey make for a challenging and rewarding hunt. "Turkey hunting," says sportswriter and longtime aficionado Charles Elliott, "is an addiction more binding than barbital, more tenacious than alcohol — more serious, even, than fishing. People occasionally overcome those afflictions. No one has ever been known to get over the disease of wild-gobbler hunting."

For all his enthusiasm about the wild birds, Jones does not expect that every turkey gourmet will take to the woods in camouflage fatigues and hide behind a tree until the spreading turkey population reaches his woodlot. No, Jones is one of a small group of bird fanciers who raise the birds in captivity for sale as day-olds to hunters, hobby farmers or backyard meat producers. His unabashed goal in life — although not even he can say it with a straight face — is to become Mr. Turkey of Canada. Those who know him do not doubt his ability to achieve that goal. Jones has the knack of directed enthusiasm that enables him to throw himself into his interests: not just a fisherman but a man who designs and ties his own flies; not a weekend sailor but one of pre-Olympic quality; a target shooter who wins trophies instead of plinking at cans; a horse rider who dresses in mountain-man garb, complete with authentic muzzleloader, to startle the neighbours; a hunter who mounts his own trophies. "I'm a dreamer and a romantic," he says, "but I can back it up with hard work." Lately, his energy has been concentrated on expanding his turkey operation.

At six foot four inches and well over 200 pounds, Jones has the build of a retired football linebacker. Born in Liverpool, England, he completed his apprenticeship as a mechanical draughtsman before coming

Tail fanned and wings drooping in a classic courting display, this gobbler struts for an unseen female.

to Canada, where he worked at his trade. Lured into the Harvestore organization by the promise of more money, he became a silo salesman and discovered a penchant for marketing and a passion for animal nutrition. Seven years ago, he bought his farm in the wooded, rolling hills south of Owen Sound, Ontario, on a ridge within sight of the Bruce Hiking Trail. For five years, he has raised pheasants there, the last three years on a full-time basis. Investing and reinvesting in the farm, he has increased his annual production level to more than 5,000 finished poults, which he sells to hunting groups or releases on his own land for parties

that pay to hunt them. He works hard to prevent the birds from becoming tame ("minimum imprinting is maximum management") and takes pride in their wildness. "When I release these birds, they don't stick around. They're not easy to shoot."

When pheasants were his bread and butter, Jones kept turkeys "as a curio," but now he is ready to become a major producer of wild turkeys. He anticipates that the birds will become popular because, in addition to their exceptional quality as a table bird, they are hardier, more intelligent and more resistant to disease than domestic birds. "And," he says, with a conspirator's grin, "the big difference between wild turkeys and domestic turkeys is that one group is controlled by quota by the provincial marketing board, and wild turkeys are raised under licence from the Ministry of Natural Resources. If you want to go out and buy domestic turkeys, you're limited to buying 50 poults. If 20 of them die, that's it, you've had your quota for the year; whereas with raising wild turkeys, a $10 licence lets you raise any number you want — there's absolutely no restriction on quantities."

This mention of quotas and provincial marketing boards is a reference to a 1979 change in the Ontario Marketing Board regulations that turned backyard turkey producers into outlaws unless they purchased their quota from the board. Public opinion forced an amendment to allow up to 50 unregistered birds per person, but Jones takes pleasure in outwitting what he sees as "a bunch of fat cats." Of wild turkeys, he says, "If you want to raise these birds for your own consumption and pleasure as a hobby or in any number for resale, all you need is the $10 permit, and you can raise a million turkeys. With domestic turkeys, you have to have a quota, and there just isn't any quota available."

Obviously not a person who abides bureaucratic boondoggling, Jones has had his share, having just emerged from a two-year struggle to secure a loan from the federally funded Farm Credit Corporation. In the spring of 1981, with his operation finally showing promise of success, Jones was saddled with a $40,000 personal debt, including an unpaid feed bill of $12,000, largely the result of start-up costs and mistakes due to inexperience. Needing money to finance an expansion and to consolidate his debts, Jones turned to Farm Credit. After his application was denied four times, he got a court order under the Freedom of Information Act that allowed him to see his file and to make adjustments to his application. According to Jones, the file revealed a "vindictive attitude" by one member of the three-man review board, a man who was a commercial turkey producer and a member of the turkey marketing board. "At one point, this guy called my operation a 'hobby farm,' and I really blew up." Jones's normally indiscernible accent creeps into his voice in recalled anger: "I mean, I had every penny I owned in the world in my operation, I was working at it 16 hours a day, I was living in a house where the roof leaked because all my money and energy were going into this thing, and then this guy has got the nerve to call it a hobby." This time, his application was approved.

Anticipating trouble with the marketing board, Jones has made sure that his birds are of 100 percent pure wild stock. "If they could prove there's domestic blood in them, I think they would have legal grounds to confiscate any surplus of the 50 birds that you may have," he says. "I think they have unfair powers."

With wild stock unavailable in Canada, Jones turned to 75-year-old South Carolina breeder T.M. Thomas, who claims to have "the purest eastern-strain wild turkeys available anywhere." Thomas still remembers being introduced to wild turkeys by Dr. Archibald Rutledge, former poet laureate of South Carolina and a prolific wildlife writer. In 1914, Rutledge visited Thomas's country school to give a nature talk. Only in the first grade at the time, Thomas was one of "a bunch of goggle-eyed school kids" who watched the guest lecturer pitch his tent in the schoolyard and prepare an evening meal of ham and grits. The next day, Rutledge spoke about local wildlife, and his eloquence about wild turkeys, combined with the haunting beauty of the paintings that he brought with him, began a lifelong fascination for Thomas, who eventually obtained a flock of birds which had been live-trapped "sometime in the 1880s." He now keeps a breeding flock of some 300 birds, divided into four strains that he carefully interbreeds to prevent genetic problems.

This spring, Jones ordered 400 wild-turkey eggs, which Thomas shipped in four crates. Separated in shipment, the crates crossed the border at two different points, and although the paperwork was in order, Agriculture Canada inspectors refused entry to two crates and delayed shipment of the other two. After the eggs had spent seven days in transit, Jones achieved a miserable 56 percent hatching rate, but although disappointed, he is not surprised: "People have experienced all kinds of problems at the border."

POULT TO POT

For those who want to raise their own wild turkeys, Jones offers encouragement. Although he sells both eggs and day-old poults, he recommends that backyard producers, unless they are experienced and have a professional-quality incubator, avoid buying eggs. Problems with fertility and hatching rates mean uncertain results, but "if you order 25 poults, that's what you get."

The first step in acquiring a flock of wild turkeys is to obtain a game-bird-propagation permit from the provincial wildlife management service. The cost ranges, according to the province, from free to $25 per producer and usually carries a provision for inspection of the premises. These inspections are not arduous and are concerned only with the housing and welfare of the birds. With permit in hand and day-olds in the coop, Jones says that in general, "what will work for domestic turkeys will work for wild turkeys too."

The major obstacle to overcome with young turkeys is getting them to imprint on their feed and water dishes. Without the example of their mother to follow, the birds need to be attracted to food and water by other means. Jones places marbles in the water dish — when the birds peck at the brightly coloured marbles, they discover the water — and starts the birds on a wire deck. Using ¼-inch galvanized wire "hardware cloth" stretched on a frame of 2 x 4s keeps the poults clean and dry because their droppings fall through the mesh. As a result, the birds are not distracted by a bed of litter, which they might otherwise peck at and digest. Jones puts their feed in 9-inch-square cake pans and sets a small piece of mesh on top of the feed. The pans provide a large surface that attracts the birds, and the mesh prevents them from scratching the feed out of the dishes. After seven days, the birds are sufficiently imprinted on the dishes to be taken off the deck, but the pans should remain until the birds outgrow them. "You'll know when the pans are inadequate,"

Dick Jones

Roy Decker

A wild turkey poult in the hand, **left,** *is worth two in the bush, where rigid controls and difficult stalking conditions give this mature hen,* **right,** *a 90 percent chance of surviving the hunting season.*

says Jones. "Common sense will dictate when you go to a tube feeder."

During the critical first weeks of life, good health is maintained by the universal requirements of clean, dry, warm and draught-free surroundings, coupled with adequate feed and clean water. As with any young birds, a supplementary heat source is necessary, and once again, common sense and a watchful eye are the most useful guides for proper use. If the birds are huddled under the brooder light, they are too cold; if spread out and panting, they are too hot.

Jones recommends a standard medicated turkey starter for the young birds, changing to a number-two starter with a larger crumb size at five or six weeks of age. When the birds are ready to go outside, they can be put on a 19 percent protein grower ration. "If it's the first time you've had any poultry in that particular area, I would just have them on a straight grower ration," advises Jones, "but as you repeat your flock on a yearly basis, I think it would be wise to have an Amprolium-medicated feed and take them off it two weeks before butchering. The Amprolium will keep them free of coccidiosis, and that's the main bug that these birds get. Coccidia, which can survive incredible extremes in weather — from heat to freezing — are in the environment and will be picked up the following year.

"I'd say 10 to 12 weeks is a good safe age to turn them outside. When you see a noticeable colouring coming into the wattle of the toms — when they 'shoot the red' — they're ready to be turned out." Still, after investing three months in the care and feeding of the birds, it is not a good idea to give them free range. "If you turn these birds out, don't expect them to come back like a bunch of domestic birds," says Jones. "That genetic wildness is there, and they'll just be gone."

The solution, of course, is a fenced run, but like any game bird, wild turkeys must not be overcrowded. Jones recommends that an adult bird be allowed 75 square feet of space in the run, somewhat less for younger birds. Thomas, who starts 50 poults in a 10' x 12' brooder house, never exceeds 300 birds in his 200' x 150' runs — a generous 100 square feet per bird. However, like love, a wild turkey will not be contained by mere walls. "These birds fly like stink," says Jones, who recommends either covering the pen with wire or nylon mesh or having the birds' primary flight feathers pinioned when they are day-old poults. "At that age, it's not a stressful experience. Of course," he adds, with a wry smile, "I've never had it done to myself, so I can't speak from experience."

The final requirement for a turkey run reemphasizes the birds' essential wildness: shade. "They've got to have quiet, shaded, secret places," says Jones. "If you turn them out into a stark pen, they'll go crashing into the wire, and you could lose some birds." He seeds the run in the spring with a purchased "pheasant pasture mix," which is mature enough by the time the birds are released to withstand their trampling. Consisting of tall, sturdy, edible plants like kale, sunflower, corn and rape, the mixture offers shade and, by giving the birds something to peck at, stops cannibalism and reduces the feed bill substantially. It also offers hiding places for the birds, increasing their feeling of security. According to Thomas, loud, strange noises can cause the birds to flock together in an open pen and thereby smother each other. And, as with any domestic bird, foraging improves the quality and flavour of the meat.

The birds are not ready for slaughter until they are 22 weeks old, compared to 12 weeks for domestic birds, and as Jones admits, "The conversion rate is terrible." Evidence of this is as close as the kitchen scales: Even after being fed for nearly twice as long, wild turkeys dress out to an average of only 12 to 15 pounds. A good, heavy tom might hit 18 pounds, but hens will run in the 8-to-12-pound range, hardly in the same league as the 25-to-30-pound domestic monsters. Still, with North American families becoming smaller and more fragmented, the market trend is toward smaller birds, thus avoiding protracted leftovers. As one consumer said of his oversized Christmas bird, "The sucker seemed to last forever."

For Jones, with his respect for the wild birds, killing day brings a new burden. "I can never feel bad about shooting a wild turkey, but to go into the barn and hang one up by the feet and hit it over the head — I can never feel good about that." Also, the bird's black plumage can produce an unappetizing-looking carcass unless each feather is faithfully removed — one reason that domestic birds were bred with white feathers.

GAME GOBBLERS

To avoid buying day-olds or eggs, the wild-turkey enthusiast may wish to keep his own breeding flock, but the process is somewhat more complicated than with domestic fowl. The first rule of game-bird management is to keep the oldest birds — those hatched from the first eggs laid — as next year's breeders. This, of course, is a luxury of choice unavailable to a first-year practitioner, or even to a second-year turkey-keeper, for only rarely does a tom become fertile before he is two years old. Aspiring breeders will have to keep some toms from their first batch of poults and some hens from the second year's purchased birds before they have any reasonable hope of hatching fertile eggs in the third year.

Overwintering wild turkeys requires no special care. They can "take incredible cold as long as they can get feed in ample supply," says Jones. Although a draught-free enclosure is an obvious advantage, Jones has left his birds out in a blizzard with only a minimal windbreak for shelter. Wild turkeys are tough and adaptable birds whose natural range is restricted not by a weather map's isocheims but by a lack of available feed in areas where winters are long and harsh. Ever the nutritionist, Jones scoffs at game-bird producers who winter their birds on a diet of high-energy cracked corn.

Shy birds that require large expanses of mature forest to survive, toms like these often exceed four feet in length.

"Sure it puts lots of fat on them," he says, "but it's not giving them the 10 essential amino acids that they need for a balanced diet."

Jones overwinters his breeder flock on a commercially prepared game-bird maintenance chow from the time they are 16 weeks of age until the first week of March. Then he gradually changes to a game-bird laying mash, which has a higher protein content than a layer ration for chickens — once again, a reflection of the wild turkeys' poor conversion rate. By the beginning of April, the birds are ready to be turned into a community breeder pen — simply a run with nesting sites for the hens, where the change in diet and the increased light bring the hens into production sometime in April. A ratio of one tom for six hens should be adequate; as Jones puts it, "With turkeys, one shot does the trick for the whole season — a hen served by a tom is fertile for the entire laying period."

Offering areas of privacy for the laying hens serves a dual purpose: encouraging egg laying and keeping the eggs clean. Some loose straw under a piece of plywood propped up against a bale of hay makes an adequate nesting site that will serve two or three hens, and Thomas claims that his birds lay until September, although the hatching rate falls steadily during the summer. The breeding flock need not be retired after a single season, but production will drop significantly after the third year.

The major challenge, particularly in mucky spring weather, is to keep the eggs clean enough that they do not need to be washed. "Washing an egg is very stressful," says Jones, pointing out that with an egg, "you're dealing with life at the embryonic stage." Very dirty eggs must be washed to prevent infection of the newly hatched chicks by disease organisms in the attached dirt. "Washing is the lesser of two evils," says Jones, "but it's still an evil; avoid washing eggs if you can." Unless the eggs are seriously soiled, he recommends removing as much of the dry matter as possible and then lightly sanding what is left with a fine garnet paper until the egg is clean again.

The reason for all this motherly concern about egg cleanliness is the unwillingness of the hens to brood in the unnatural atmosphere of a farm operation. "If you've got hen turkeys that will sit on eggs in captivity, they're not true wild turkeys — they've got some domestic strain in them," pronounces Jones, who hatches his poults in a 4,800-egg incubator. He advises that beginners place their eggs under what he calls "a living incubator," a female Bourbon Red turkey that, like a banty hen, will adopt orphaned eggs. "She'll raise them very diligently and lovingly, and you can have your barnyard turkeys that way. But the problem is that as the poults get bigger, she'll range farther, and if you've got a woodlot or a bush, she'll range in there. One day, she'll come home on her own, and the poults won't come back."

Despite Jones's insistence on the inherent wildness of his birds, there are those who disagree. Paul Prevett, regional ecologist with the Ontario government, explains: "When these birds are first penned up, the spookiest ones fly against the fences and are injured or killed. In a very few generations, the real wild stuff dies out. Game farm birds are not as secretive, wild or wily as the real wild birds. They're easier to hunt and are more susceptible to predators." Game farm birds — the phrase brings a sneer to the lips of naturalists and wildlife workers who still remember the failure of the mass release of hatchery-raised birds in the '30s and '40s. Today, it is felt that releases of pen-raised birds actually have a negative effect on the wild population because they carry barnyard diseases and parasites. At the same time, the farm-raised birds, imprinted on the feed trough, are not able to feed themselves well enough to survive harsh winter weather. This was vividly demonstrated by the release of 88 turkeys in the Porcupine Hills of southern Alberta in the spring of 1973. Seventy-five of the birds were hatchery-raised, the other 13 were live-trapped in Nebraska. When the snow melted the following spring, only 12 birds remained — all of them live-trapped transplants.

In Canada, there are wild-turkey populations scattered in every province west of Quebec, with the largest and most successful in Manitoba. According to Wildlife Programme Coordinator Ron Larche, the Manitoba stocking was begun in 1958 by Wild Gobblers Unlimited, a privately funded special-interest group, and the birds' range now covers most of southern Manitoba, wherever there is a large stand of mature nut-producing trees. "The birds are not able to survive the winters by themselves, so they congregate around cattle operations, eating grain and scratching in the hay." In fact, the only wild-turkey population in Canada not dependent on the generosity of interested farmers is in the Cypress Hills area along the Alberta/Saskatchewan border, where a 1962 stocking was all but wiped out by the severe winters of the late '60s. Discouraged, biologists turned their attention to the milder Porcupine Hills region, but a small flock of genuinely wild turkeys still ekes out a precarious existence at the original site.

By and large, provincial governments are receptive to wild-turkey stocking programmes, although funding is left to private groups. With numerous projects across Canada in various stages of organization or implementation, it would be scurrilously irresponsible for any individual to release farm-raised birds that may, like a measles-ridden wagon train heading into Indian territory, wipe out a beleaguered native population. Irresponsible and, in most provinces, illegal, without a special permit.

Although Dick Jones is sympathetic to attempts to place turkeys in the wild again, he is far more interested in placing them in a roasting pan. "You can't go into the wild and shoot a bird that tastes as good as these pen-raised birds," he says. "They pick up delicate flavours from the greens they peck at, but they also have the benefit of a controlled diet, and that makes a big difference." He is a firm believer in allowing the birds some free range to enhance the flavour of the meat and says that although a wild turkey will never taste like a hybrid, proper management can make a significant difference where it counts — at the Christmas dinner table. "The bird has the genetic potential to be an absolute gourmet delight," says Jones, warming up to his favourite topic, "but if you take shortcuts and get cheap when you're raising the bird, you're going to be disappointed.

"They're a long, lean, gangly-looking bird, but when I finish them on my feeding programme, I find I get a well-rounded breast and flavour and texture you just can't compare. You don't see the marbling in poultry flesh, but it's there — the fat is permeating the meat — and when you cook the bird, it bastes so evenly that the breast meat is as moist as the leg meat. I'd rather eat an eastern-strain American wild turkey than I would one of those coconut-oil-injected cotton wads. If we've got a choice, that's my choice, and I don't need anybody's blessing or their damn quota." ∎

All White Meat, No Crowing

Reconsidering the humble rabbit

By Ron Allensen

As a child, I always found it strange that my mother put such dogged faith in the miraculous charms of two small mauve and yellow paws she dropped in her purse prior to her Thursday night departures for the bingo hall. Had my perennially lucky Aunt Olive taken to using the same charms, I'm sure I would have gained great faith in their magical powers. As it was, my aunt usually returned home with the winner's share of the loot, but my mother, more often than not, came home empty-handed, despite her amulets.

Folklore, mythology and half-truth have accompanied the rabbit — and its paws — wherever it has gone, from the outback of Australia where rabbits are said to be as plentiful as zebras on the Serengeti, to Wales where newborn babies are wished good health with the touch of a rabbit's foot, to North America where a cutesy, sugar-coated mythology reigns and rabbits are ubiquitously associated with everything from "What's up, Doc?" to *Watership Down*. More than any other myth, it is this cartoon fantasy that has hindered the rabbit's acceptance as a meat animal.

For instance, I recently asked a friend why she didn't buy rabbit meat. She confessed that every time she sees a sign in the local butcher shop that reads "Fresh Rabbits on Ice," all she can think of is Thumper coaxing Bambi onto the pond. Although rabbit meat was as popular as chicken or pork at the turn of the century, it is only now gradually overcoming such sentiments to regain its position as a meat of choice, especially as downtown supermarkets begin to carry it and rabbit

hutches become ever more popular features of the backyard.

Those who do decide to raise their own rabbits discover, as Europeans and Chinese have known for centuries, that the animals are as easy and economical to raise as chickens and have several other attributes besides. Rabbit stock is relatively inexpensive to obtain, thrives almost anywhere, is clean and legendarily prolific. As one 19th-century writer recorded, "Their amazing fecundity renders the keeping of a few of them in a tame state an object of some consequence in the cottage economy."

Where space is limited, in the city or village, raising a few rabbits for the family larder is simple and practical. A single doe in a small hutch can produce 70 to 95 pounds of dressed meat in a year. Two does can produce one rabbit meal a week, year-round. Three or four hutches will usually house just about all the rabbits an average family can eat, producing some of the best-tasting meat available anywhere. And rabbits will never be caught crowing at the neighbours at 5 A.M. Some apartment dwellers have even managed to raise a few almost unnoticed on the balcony.

One struggling author who turned to rabbits to supplement his income says he never again will be afraid of starving, even if no one buys his books. "I have learned enough about rabbits," he says, "to make them provide me with an old-age pension." The versatile little lagomorph is not only an excellent source of delicate white meat, but can provide several other sources of potential income, including the sale of breeding stock,

wool, pelts and the best natural garden fertilizer available.

Exactly where and when the wild rabbit was first domesticated is a matter of some dispute, but selection and crossbreeding have been employed to such a large extent that there are now more than 50 distinct breeds, from 2-pound dwarfs to the long-haired Angoras to 20-pound Flemish Giants.

Large-scale producers generally choose one of the medium-sized breeds, such as the New Zealand white (also available in red or black), or the Californian, which has white body fur with black or brown extremities. These animals weigh 10½ to 12 pounds at maturity, although they are usually butchered at about half that weight. Like hybrid meat chickens, these two breeds have been developed for consistent performance in superior conversion of feed to meat, in disease resistance and fertility. Less popular but similar in size and habit are the Palomino, Martens and Silver Fox.

Before one chooses a breed, he must decide which aspect of rabbit breeding is most appealing to him, taking into consideration the space he has available. Those who have limited space and do not care for large meat animals might choose one of the dwarf breeds, which rarely weigh more than five pounds at maturity but are just as edible and prolific as the larger breeds. Almost all breeds, including Angoras, are suitable for the production of meat for home use, but anyone who wishes to raise rabbit meat to sell must consider the desires of

Although most meat rabbits are white, other shades find favour among some breeders.

the market, whether it be a larger commercial processor, the local food store or the neighbours. Throughout much of Canada, there are regional processors who will often buy live animals, but contact the closest before investing in rabbit stock. The prices they pay vary widely, but currently run from 75 to 80 cents a pound for live fryers (four to six pounds). Rabbits over six pounds are considered roasters. As they are in less demand than fryers and may be tougher, they command a much lower price, only 35 to 40 cents a pound at present.

The number of rabbits one purchases will depend upon one's choice of breed, especially whether they are small or large, the amount of space available and the size of operation envisioned. In any event, start small. Those who do want to sell meat commercially and who have found a market for the meat might want to buy five or six does and a buck, while anyone who simply wants a few rabbit dinners for his family could get by without a buck at all, buying just one doe that he will take to someone else's buck for servicing.

Jack and Marg McCallum of Lambeth, Ontario, are a good example of a family who started small. They raised a few rabbits for show in their city backyard, until they found that their herd contravened local by-laws, so they relocated, expanding their operation to include a small processing plant. "It is a seven-day-a-week job," says Marg, "and you can easily get discouraged while you are building up your herd and your feed bill begins to look like the national debt." Keeping rabbits is not a venture that should be undertaken with the sole idea of making money, at least not initially.

Jack recommends not only that the beginner start small but also that he pay less attention to breed and more to the animal's overall suitability for his purposes. "Above all," he says, "I look for a broad, meaty animal that has good-sized litters and outstanding milking ability."

This kind of information is available only from the breeder who has kept a record of the performance of his animals. While registration is not necessary in a meat production herd, it would be wise for the husbandman to obtain a pedigree, a record of the family lineage, for each rabbit purchased. For one thing, if all the stock is purchased from the same rabbitry, consulting the pedigrees will enable the new breeder to prevent too-close inbreeding.

REGISTERED STOCK

Registration papers will provide the buyer with even more information, but many topnotch registered show animals would definitely not make the best meat animals and will certainly cost more than unregistered animals. These animals are not judged primarily on their performance as parents but simply on their condition, fur and conformation.

When buying stock for large-scale meat production, it is most important to ask to see the records of the parents of the animals offered for sale, however. Any breeder who has a really good herd will not refuse this request. Many breeders of meat animals claim that crossing the pure strains will often produce a meatier rabbit. Cross-bred stock that shows consistently high production levels should not be rejected out of hand.

In any case, be sure to buy from a breeder whose rabbitry is clean and neat and who will stand behind what he sells with a guarantee. The beginner may choose to buy either one or more mature animals ready to breed or young stock, which will, of course, be less expensive, since does must be six to eight months old before they can be bred.

In selecting any stock, thoroughly examine the rabbits offered. The fur should snap back into place when you run your hand from tail to neck against the grain. The eyes should be clear and bright and the fur below them dry and unmatted. The two upper front teeth should be straight and meet or overlap the lower ones — never the lower over the upper ones. The fur pads on the soles of the back feet should be very dense and somewhat coarser than the body fur. This is essential in rabbits kept on wire floors; rabbits with less than adequate foot pads will develop sore hocks. In young rabbits, the back feet should track straight with the body and not stick out at the sides. Fecal matter should be in the form of hard, round pellets, dark brown or lighter, depending on the foods consumed. Above all, choose a rabbit that is active and lively, with ears that are constantly moving one way or another to catch any

sound and a nose that is twitching and shows no sign of discharge.

Rabbit sources are plentiful in most areas of the country. Buying a rabbit will simply mean a short car trip with a cardboard box to a spot listed in the local newspaper's classified ads. If the beginner is after a certain breed or lives in a remote area, however, he may want to contact some of the rabbit societies listed in Sources at the end of this article.

Before the new rabbit owner arrives home with his charge or charges, he must have made some provision for housing. Keep in mind that while rabbits can tolerate cold, the keeper who allows them to remain damp for any length of time is courting disaster, often in the form of pneumonia. Ventilation (but not draughts) and dryness are the top priorities for the rabbitry. In summer, it is most important that the building not become too hot, so a partially shaded spot is preferred. Vines can also be used to help shield the building from the direct summer sun. If constructing a new rabbitry (the building to house the hutches), one should locate the long axis east-west, if possible, to make use of prevailing winds for ventilation in summer.

Hutches, the "single-family dwellings" for rabbits, can be situated outdoors on their own or, as is more popular in Canada, inside a larger building such as a barn or shed (either already present or specially constructed). This way, the animals are protected from severe temperatures and winds. Only in relatively temperate parts of Canada can a hutch be left outdoors all year, and in this case, it should be situated against the south wall of a larger building and placed on legs at least three feet above the ground to help prevent predator invasions and reduce dampness.

In very frigid areas of the country, any rabbit shelter must be well insulated if breeding is to continue through the winter. Jack and Marg McCallum utilize heat lamps to "dry the dampness off" occasionally in their unheated rabbitry, where the rabbits breed successfully year-round. "I find a change in the weather is a far greater problem than cold," says Marg. "Rabbits are very susceptible to pneumonia, and when the weather is constantly changing, we have our greatest problems."

As far as hutches go, durable and relatively inexpensive ones can be homemade using a wooden framework and square-mesh rabbit wire. A practical size will accommodate a doe and her litter and yet not be larger than the full reach of the breeder, so that he may easily examine the nest box or catch an individual rabbit. A hutch 36" x 30" x 18" high or 40" x 24" x 15" high is adequate for a medium-sized doe and her litter, who should be provided with at least six or seven square feet. The door should be at least 18 inches square. The main frame should be made of 2 x 4s or a combination of 2 x 4s and 2 x 2s. If it is outdoors, the roof should overhang the hutch by at least eight inches on each side to provide some shade and protection. Ordinary shingles or tar paper are preferable to tin, which becomes excessively hot in the sun.

Several of these basic units can be attached to an inside shed wall, placed in rows or one above the other with deflecting metal or wooden panels below each, which slant backward to catch and direct the droppings. In a two-tier arrangement, locate the bucks on the lower tier to avoid the unpleasant possibility of being sprayed with urine.

RABBIT WIRE

Avoid poultry mesh in construction, as it is extremely fragile and is easily corroded by rabbit urine. Instead, use 16-gauge 1" x 1" galvanized square screening for the ends and sides of the enclosure. Fourteen-gauge 1" x 1½" screening on the floor will support a doe and her litter and will allow droppings to pass through. Even this thick-gauge wire may begin to show rust spots after a few years, however; this tendency can be considerably slowed by the application of fast-drying aluminum paint.

Baby-saver wire is used by some breeders to prevent the loss of young born outside the nest box. This mesh, available from rabbit supply houses, has 1" x 1½" openings for the bottom four inches, the remainder being 1" x 1". Remember that wire should be attached to the inside of the framing to prevent any exposed wood from being gnawed.

Those who opt to build the hutches into a larger building often choose all-wire cages rather than wood/wire hutches. Cages are favoured by commercial breeders and are available from rabbit supply houses. Including built-in feeders and dropping catchpans, they are well designed and durable but quite expensive. Similar cages are fairly easy to construct and just as easy to clean and disinfect. Use the same special rabbit wire recommended previously for the hutches, joining it at the seams using J-clips, available from most feed companies and rabbit suppliers. These clips should be applied every four inches or so to ensure that the wire does not separate. Use the same dimensions as those recommended for hutches. Cages or hutches for bucks can be slightly smaller but must allow enough room for exercise.

Make a few hutches to finish out any fryers that fail to reach the desired weight by the time they are weaned, or to house a young doe or buck kept as a future breeder. Those who wish to keep only a few rabbits should place a single tier of wire cages just above waist height to avoid constant bending over and to aid in cleaning. Some breeders prefer to construct a metal framework for cages out of perforated steel angle-iron, which is assembled with nuts and bolts much like a child's construction set. With two tiers, leave at least 18 inches between the bottom tier and the floor. If more than one tier is used, don't forget to install a dropping board between each tier.

Besides hutches or cages, there are several other essential pieces of rabbitry equipment. One of the most important is the nest box. There is a variety of nest boxes available, including all wire and all cardboard models, but the most satisfactory for cold climates is a box made of wood. These boxes can have an entirely or only partially covered top. However, Hardie

The Champagne d'argent is a rabbit show favourite, but far too exotic for farmyard stock.

Brown, a longtime breeder in London, Ontario, claims that a covered nest box will make "all the difference in survival rates," particularly during very cold winters.

For a New Zealander or other medium-sized doe, a box measuring 20" x 1' x 1' high will avoid crowding while allowing the young to stay warm. Cut a 7" x 7" hole in the upper front of the box, five inches above the floor, to allow the doe entry. The floor of the box should be removable to facilitate cleaning and should have six or eight ¼" drilled holes for ventilation and drainage.

Whatever its quarters, the rabbit must have access at all times to clean, fresh water. This can easily be provided by inverting a large pop or liquor bottle filled with water outside the cage and placing its neck in a small water dish, which will fill automatically when the water level drops. Thirsty rabbits will not eat. Be sure in winter that the water supply has not frozen and in summer that the supply does not run out as the animals' drinking increases. Does that are nursing have an especially great need for fresh water.

A sound feeding programme is the foundation of fast growth and good meat production. Years ago, it was quite a task to guarantee that the available feed provided the essential nutrients rabbits need. Today, modern research has resulted in bite-sized pellets which contain everything that rabbits require. They can thrive on a combination of other feeds, but pellets save time, avoid wastage and assure the owner that the rabbits have a proper diet. I advise beginners to stick to commercial pellets.

John Seymour, writing in *The Self-Sufficient Gardener*, believes, however, that "the best approach is to strike a happy medium and feed some grain — oats are best — mixed with hay and greenstuff and, if you can get it, with whole or fragmented bran. Rabbits also like potato peelings, boiled potatoes and all the root crops: turnips, mangels, parsnips, carrots and radishes. Sugar beet is fine for fattening young rabbits but not for breeding stock; it makes them too fat.

"Four ounces of pellets or six ounces of oats per day with as much hay and greenstuff as they want is a good ration for adult rabbits, but this amount must be increased for a pregnant doe to eight ounces per day until the young are weaned so that she has enough milk."

Among "greenstuffs," Seymour includes grass, dried nettles, kale, root tops (but not potato leaves) and many other assorted greens. Those who intend to supplement or replace commercial rabbit pellets must keep in mind three categories: dry roughages, green roughages and concentrates, all of which should be provided. Preferred dry roughages are good quality cover or alfalfa hay, but other good quality hays will do. Green roughages should be fed in small amounts. They include carrots, rutabagas, turnips and lettuce. Cabbage should be avoided or fed in very small amounts only, and never to young rabbits, as it will cause diarrhoea. The concentrates include grains such as corn, oats, wheat and barley. Beet pulp or soybean meal may also be used if available. Hay can be fed by placing it on top of the cages where the rabbits will reach for it. The other feeds should be placed in a compartment feeder because the rabbits are likely to scratch them out and waste them if several feeds are combined. Breeders who do not feed pellets must provide mineral salt in a block or spool in each cage.

Because all rabbits do not have exactly the same feed requirements, many breeders provide access to food throughout the day. This is especially recommended for does in late pregnancy and those suckling rabbits. All breeding stock should be kept on the lean side, however, as fat animals produce poorly or have more difficulty raising their young.

Domestic rabbits, like their wild cousins, are more active during twilight and early evening and so will eat more readily at this time of day. If this is not convenient, rabbits can adjust to any schedule. The most important thing is regularity: rabbits should be fed at the same time every day. If feed is not always available, allow the animals only what they will clean up in a half-hour.

The easiest feeding method utilizes a self-feeder that can be filled from the outside and is attached to the side of the cage. Some breeders use earthen crocks or feed troughs, but these can be easily soiled, and cages must be opened for them to be filled or cleaned.

The propagative propensities of rabbits are legendary, but their capacity for family plannning is rather limited. Although one breeder swears that a mother rabbit was overheard explaining to her daughter that at her age she was already married and the mother of 176 children, it is not very likely that most domestic rabbits will achieve this kind of unmitigated breeding success if left to their own devices. Selective breeding in the rabbitry is a must for ensuring a continuing line of high-quality animals that mature early.

Does and bucks of the medium breeds are ready for breeding at about six months of age. "Bucks are half the herd," says McCallum, "and they should be as rigidly selected as the does."

Both the buck and the doe should have a coat that shines, with little shedding fur. Both animals are best on the slim side. An especially fat doe will have a difficult gestation. If both prospective parents look good to you, take the doe to the buck's hutch. Never make the mistake of taking the buck to the doe, as they will usually fight rather than fondle.

When handling a rabbit, never lift it by its ears or legs. Instead, grasp the loose skin over the shoulders with one hand, and place the other hand under the rump to support most of the weight. Hold the rabbit outward to avoid being scratched if it struggles. A very large rabbit or one that struggles excessively may be turned around and held snugly under one arm, placing the other hand under the hindquarters to support its weight.

To examine the doe for readiness to breed, pick her up by the loose hide over the shoulders, and set her upside down against your lap. With the other hand, lightly press either side of the vent. If the vulva is a deep reddish-purple colour rather than pale pink, the doe is probably ready to breed. In any case, she should not be less than six months old.

Rabbit breeding is definitely unromantic. If you blink, you are likely to miss it. Those who manage not to blink at the wrong moment will observe the buck mount the doe, service her and fall over backwards or on his side. Occasionally, one may even come across what is known as a "screamer." These bucks will stand straight up when they ejaculate and let out an ear-piercing scream. Don't be alarmed. Whether silent or noisy, the buck will probably regain his composure in a moment or two. After mating, the doe should be gently removed from the buck's cage. Hold her rump up rather than down to help retain the semen.

If, for some reason, the doe will not accept the buck, remove her and try again the next day. If this doesn't work, try her with another buck. The vast majority of the time, the buck is ready to mate, but occasionally, the doe is not. Sometimes it helps to allow the buck and doe to exchange hutches for an evening so that they will acquire each other's scent. Other handlers restrain the doe to allow the buck to service her, but this is rarely necessary.

Some breeders advise against overworking a young buck, insisting that it is best to limit his use to twice weekly. Hardie Brown dismisses the notion as "strictly ridiculous," saying that bucks can be safely bred every day with no ill effect and citing a university veterinarian who claimed he sometimes used his service bucks every two hours for extended periods. Brown insists that

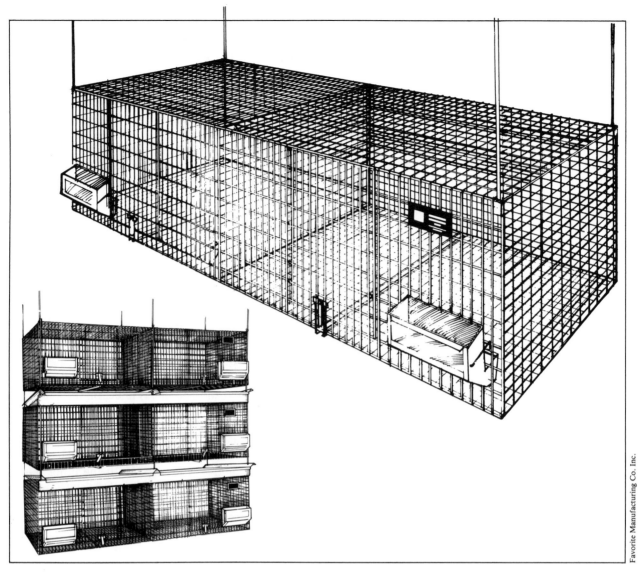

Favorite Manufacturing Co. Inc.

The narrow-meshed floor of this hutch serves to protect young rabbits from falls. Hutches may be used singly, combined in single rows or hung from overhead frames to provide a solid wall of rabbit housing.

three bucks can easily service 35 to 40 does and will not be used to anywhere near their limit. Marg McCallum more conservatively recommends one buck for every eight does. She adds that she always likes to have a couple of spares, "because you never know when one is going to go toes-to-the-sky."

How does one know whether the mating was a success? It has been variously reported that the female rabbit is fertile 365 days, or that she is fertile for 12 days, followed by 2 to 4 days of infertility. Whatever the truth, it is known that the sperm remains viable with the doe for up to 30 hours after mating and that upon sexual stimulation, her eggs will begin to descend. The time required for fertilization (for the eggs to meet the sperm) ranges from 8 to 10 hours, usually ensuring that conception will take place. Many breeders put the doe back in the buck's hutch on the 5th and 18th days after the first breeding. If she runs from the buck and growls, it is a fairly good sign that she has conceived. If she allows the buck to service her, however, note the new date, because she may now be bred if she isn't already pregnant.

There are a couple of ways to determine whether or not the doe has conceived. First, weigh the doe at mating time and record the poundage. If, two weeks later, she has gained a pound or more (on the same feeding

programme), she is probably pregnant. The second method is to palpate, to feel for the young. Place the doe on a flat surface, and hold her by the scruff of the neck with one hand, gently sliding the other hand under her belly. Within two weeks after mating, the developing young will feel like large marbles on both sides of centre, just forward of the groin area. While some practice is necessary to determine the presence of young by this method, once it is mastered, it can save time by eliminating falsely pregnant does.

The gestation period in rabbits varies from 28 to 34 days, so the 27th day after mating, a nest box should be provided in the hutch. Avoid the temptation to put the box in before the 27th day, as the doe will soil it before the babies arrive. For nesting material, use plenty of clean, soft hay with an optional layer of wood shavings on the bottom to absorb moisture. Do not use sawdust, as it will suffocate the young. Supply some extra straw outside the box to satisfy the doe's packing instinct; most does are quite industrious in nest building. A day or two before the litter arrives, the doe will pluck her belly and sides. This instinctive behaviour serves to provide a final bedding to line the nest, while baring the nipples so that the babies can nurse easily. The doe may go off her feed slightly at this time, but be sure that feed and water are always available. The doe should be left alone when her kindling (birthing) time nears.

Occasionally, outside disturbances, a lack of protein or simple nervousness may cause a first-litter doe to eat or kill part of her litter. Make a note of her behaviour and provide her with extra protein for her next litter. The young doe should be forgiven her first offence, but if she eats part of her second litter, she is best culled from the herd.

The day after the doe has kindled, offer her a tidbit of carrot or apple to keep her occupied while inspecting the litter. Count the babies and remove any dead ones. If there are more than eight, it is best to foster the extras off to another doe who was bred at the same time and has fewer than eight. Mark the ear of any transferred youngsters with ink so that you can keep track of their parentage. If the two litters are within a few days of each other, most does will readily accept young from another mother. If you aren't sure about the doe's acceptance, rub a little vanilla extract on her nose. This will disturb her sense of smell long enough for the fostered baby to pick up the scent of the rest of the litter.

With the new litter nursing, the doe will benefit from an extra lettuce leaf or carrot each day. She should be given all the pellets she will eat mixed with a tablespoon or so of dried milk each day to aid her in providing the nourishment her litter needs.

After the initial inspection, it is best that the doe and her young be disturbed as little as possible and only for very brief periods to check their progress or remove any young that have died.

The origin of the superstition concerning the luck of the rabbit's foot is said to have sprung from a belief that young rabbits are born with their eyes open and thus have the power to ward off evil. Contrary to this belief, rabbits are born naked with their eyes tightly closed and remain that way for 10 to 12 days after birth, during which time the young rabbits grow rapidly. If a single baby is ever found outside the nest, it should be returned at once. It was probably pulled out of the nest while hanging on to the mother's teat.

When the babies do start coming out of the nest at about three weeks of age, they will sample the foods provided for the doe. Very slowly add more feed to the doe's ration, but once the little rabbits leave the box, all green feeds must be stopped until the babies have been weaned.

When rabbits are about five weeks of age, they will begin to increase their intake of solid food substantially. Creep feeding — providing special high-protein, small pellet rations — will boost the young rabbits' growth, allowing the farmer to breed the doe sooner than would otherwise be possible. Special creep feeders are available, permitting access only to the young rabbits. By the time they are four or five weeks old, the nest box may be removed. It may be necessary to provide clean bedding straw when the nest box is used for this length of time.

Advances in feeding, including pellets and creep-feeding techniques, now make it possible to maintain the doe in good condition even if she is bred again when the litter is just five or six weeks old. The young are weaned at seven or eight weeks, at which point they may be butchered as fryers. This regime will give the farmstead about five or six litters per doe each year, allowing her a week or two before kindling without the nursing young. The doe is ordinarily more easily bred again if her previous litter is still running in the hutch with her; after a rest, she is apt to get fat and have difficulty conceiving. After mating, she should be returned to her cage and her young, who may remain with their mother for another couple of weeks with no ill effects on her health.

Weaning should be a gradual process, taking place over a period of about a week. Taking away the biggest youngsters first will help the mother to dry up gradually, allowing the little ones some extra milk. The litter may remain together in a single hutch until the young are three months old, but then each young buck who will be kept for breeding will require a hutch of his own. At this stage, it becomes necessary to sex the rabbits.

The gender of young rabbits can be determined by pressing open the sexual aperture just below the anal opening, using the thumb and forefinger. In does, a longitudinal slit is observed; if the little rabbit is a buck, a minute tubular protrusion will be noticed.

Young does that are to be kept for breeding stock can be accommodated two to a hutch. Most of the rabbits should be ready for butchering at eight weeks, so there need be few growing pens unless the herd size is to increase. It is difficult to measure a rabbit's potential as a future breeder when it is only eight weeks old. To properly assess them, let the young develop to at least three months of age. Then always select the finest animals in the litter. Choose daughters from does that show strength, stamina and resistance to disease. The young stock of does that have few problems kindling, are good milkers and breed readily are the ones that should be considered. Many smallish does are far superior to large animals when it comes to nest building, milk production and the ability to produce year-round, so think twice before rejecting any doe simply because of her small size.

See to it that the doe's breeding record card is always maintained. This card should include her birth date, name, or identification number, and those of her sire and dame. There should also be spaces to record the identification of the buck she was served by, date kindled, number of young born, raised, adopted and those that have died. Additional columns may indicate whether progeny were saved for breeding, average weight of young at weaning and additional remarks. Buck record cards should have space for the farmer to record each doe served, date, resulting litter size, weight and remarks. Breeding record cards similar to these can usually be obtained from your feed dealer, but homemade cards are adequate for the backyard rabbit herd.

Faithful record keeping will provide any rabbit

keeper with information essential in planning matings and monitoring the progress of the stock. Every breeding rabbit in a herd should also have some permanent means of indentification. A starter tattoo set with numbers zero through nine is well worth the small investment. It is simple to use: Insert the numbers into the pliers, squeeze firmly over the left ear, and rub the tattoo ink into the ear. A coding system combining letters and numbers can easily be devised to record month and year of birth, an identifying number and perhaps the keeper's initials.

Rabbits are extremely hardy, disease-resistant creatures. There are a number of rabbit ailments, however, most of which are only positively diagnosed by experienced handlers. Certainly the best cure for all of them is prevention. By keeping the pens clean, dry and free of draughts, the rabbit tender is likely to have little problem with disease. Cage floors should be brushed clean every few days and completely disinfected with a propane torch or disinfectant cleaner every few months. Many rabbits display a strong dislike for the odour of chlorine or ammonia used around their cages; it is best to use a less offensive smelling cleaner. The nest box as well must be thoroughly scraped and cleaned after each litter. Wash it with a mild disinfectant, and allow to dry inside and out before using again. Manure must not be allowed to build up under the cages. It should be removed every couple of weeks and composted or collected in a central location to dry.

The many attributes of the rabbit include the somewhat dubious but undisputed title of king of the dung heap. Although some of their other claims to fame may be debated, no experienced vegetable gardener would deny that rabbits produce one of the most effective natural fertilizers available for garden soils. I have known several gardeners and nurserymen who keep rabbits for this reason alone. Many of them have tried commercial fertilizers, other animal manures and various combinations, yet they still swear by the efficacy of rabbit manure. Unlike most manures, rabbit manure is easy to collect and distribute, and is available in almost odourless, small, dry pellets. In addition, it can be spread on garden soil directly, without ageing, with no danger of nitrogen burn.

As well as maintaining a clean rabbitry, fight disease by constantly watching for its symptoms and isolating any sick animals at once. Be on the lookout for generally slow or listless animals, frequent sneezing, open sores, watering eyes or a general lack of appetite. After isolating these animals, consult a thorough text or veterinarian regarding the symptoms and possible treatment.

Many breeders believe that treating diseased animals is a waste of time and promptly dispose of any animal that shows signs of severe illness. Marg McCallum is one of these. She says disease will "spread like wildfire through your herd," and claims it is best to kill a few animals for the sake of a healthy herd. She states flatly, "I don't believe in medication, with the one exception of coccidiosis."

Coccidiosis is caused by a small intestinal parasite which many believe is present in virtually every rabbit herd at subclinical levels. As a precautionary measure, many breeders routinely treat their herds for coccidiosis. The medication, available from rabbit suppliers, is added to the drinking water for three consecutive days once every few months.

Ear mites are a fairly minor but common problem. Microscopic in size, they're first apparent when tiny red spots appear on the inside of the rabbit's ear. Advanced cases will cause brownish-red scabs. Medication can be purchased from suppliers, although some breeders apply cooking oil to suffocate the mites. McCallum gets a local druggist to make up a mixture of olive oil, iodoform and ether, a combination that is inexpensive, kills the mites and heals any infection at the same time. A small plastic squeeze bottle with a pointed, cut-off tip makes an ideal applicator.

Providing quality feed, clean water and maintaining good quarters will help ensure disease-free stock.

KILLING & DRESSING

There are probably as many ways to butcher animals as there are butchers, but whatever the method, be sure to withhold all feed, giving only water for 12 hours prior to killing. One of two preferred methods of killing a rabbit is to hold it by the hind feet and quickly snap its head downward and backward, breaking its neck. This type of killing takes a knack and is best learned from someone who is experienced. A second method is to stun or kill the animal with a well-placed blow behind the ears with a heavy stick. Whichever method is used, proceed by immediately cutting off the head and tail and suspending the carcass by the hind legs on hooks or nails provided for this purpose. Some breeders hang a plastic garbage bag on the nails below the rabbit to catch the blood and entrails and to speed cleanup.

After the rabbit is hung, remove the front feet. Now cut the skin just below the hocks (around each back foot) and inside the legs to the root of the tail. The flesh is thin in this area, so care should be taken to prevent puncturing the intestine. Now, using both hands, simply peel the skin down over the carcass. Put the skin aside, and slit the carcass through the abdominal wall along the median line from tail to abdomen. The kidney, liver and heart should be saved, but allow the rest of the viscera to fall into the bag. Wash the carcass in cold water to remove hair and excess blood, and place it in a tub of ice. Do not allow it to soak in water, as this will give the meat an undesirable colour.

What is now done with the carcass depends on the producer's preference, whether or not he intends to sell the meat, and how he intends to cook it.

A dressed rabbit can be neatly cut into several serving portions or left whole. A rabbit with a dressed weight of two to three pounds is considered a fryer and is usually cut into pieces. A medium-sized rabbit between 8 and 10 weeks old should yield about 2½ pounds of meat. Roasting rabbits, those over three pounds dressed weight, are usually slightly older does and bucks that have served their period of usefulness in the herd, or breeding stock that has been culled. Many families choose to allow their rabbits to attain this larger size simply because they prefer the larger carcass. In Europe, roasters are generally preferred over fryers.

After completing the butchering, turn your attention to the rabbit pelts. These are an additional, although minor, source of income to the breeder, usually bringing about 20 cents a pelt. Some regional processors will accept the pelts frozen while others will request that the pelts be dried, which requires the the use of stretchers or shapers. Shapers can be purchased ready-made, or they can be fashioned from #9 galvanized wire. Pelts should not be dried in the sun and, once dried, should be packed in a tight box with moth balls. You may want to have them tanned, or try tanning them yourself for home use. The pelts from older rabbits — roasters — are more durable, larger and more valuable than those of fryers.

Farmsteaders who have chosen to raise the longhaired Angora rabbits have yet another income possibility. Although Angora rabbit wool is said to be warmer than the finest sheep wool, the mills will not be beating a path to the door of the Angora breeder. The commercial market for Angora wool has not been developed in Canada, so it is unlikely that one will make a large profit by selling wool alone. On the other hand, for anyone who has a ready market, Angoras can certainly add to the economic viablility of the rabbitry.

The basics of raising Angora rabbits vary only slightly from those of raising meat rabbits, although the stock is more expensive. Expect to pay $20 for six-to-eight-week-old youngsters and $45 or more for mature animals. Common commercial practice involves shearing rabbits four times a year, allowing the wool to attain a length of 2½ to 3½ inches during the three-month intervals.

Leopoldine Meyer, however, who has been breeding Angoras for over 40 years, first in her native Holland and now at her home in Sharon, Ontario, prefers to comb out the wool once a week. She claims that this method produces superior quality yarn and garments, which "do not shed and can be washed like cotton."

A mature Angora rabbit will produce about 12 ounces of wool a year, an amount that can be enhanced somewhat by intensive feeding. Meyer conceded that there is no "steady" market for Angora wool, but she added, "Being a member of the Toronto Spinners' and Weavers' Guild, I never have any trouble selling my wool." If a commercial buyer cannot be located for the wool, many breeders simply spin wool and knit the yarn into garments for home use. Alternatively, several breeders may pool their wool and sell to individuals who have a local cottage industry in spinning or weaving. In this way, Angoras can enhance the pleasure and value of rabbits in the farmyard or backyard.

Those "lucky" rabbits' feet may be unlikely to help anyone win the lottery, but by keeping one's faith squarely placed in the rabbit's amazing reproductive ability and hardiness, one will seldom be disappointed by his furry charges. ∎

Ron Allensen, a resident of Waterloo, Ontario, maintains an ongoing interest in small stock.

Sources

Publications

RAISING RABBITS
Available from Information Services, Agriculture Canada, Ottawa, Ontario K1A 0C7. Publication #1200. Free.

RAISING RABBITS
By Ann Kanable
Rodale Press
191 pages
204A — paperback, $8.95
Available from Harrowsmith Books, Camden East, Ontario K0K 1J0.

RAISING RABBITS THE MODERN WAY
By Robert Bennett
Gardenway Publishing
156 pages
33A — paperback, $7.75
Available from Harrowsmith Books, Camden East, Ontario K0K 1J0.

RABBITS MAGAZINE
Route 1, Box 7
Waterloo, Wisconsin 53594
(414) 478-2115
One year, 12 issues, $16 (U.S.).

Breeders & Suppliers

Sources of rabbits can be often found in classified ads or by word of mouth. For specific breeds, however, write:

THE DOMINION RABBIT & CAVY BREEDERS ASSOCIATION
Rene Clark
Box 51, Station L
Toronto, Ontario M6E 4Y4
(416) 922-8891
Single membership $7.50 per year, $10 family; includes breeders' directory and newsletters.

CANADA RABBIT HOUSE
Box 109
Fordwich, Ontario N0G 1V0
A "Canadian Rabbit Directory," including sources of further information, provincial associations, equipment and some breeders, can be purchased for $2.00.

Guinea Fowl and Fare

The most primitive and practical of domestic poultry

By Helen Molitor

It may be the only bird that demands its feed by name: "Buckwheat. Buckwheat." And the only one that practically never stops saying it. Guineas are by temperament aggressive and noisy birds. In fact, when my husband and I lived in Minnesota and had trouble with hawks taking our chickens, we added a few guineas to our flock. The guineas seemed intent only on eating, but as the hawk circled slowly overhead, they kept a careful eye on him. When the hawk lunged in his strike, the guineas let loose their appalling squawk and actually ran or flew to intersect that plunge. Few hawks were willing to meet the double challenge of guinea bravado and piercing guinea sound — "Buckwheat! Buckwheat!"

The qualities that make guineas superb hawk deterrents are some of the same ones that discourage the inexperienced from trying to raise them. Yet anyone who has had some experience with chickens and turkeys can manage guineas successfully — *provided* he or she is willing to consider how guineas differ from other fowl.

Guinea fowl, named after the area of western Africa from which they were exported to Europe, have been around in their present form for a long time. Dr. Mary Leakey, at her famous excavation in Tanzania, has found guinea tracks identical to those of the modern bird in a level estimated to be over 300 million years old. And we know that in the relatively modern era, the Greeks of Plato's time raised guineas which were also featured items at Roman banquets.

Since guinea fowl have obviously passed the rigours of survival of the fittest, one might expect them to be quite hardy, a popular kind of fowl on small farms, providing, as they do, a source of both homestead meat and homestead income. (Their price is about the same as pheasant — three dollars or more per pound, dressed weight, in most parts of North America.) Yet

few farmers think to raise them.

The reasons are not hard to discover. First, guinea meat is dark and gamey, much closer to the meat of wild fowl than to the flesh of any other domesticated poultry. For gourmets, this flavour is, of course, a major point in the guinea's favour; but for many moderns who expect all poultry to look and taste like supermarket chicken, the guinea comes as a shock.

Secondly, guinea fowl, despite their long association with man, are less domesticated than any other kind of poultry, preferring to nest in long grass and hedgerows, to roost in trees and to range freely, very freely.

The first thing to take into account when deciding whether or not to raise guineas is where you might keep them. Although the birds originated in Africa, they are relatively hardy and do not need heated winter quarters. But they must have shelter at night, with plenty of roosting area and a nest for every two or three hens.

Guineas lay mostly in spring and summer, when some will be very protective of their nests and unwilling to share them.

Guineas prefer free range; in fact, you'd need golden eggs to finance really guinea-proof fencing. Thus, you will need an area at least as big as the average yard around a country homestead for a small flock. A couple of acres is even better if you contemplate a flock of more than 30 or so hens. Ideally, this guinea area should be behind the house, away from any sort of intrusion by mailmen, visitors and such, since guineas, especially as they settle into new surroundings, are easily roused, and when roused, they let you know they are upset. So the calmest area of the homestead is the best.

Those who do have such a quiet area have only two questions to answer. Is there a market for guineas nearby? Is there a convenient source of a good pair or some eggs? One's guinea market may, in fact, be his own family, in which case the first queston is easily answered. Those, however, who want to sell fowl will need to do some investigating.

Basically, guinea markets are the so-called "gourmet" and "ethnic" markets, which sometimes overlap. For example, French, Chinese and Indian restaurants may be interested in guineas, either as regular items on their menus or for special banquets. In the early '60s, one Indian restaurant in New York offered baked guinea fowl, with a special dressing and wrapped in gold foil, for $50 for two people. And that was when dollars were dollars, and gold was cheap.

Gourmet and specialty shops, restaurants specializing in game, European and Oriental food stores are other possibilities. In every case, check on whether the outlet will want a year-round supply (a difficult feat to achieve) or will be content with a fall seasonal supply (very easy). In these days of freezers, one wouldn't suppose it would make much difference, but genuine gourmet restaurants often will *not* serve frozen foods to their customers, so it could matter significantly to the enterprise. These same genuine gourmet places are also most apt to understand the seasonal nature of supplies of certain kinds of food and be prepared to vary their menus according to the time of year. So whether the market is pro-freezer or anti-freezer, the attitudes toward guinea supplies are apt to balance out.

TYPES OF GUINEA

Those who will be selling fowl should be particularly careful about the variety chosen. There are three major varieties, named after the colours of their feathers — Pearl, Lavender and White. The Pearls are basically dark purple-grey, while the Lavenders, as might be expected, have paler feathers. Both varieties have distinctive, regular patterns of white dots "pearling" their plumage. The Whites, predictably, are pure white. A subvariety sometimes available is a cross between the White and one of the other two types, with the colouring of the darker parent but with a white breast and white flight feathers. This type is called the Splashed Guinea.

All of these varieties are similar in weight, behaviour and flavour. All need the same ratio of one cock to every five hens on free range; all are about the same in hardiness. The only significant difference is that the skin of the Whites is lighter and may be preferred by some restaurants. Do check with the market to be sure of its expectations.

The right choice of breeding stock usually does not depend upon the variety. It is the training of the birds that makes the crucial difference between success and failure in raising guineas. Whether one buys keets (the young birds between the ages of 3 and 12 weeks) or mature stock, one should be sure to get affirmative answers to three essential questions:

1. Are the birds trained to come into the shed or barn at dusk for their evening feed?
2. Are they used to having people around?

3. Have they had their flight feathers removed or their wings clipped?

One would do well to arrive around dusk to see if the guineas do, in fact, go into the building readily. Do they respond sensibly to the traditional "shooing" gestures (arms held loosely at the sides, hands making gentle scooping motions, a soft and soothing voice saying anything from "now, now, now" to "would you damn fools move along?")? By contrast, do they rush about hysterically with numbers of them turning on the drover, swelling up, spreading their wings out to drag along the ground while that enraged guinea shriek fills the air?

See if the owner can pick up one or two of them and present the clipped wings or the place where the missing flight feathers would be. (One advantage the Splashed variety has is that the white flight feathers are very easily seen against the darker background, and their absence is obvious.)

A BIRD IN THE HAND . . .

Unless the answer to the above questions is yes, I wouldn't buy the flock. A buyer may save money on the half-wild guineas of someone who is giving up in despair, but those initial savings will rapidly disappear as the birds vanish into the brush or die of exposure on the first really cold fall nights. Further, one could wind up several years older without ever laying eyes or hands on a guinea egg.

The wing clipping of mature guineas is a gory business, for the birds bleed heavily, and their wings must be tied up until the bleeding stops. Even cutting the flight feathers on a wild and suspicious flock is a chore to be avoided if one ever hopes to live at peace with one's guineas.

By contrast, wing clipping a *young* guinea is relatively painless — for both participants — if it is done when the birds are a week to 10 days old. Any younger, and it is hard to clip just the first joint; any older, and the stress is greater.

Therefore, either buy a well-trained wing-clipped flock, or if the cost of such birds is too high, the very best bet for anyone who wants to begin with guineas is to buy some eggs. I'd try about 25 of them, planning to eat the extra males as soon as they reach slaughter weight.

Guinea eggs may be artificially incubated; they take about 28 days to hatch, and require, in the usual homestead incubator, a temperature of 102 degrees F, rising to 103 degrees in the fourth week. The humidity should be 58 percent. If the incubator has a setting for turkeys, that is an appropriate one to use for guineas; just be sure the humidity is correct. No matter what the instructions say, turn the guinea eggs four times a day if possible for the first 24 days; then leave them alone until they hatch.

Of course, if there is a handy broody hen, she can incubate the eggs. A large, old-fashioned meat-type hen can manage all 25 guinea eggs, since they are much smaller than her own, but two such hens will look after

Guinea fowl are excellent foragers, ranging widely in their search for insects, worms and seed.

them better. Bantams can manage 8 or 10 each and are even better foster mothers because they often have more patience with a long hatch than the larger breeds do.

ADOPTED CHICKS

The advantages of foster mothers for guineas are several. The hens will help to civilize the guinea chicks, for they will imprint some chicken behaviour. For example, if the hens trust their owner, the chicks will not receive any reinforcement of their fear of strangers. As keets, they will be less likely to stray, and even as mature birds, the guineas will tend to associate with their "mother," using her location as a central point about which they forage. Her return to the coop at night will be a signal for theirs.

Whether incubated or fostered, Canadian guinea chicks will need to be kept indoors for the first few weeks, inside *very* fine mesh. They are so small — about half the size of hen's chicks — that they will walk right through 1-inch mesh without noticing it is there; even ½-inch will cause only a moment's hesitation. So fine mesh or a solid barrier is best.

Wing clipping or pinioning should be done when the chicks are a week old. With very sharp scissors or clippers, remove the last segment of *one* wing; that is, cut at the first ("wrist") joint. The wound should heal rapidly.

Fostered chicks can spend some time outside with their mother hen as soon as there are some bright warm afternoons (75 degrees F), but incubated ones take more preparation. Immediately after hatching, they should be given a high brooder temperature, around 95 degrees, which should be dropped over the next four or five weeks by five or six degrees per week until it reaches natural daytime temperatures. At this point, they may go outside. Since many guineas hatch in the spring and are fully feathered out (in four weeks) by May or early June, one may find that fostered and brooder chicks wind up going outside at about the same time.

As chicks and keets, guineas are quite beguiling, especially the pearled varieties, with their immature feathers looking almost like those of quail, in shades of dark brown with lighter tan on the chest and belly.

Take advantage of this period of charm and start picking them up and handling them on the third day. Try to establish in the guineas' minds, such as they are, an association between being handled and being fed.

Finally, keep both keets and mature breeding stock inside in the morning until the dew is off the grass and the eggs have been laid. If necessary, breeding hens may be kept indoors until early afternoon to control their desire to lay their eggs across the countryside. From their first day outside, always round the flock up at dusk, give them an especially good feed, and lock them up for the night.

The starting mash for chicks for the first six weeks should contain 25 percent protein; they can then spend two weeks on growing mash and grain, fed either free choice or four or five times a day. At 8 to 10 weeks (depending in part upon the weather), they can go on the same regimen as the breeding flock.

Commercial game bird feed is a good choice but relatively hard to find. Turkey feed will also suffice but, again, is scarce except in areas where the birds are raised commercially. Chicken feed is second best, but often the only accessible one.

One guinea raiser, W.H. Harrison, makes his own feed, as he writes in *Guinea Fowl* (see Sources): "The guinea chicks when hatched soon want something to eat, and the first meal may well be a mixture of bread crumbs and finely chopped hard-boiled eggs. Stale bread moistened with milk is also a good feed. After they get a few days old, clabbered or sour milk is appropriate as well. They should be fed at least four or five times a day for the first week or 10 days. . . .

"As the birds get older, they can be fed cracked corn, wheat, oats, et cetera. It is essential to feed some sort of grain ration during the winter months. Grit and oyster shell and an ample supply of fresh water must be available at all times."

Those who do choose to feed commercial mixes should be careful not to purchase medicated feeds, as the additives are proportioned for chicks or turkeys, not guineas, which in any case, are seldom troubled by disease.

SUMMER OMELETTES

Like wild birds, guineas have a very restricted laying season. Dr. R.D. Crawford, who keeps a flock at the University of Saskatchewan in Saskatoon, says, "They are very poor layers. Here, they don't start laying until May. They seem to have to have a warm temperature as well as the longer day length before they start laying, and on the Prairies, that presents a problem. They reproduce here through June and July and then stop laying again. So they're not a good idea for self-sufficiency, if that's what your're looking for."

The hens usually lay 25 to 30 eggs and may then become broody. If you want to improve egg production, never leave more than two eggs in the nest, and get batches of eggs to the incubator or under foster hens as soon as possible. Never keep eggs more than a week before starting them, and for that week, keep them cool (about 55 degrees F).

If pressed, guinea hens are reported to lay up to 100 eggs per year in some commercial hatcheries. (In France, especially, guinea raising is a well-established commercial enterprise.) But in northern areas, 40 to 50 is a good production. At the end of the laying season, the flock can go on to a maintenance ration, identical to a standard turkey or chicken maintenance feed.

Of course, those who want to save some laying hens will need to discern the sex of the birds. Like all fowl, guineas are somewhat hard to sex when young. In fact, they are almost impossible to distinguish. When they are between three and four months old, however, the "helmet" and wattles of the male birds become larger, coarser and thicker than those of the female. Further, the males have only a one-syllable shriek, while the females, when contented, have a quieter, two-syllable cry, with the stress on the first one, which sounds rather like "*puck*-weet, *puck*-weet" and so, of course, has been translated as a demand for "buckwheat, buckwheat." Hence, by the time you are ready to slaughter the guineas, you can save breeding stock fairly easily.

Keets ought to reach slaughter weight of 3 to 3½ pounds at 16 to 18 weeks of age. If you are lucky, your buyer will take them live. But it may be necessary — and is sometimes economically advantageous — for you to do the processing. Some guinea raisers recommend dry plucking, but it is somewhat tricky, and I would recommend, instead, the usual slaughter method for chickens, followed by scalding and then plucking. Tedious as this work is, guineas are worth much more than chickens per pound, so you will come closer to being decently paid for your time. If you are selling to game restaurants, you just might get lucky: some of those restaurants will serve guinea as they do pheasant and chukar — they will want the feathers left just as they are.

Those who have raised their own guineas can enjoy a gourmet meal without the corresponding price tag. I have two rules, however, to ensure that this feast is as memorable as possible. The first rule: Always eat a young guinea, never one more than four or five months old, unless you have absolutely no choice. The second rule: Always lard your bird to prevent its drying out and becoming tough as it is roasted. Cover the entire bird with a thin layer of lard or bacon strips, not forgetting to insert a piece between each leg and the breast. Roast for 45 minutes at 350 degrees F (one hour if the bird is stuffed), remove larding 10 minutes early to let the guinea brown a little.

Traditional guinea stuffings include wild or white rice, often with mushrooms, occasionally with chopped dried apricots. The usual sauces involve simply making a roux with a tablespoon of flour in the fat, browning bits from the bottom of the pan and then adding a cup of liquid — a combination of chicken stock, water and white wine, or water and sour cream. For variety, I make a medium-thick white sauce, substituting a half cup of wine just a few minutes before serving to avoid curdling the milk sauce.

Meals such as this one can become Thanksgiving traditions if one always overwinters a few guineas for eggs the following spring. Such meals may even be free of charge if the guinea enterprise is supported by the sale of some birds. As Dr. Alan Grunder of Agriculture Canada's Animal Research Institute says, "We think there is a market for guinea fowl in Canada. It's probably limited to a gourmet market and could be saturated easily, but nevertheless it is there." ■

Helen Molitor, a former English professor, lives on a farm in Oregon.

Sources

Hatcheries

There is no commercial source of guinea fowl for Canadians, so those who want the birds or eggs should advertise locally; small flocks are scattered all across the country, and farmers are often willing to sell a pair or a few eggs. Readers may wish to advertise in Feather Fancier Newspaper, R.R.5, Forest, Ontario N0N 1J0, (519) 899-2364. There are several choices for U.S. buyers, including the following:

RIDGWAY HATCHERIES
LaRue 14, Ohio 43332

WILLOW HILL POULTRY FARMS
AND HATCHERY
R.D.1, Box 100
Richland, Pennsylvania 17087
(717) 933-4606
Guineas available from June to September. Write for price list.

Books

GUINEA FOWL
Van Hoesen-Stromberg, Publishers
Available from Fanciers Specialty Co., Paris, Ontario N3L 2E3, (519) 442-4038. This book consists of separate articles on various aspects of raising guinea fowl. $6.25.

Associations

CANADIAN ORNAMENTAL PHEASANT
AND GAME BIRD ASSOCIATION
R.R.3
Rockwood, Ontario N0B 2K0
Offers a monthly magazine, and new members receive a yearbook containing a list of breeders.

The Compleat Fowl Yard

Being a short treatise in praise of ducks and geese

By Jennifer Bennett

To those travelling north from Kingston, Ontario, on Highway 38, the sight of Maas Dirksen's pastured flock of snow-white geese is as dependable a sign of late summer as are the first yellowing leaves. A sign of the approach of winter is the disappearance of the geese every November, replaced by the elegy on Dirksen's front lawn: "Order Your Christmas Goose Now."

Dirksen, whose own family has always shunned festive turkey and mundane chicken in favour of the dark richness of goose or duck meat, is taking advantage of a double-barrelled phenomenon that benefits the rural smallholder. Geese and ducks vary from nonexistent to prohibitively dear in butcher shops, but on the farmstead, they are the easiest to raise of all poultry: hardy, disease-resistant and practically self-sufficient. Some ducks actually outlay chickens, and Embden geese gain weight more rapidly than any other poultry.

"I lost 1 out of 103 geese this year," says Dirksen, who buys day-old White Embdens from Webfoot Hatchery in Elora, Ontario. "We used to raise 400 a year, but a lot of people are raising 8 or 10 now, they're so easy to take care of. Right now, we raise 100, and we have no trouble selling that many."

Equally fond of goose meat but not overly enamoured of goose personality is Douglas Green of Kemptville College in Kemptville, Ontario. "I can remember when I was four years old being chased by my grandfather's geese. Thanks but no thanks." Green has put off raising geese until his children have grown big enough to "give them a boot" when necessary. In the meantime, Green is content with his ducks; his Pekins, Rouens and crosses. "They taste as good, and they're just as easy and cheap to raise."

Whether one will choose to raise ducks, geese or both depends on a number of factors. Anyone with less than a half acre of land should not even contemplate raising geese; these big noisy birds love to graze, and they need space. On the other hand, we have seen a pair of ducks raised by a Chinese family in a downtown Toronto backyard. No doubt, some sort of bylaw was being contravened, but from their infancy in a cardboard box until their demise in late summer, no one but we onlookers from the office building next door was probably any the wiser about their presence. In a coop, one should be prepared to allow at least 2 square feet of space per duck, 10 per goose. In the run, allow another 6 square feet per duck, 80 for a large goose.

Waterfowl may be adaptable, hardy livestock whose culinary possibilities are delicious and endless, but according to a recent census, there were less than 600,000 ducks and just over half that many geese raised in Canada in 1976. That's an annual duck dinner for only 1 in every 42 people and doesn't even take into consideration the fact that many Canadian geese and ducks are exported. Northern Goose Processors Limited of Toulon, Manitoba, is Canada's largest goose meat and down producer, buying, killing and packaging more than 200,000 White Embdens a year. According to manager Don Alkeld, "We probably export three times as many as are consumed in Canada." The manager of the Feather Industries division of Canada Packers

of Toronto adds, "There's no reason why Canadians couldn't grow more ducks or geese — but where are you going to sell that meat? When was the last time *you* had a duck or goose?"

No, there is no point in raising ducks or geese if you don't like the meat, but try it, by all means, before deciding against raising these versatile birds. Goose and duck flesh is all dark, fattier than chicken or turkey, but milder in flavour than wild waterfowl. It is high in both protein and iron; the U.S. Department of Agriculture reports that one pound of goose meat contains 5.32 grams of iron; duck, 4.67 grams; turkey, 4.29 grams, and chicken, 2.25 grams. Duck and goose eggs are larger than chicken eggs and slightly different in flavour and texture. The yolks have a buttery richness, while the whites can be more rubbery than chicken eggs when fried. In Holland, where duck eggs are big business, most of them find their way to the baking industry.

PRICEY DAY-OLDS

Except among Oriental and German neighbourhoods, the lack of a large Canadian market for duck and goose has been the main reason that the industry has not developed much in the North. But also, ducks and geese, except those breeds of duck that excel in egg laying, lay too few eggs to enable the price of day-old birds to come anywhere near that of baby chicks. Prices of two to four dollars for a gosling are likely to limit the size of one's flock, at least in the beginning.

Although it is expensive, buying day-olds is usually the way one gets started in duck or goose raising. One may, however, be able to purchase young or mature birds locally, and this is the best idea, as any stress in the transportation of the birds can be minimized. Check newspaper ads, or put up a notice in the general store. A list of mail-order suppliers follows this article.

The breed of duck or goose one chooses will depend to some extent upon what is easiest to come by and to some extent on one's preference. Geese are differentiated mainly by size, with the larger breeds tending toward more economical meat production, the smaller ones laying better. Ducks, however, are quite easily divided into three categories: egg birds, meat birds and dual-purpose breeds.

The most common breeds of domestic geese in Canada are the Embden, Toulouse, Pilgrim and Chinese. The first three are descendants of the Greylag goose of Europe, a Mother Goose type, brownish-grey and averaging 8 to 10 pounds. Through centuries of domestic selection, the Embden has become its largest descendant and the most popular meat and down breed in North America. Embden ganders may reach 30 pounds, although they are usually butchered at about half that weight. Hutterite colonies are Canada's most active goose producers, and they rely almost exclusively upon White Embdens.

The Toulouse is another big goose, although it tends to be somewhat smaller than the Embden. It does have a more docile disposition, but its grey feathers may result in a slightly less attractive roast, as the dark pin feathers produce a spotty-looking carcass.

The Pilgrim, smallest of the Greylag descendants, attained its name from its association with the Pilgrim fathers that settled in New England. Its colouring is sex-linked — the ganders are white and the geese grey — and it is a fairly good layer.

Chinese geese look much like their larger version, African geese, and both probably derive from the same ancestor, the swan goose of Siberia. The Chinese, a graceful, swanlike bird, reaches a weight of only 8 to 12 pounds at maturity. Chinese and African geese tend to be noisier than other breeds (all of whom can be raucous when the mood strikes) and, because of a frost-sensitive knob on the bill, are less well suited to northern climes than are the Greylag breeds.

Among meat breeds, the most common ducks are the Pekin, Aylesbury and Rouen. Dual-purpose breeds include the Cayuga and Muscovy, and those usually raised primarily for eggs include the Khaki Campbell and Indian Runner.

The white-feathered Pekin is favoured almost everywhere as the best meat bird, dressing out as heavy as 10 pounds, the weight of a small goose. In the United States, it is often called the Long Island duck, as more than half the American Pekin population is raised there. One of Canada's largest duck ranches, Brome Lake Ducks of Knowlton, Quebec, raises about 118,000 White Pekins for the international duck market.

The Aylesbury is almost identical to the Pekin, except that its skin is white while that of the Pekin is yellow. The Aylesbury was once the meat bird of choice and is still very popular in Britain.

Although both the Pekin and Aylesbury are descended from the wild Mallard, it is another descendant, the Rouen, that most closely resembles that colourful bird, looking much like a larger version of it. The Rouen will grow as large as the Pekin or Aylesbury although it generally does so more slowly, and its dark pin feathers make the carcass less appealing. Although none of the three meat breeds is likely to lay more than 100 eggs a year, the Rouen usually is the best mother of the three.

Another Mallard descendant, the Cayuga, is an American breed, black with a green sheen, that attains a weight of about eight pounds. This bird is hardy and a fairly good layer and sitter, but its main drawback is that, like the Rouen, its dark pin feathers are unattractive on the finished bird.

Better as a household dual-purpose bird is the Muscovy duck. This quiet species, beloved of suburban farmsteaders, has earned the admiration of Maas Dirksen as well: "I've tried them all — Rouen, Pekin, Muscovy. The Muscovy is just about as nice a duck as you're going to get." This bird has an entirely different background from the others. Of South American ancestry, it seems almost a duck-goose amalgam. Muscovy drakes spar like ganders, and although they will mate with other breeds of duck, the eggs will be sterile. The drakes dress out as heavy as 12 pounds, producing a relatively easy-to-pluck carcass that has a uniquely mild-flavoured meat. The ducks are good layers and

very good mothers.

The Khaki Campbell is the Leghorn chicken of ducks. It is often known to lay more than 300 eggs a year and has been known to lay 364 (a remarkable achievement of domestication when one considers that the wild Mallard lays only about 15 eggs a year). The Khaki Campbell is not, however, inclined to broodiness.

The Indian Runner, or Runner, is a remarkably shaped bird, sometimes aptly called the Penguin duck, that lays about 200 hen-sized eggs a year, but thanks to its small size, does so on less feed than any other domestic duck. Runners, like Campbells, are not inclined to set on their eggs, and may be flighty and excitable.

There are also bantam ducks, miniature birds under 4½ pounds, used most often for setting on the eggs of other breeds, as they are very inclined to brood.

INSULATED BABIES

Day-old ducks and geese are far more resilient than young chicks or turkey poults; the insulating quality of duck and goose down is not only of benefit to producers of pillows and sleeping bags. Reporting on an experiment at Agriculture Canada's Ottawa station, Dr. J.R. Aitken says, "The chick doesn't have the ability to maintain its body temperature, so it must be given heat, but the goose can control its body temperature

When ducks interbreed, the results may be useless for show but can still be colourful providers of meat and eggs.

right from when it is hatched. In our research, we raised geese without brooder lights in the spring. The only important thing is that they must be kept dry, or the insulation value of their down is lost."

In the pamphlet, *Raising Geese*, however, Aitken and a colleague do recommend that brooder lights be used for young goslings. Few of us operate under the controlled conditions of an experimental station, and if the weather gets chilly, the young birds may pile up and suffocate. Certainly brooder lights or some other source of heat are required with ducklings, although, again, temperatures are not as critical as they are with other young domestic birds.

The most convenient source of heat is a brooder lamp suspended about two feet above the litter in the coop. One lamp will be sufficient for up to 40 goslings or 100 ducklings. Maintain a temperature of about 85 to 90 degrees F for the first week, 75 to 80 for the second, 70 to 75 for the third and 70 thereafter, reading the temperature on the floor directly under the lamp and raising the lamp as needed. The birds will indicate their need for more heat by bunching under the light and will move into the far corners of the coop when too warm. "You'll see when they're done with it," says Dirksen. "They'll stay under it until they don't want the heat anymore."

As important as warmth for the babies is a secure,

draught-free, dry enclosure. Be sure that they are safe from cats, rats and other predators. If the birds are to be kept only until butchering time, this shelter can be quite rudimentary, as once they are fully feathered, they need come back to it only during very bad weather and perhaps at night. Allow about one square foot of space per duckling, two per gosling. Cover the floor with a dry, nonslip litter; paper towelling or burlap is excellent for young waterfowl, who produce copious quantities of semi-liquid droppings.

Throughout their lives, waterfowl require a source of drinking water that enables the entire head to be submerged. When they are young, a chick fountain may be deep enough, but later on, special waterers must be provided, ones that will allow the birds to dip their heads but will not let them paddle, as this quickly results in sodden litter and a damp, smelly coop, just ripe for disease.

It is seldom necessary, however, to allow domestic waterfowl to swim, and, in fact, before they are feathered, they should not be allowed to swim. (If one is planning to keep some birds over for egg laying and breeding, a pond or some other water source may be necessary.) Similarly, although the young birds can be let outdoors in fine weather when they are only 10 days old, until three weeks have passed, they must be driven inside when it is cold or rainy and at night. Dirksen says that not only can the birds become fatally chilled if soaked, but also "they can drown in rain. They'll just stand out there with their heads up and their beaks open."

Sounds suspiciously like turkey behaviour, but one must remember that these are waterfowl, meant to be (and soon to be) water repellent, and until then, there is supposed to be an adult bird around who knows the ropes. Once they are feathered, the birds will be impervious to all but the worst winter weather.

For the first three weeks, provide the birds with chick grower in pellet form if it can be bought or, alternatively, as crumbles. Mash, which the birds find difficult to eat, is the third choice. While special duck and goose rations are manufactured, they will be available only if there are commercial poultry establishments nearby. Do not feed any medicated ration, such as chick starter, as the dosages of medication are not calculated for waterfowl, and such feeds can be fatal. Ask for unmedicated feed at the store. The food can be given twice daily and then removed after 15 minutes (which is less messy), or it can be constantly available (which is easier), but in all cases, water must be available to the birds while they are eating.

The fowl will enjoy a sprinkling of fresh, unsprayed greens over their food. Allow them access to finely ground, clean gravel as well; grist for the mill, as it were.

Once they are outdoors full time — at about four weeks if the weather is warm — both ducks and geese will do a great deal of foraging. Geese are true grazers and can actually feed themselves entirely on pasture such as timothy, ryegrass or clover. Depending on the size of the breed, the age of the birds and the quality of the pasture, an acre can support from 2 to 100 geese.

Pasture growth must be young and succulent, however, and some mowing may be required to keep it suitable for the birds.

To ensure that their growth continues, pastured geese should still be provided with one or two pounds of feed each week, divided into small daily feedings. Be sure the feed is distributed so that all birds have access to it. Chicken "scratch" will do now. If the birds appear to be thriving on the pasture, it is possible to do without supplementary feeding. Grain is absolutely necessary only during the first three weeks, during fattening and when hatching eggs. Watch the birds carefully, however, to ensure that weight loss and weakening do not occur.

If little or no pasture is available, a full-grown goose will consume up to two pounds of feed daily, although this may contain kitchen scraps such as bits of meat, vegetables and grain. A mature duck will consume about a quarter pound of feed a day, but, like a goose, it will do considerable searching for its own feed if given the chance, although it cannot survive on pasture alone as a goose can. Still, on its daily wanderings, it can consume about half its diet in greens, grain, insects, snails and such.

CHINESE WEEDERS

It is the goose's tireless foraging that has contributed to its reputation as a weeder. Chinese geese are often dubbed "weeder geese" because their small size and active nature makes them especially suited to this task. Dennis Sewald of Idaho actually rents out young Chinese geese to organic farmers with weeding chores. He estimates that 6 to 10 young geese can take care of an acre, specializing in weeding potatoes, strawberries (before they fruit), onions, fruit trees and other crops that geese do not relish. Some crops such as leafy greens and small grains they will consume in preference to the weeds.

Any goose, not only the Chinese, will weed, but the larger the breed and the more mature the bird, the more likely it is to damage crops as well. If necessary, they should be moved from field to field as they graze. They must be fenced in, and drinking water must be available within the fenced area. If the weather is hot, be sure some shade is provided — boards resting on straw bales will suffice. Young birds exposed to hot sunlight sometimes develop a form of heat stroke known as staggers, a disorder that can be fatal.

Geese are quite territorial and may fiercely defend any space they consider their own. They should, then, be kept out of roadways, gardens and porches, where they will not only make a mess but also will stop traffic and chase strangers. Not for nothing have they acquired a reputation as "watchdogs." One company in Scotland, seeking to cash in on this reputation, in-

---

Top, *Rouen drake and duck are easily distinguished.* **Bottom left**, *Peking ducks are raised worldwide, their white feathers making them a more popular table bird than the Rouen.* **Bottom right**, *the Toulouse goose, bred in France, is also favoured for meat.*

Top, left to right, *Indian Runner ducks, named for their distinct carriage and gait, are small, four-pound birds developed for the economical production of white-shelled eggs. The lustrous, greenish-black Cayuga is an American breed, raised for both meat and eggs. It attains a size of seven or eight pounds, laying eggs that are initially black-shelled, becoming blue as the bird matures. The Embden goose is the worldwide favourite meat breed, especially favoured by Europeans, for whom it surpasses the turkey. Ganders grow to about 30 pounds. The African goose, the larger version of the Chinese, has a different family tree from the other domestic geese.* **Bottom left,** *the Muscovy, too, has unusual origins. Although most farmers select the white-feathered Muscovy, the coloured strain shown here is also hardy, mute, a good meat bird and a good mother.* **Adjacent top,** *as soon as the strain was bred in England, the Khaki Campbell duck established its reputation as the best layer of all, laying as many as 364 white-shelled eggs a year. Slightly larger than the Indian Runner, it shares the traits of nervousness and little inclination to brood.* **Adjacent bottom,** *the Aylesbury is a less popular meat duck than is the Peking, because its skin is white, rather than yellow.*

Domestic waterfowl have more "personality" than other farm-yard birds. Some are pets; others are the terror of the neighbour-hood.

stalled geese to guard its property during off-hours, but did not plan for the yule-spirited Scots who rustled all the birds away during the graveyard shift. Dirksen says that although his geese know him well and will come to his call, "they really carry on" when a stranger enters the field. Ducks, however, are quite peaceful, although individual drakes or setting ducks may be feisty.

GENTLE HUSBANDING

Ducks and geese, especially flighty breeds such as Indian Runner, Muscovy and Chinese, should be wing-clipped to ensure that they will remain within a four-foot fence. Be sure, too, that fencing is kept in good repair, as birds that escape often become lost. To clip a wing, cut the long primary feathers from the tip of *one* wing of each bird. These feathers will regrow every year after the moult.

It is important that pastured geese or ducks be kept free of undue stress. Dogs love to chase landlocked birds, but such excitement can cause stress lameness and a loss of appetite that can actually lead to death. Like all birds, waterfowl appreciate consistently gentle treatment.

Geese, like goats, will eat almost anything. Their at-

traction to bright objects apparently won them some favour amongst early prospectors, who often found a nugget or two in the gizzard of the Sunday roast. Dirksen says that neither glass nor nails will kill a goose, however, "When they start limping, you can bet they've got a piece of glass in their stomachs, and they'll just keep limping until it passes out of them."

Unlike other fowl, ducks and geese are nocturnal foragers. They simply sleep when they are tired, day or night, so they will not naturally move indoors at night as chickens do, at least not unless they have been trained to do so. If predators are a problem, if eggs are being laid, or if the weather is very cold or wet, the husbandman should drive the birds into overnight shelter.

Should you need to pick up one of the birds, do not grab it by the legs as you might do with a chicken. Waterfowl legs are quite weak, and such a grasp could easily cause lameness. Instead, grab the bird around the base of the neck or by the body, and carry the bird pressed against your body so that its wings cannot flap.

If fed exclusively or almost so on mixed grain rations, a goose, according to Dr. Aitken of Agriculture Canada, will be of the best size to butcher at 12 weeks, but its feathers will not be sufficiently developed to make plucking possible until it is 15 weeks old, the age commercial establishments aim for. At this point, the live weight of an Embden is about 14 pounds; dressed weight about 10. Geese butchered before they are fully feathered are a mass of tenacious pin feathers.

Because Dirksen's geese spend most of their lives on

pasture, they take much longer to grow than do "full-fed" commercial geese, although such pasturing is economically efficient and results in a meat some find better tasting. Dirksen butchers his geese at about six months. He buys his day-olds in late May, feeds them grower for two or three weeks and then pastures them on a lush, 10-acre field until September, when he begins to fatten them on grain.

Fattening takes place in a fenced enclosure, small enough to restrict the birds' movement so that they do not exercise away the profits. Both ducks and geese are ready for fattening when they are fully feathered; that is, when the primary wing feathers extend to the tail, and patches of down are not visible. Fattening usually takes about a month, during which time the birds are allowed to eat all they want; both feed and water are constantly available. Chick grower pellets can again be utilized for fattening. Adding cracked corn will help to ensure rapid weight gain. Traditionally, cooked and cooled rice was used to fatten ducks, and if it can be purchased cheaply in bulk, it may still be used. Greens must also be provided — boiled nettles (use leather gloves to pick them), wilted cabbage and lettuce leaves and grass clippings will be fine. Provide grit as well.

Dirksen says he finds it easy to tell when the birds are ready to kill. "Around mid-November, all of a sudden they stop eating. You can put out two pails of grain for them, and they'll only eat one-third of a pail. That's their instinctive way of getting ready for winter, and that's when they're done."

In commercial establishments, ducks are killed at seven weeks, when Pekins are about 6 pounds live weight and 4½ dressed, but home duck owners will probably rely on pasture feeding to some extent, so weight gain will be slower. Usually they are left for 12 weeks, with Muscovies requiring a month more. As both ducks and geese will become tougher as they age, for the best and most economical results, do not let geese or Muscovies go longer than 10 months before butchering, or other ducks go longer than four. Besides, if the birds are left until they are in full moult, they will be very difficult to pluck.

Do not allow the birds to feed for about 12 hours before butchering, but provide water as usual. On butchering day, have a very large pot ready for scalding, killing cones or a butcher block and a very sharp hatchet, a good sharp knife for gutting, and all the friends you can find.

The killing of ducks and geese is most simply done with the help of a killing cone, an open-ended receptacle into which the bird is placed head down. Its wings are held securely against it while its head is turned to one side and chopped off against a butcher block. Alternatively, the head can be chopped off without the use of a cone, although with geese and Muscovies, this will be a two-person operation, as the flapping wings of a mature goose — both before and after decapitation — can inflict some painful blows.

As soon as movement has stopped, the bird should be dipped for one to three minutes in a very large container of 140 to 145 degree F water into which a few drops of dish detergent have been added. Such an additive helps dissolve the oil on the feathers, facilitating both soaking and plucking. A wooden spoon will be required to push the bird under the water, as it is naturally inclined to float. Hold it by its feet, and bob it up and down a bit so that the feathers are thoroughly wetted right down to the hocks.

Dry plucking is a possibility and a good idea for those whose main aim is clean down. But it is very difficult to do without tearing the skin — waterfowl feathers are much more tenacious than those of land birds — and is not recommended except for the truly patient.

Whether wet or dry, the feathers should be pulled off just a few at a time and in the direction of growth. Pulling too many or tugging in the wrong direction can, again, tear skin. The wing primaries are very difficult to remove, so some farmers such as Dirksen simply remove the wings at the first joint — "there's no meat there anyway." He saves these feathers for use in feather dusters. Legs, too, will be removed at the first joint.

The down may be collected separately for later cleaning and drying. While the wet down tends to stick to the fingers, and the dry stuff disappears in clouds, diligence in this area will pay off, as goose down sells for $60 per pound. It takes, however, about 40 geese to produce a pound of down. Pile the dirty feathers in a pillowcase (or a bag made especially for the purpose), and place it in the washing machine with a mild soap. When laundered, hang the bag outdoors, fluffing up the feathers occasionally until dry and ready to use.

Pin feathers can be removed with wax. Commercially processed birds are dipped in a vessel of special wax, but at home, melted paraffin can be poured over the bird. Melt paraffin in a double boiler, as it can ignite if overheated. Apply several layers, allowing each to cool and harden before applying the next, and then scrape the wax off. It may be used over and over, even as it becomes filled with feathers. To clean it, periodically strain the melted wax through a nylon stocking. When hardened, scrape any dirt off the bottom of the block of wax.

DRESSING OUT

Gutting is done in the same way as with other poultry, although waterfowl seem to be somewhat easier to handle, their organs being a little "looser." Place the bird on its back, its tail toward you. Insert the point of a very sharp knife at the base of the breastbone, and cut downward toward the vent. Placing a couple of fingers in this incision, cut carefully around the vent, being careful not to pierce the intestine. Now reach into the hole and pull out the guts. All, including the crop in the neck, can be removed through this lower opening.

Retain any desired giblets, especially the livers, which are gourmet treats either stir-fried or used in pâtés. Those who find duck or goose too greasy may choose to remove the pockets of fat just inside the rear opening.

Although waterfowl need not always be provided with a pond, there are few homestead sights as satisfying as that provided by the home flock on its own element.

When the inside is completely clean, cut out the oil gland at the base of the tail on the bird's back, and cut off the neck to the desired length, ensuring that both crop and wind pipe have been removed.

Cleaned and washed in cool water, the birds may be cooked fresh or chilled for a day and then bagged — "kitchen catchers" are good for geese — and frozen or pressure-canned.

If space and facilities permit, one may decide to keep a few geese or ducks over the winter for eggs or for breeding. Keep in mind that few breeds will provide eggs economically. In the duck line, only Campbells, Runners and sometimes Muscovies are suitable. Chinese geese may provide 50 to 100 eggs per year, although these will be much larger than chicken eggs. Most geese, in fact, do not even hit their laying stride until they are at least two years old, nor are most ganders fully mature until two or three years. Douglas Green, however, keeps a few ducks over the winter just to lay what will be next year's meat.

Those who do wish to have the birds raise their own young should choose a breed with a propensity to do so; Muscovies make very good mothers, but banty ducks will probably be necessary to hatch the eggs of Khaki Campbells or Indian Runners. Embden geese are quite likely to go broody, but the expense of keeping them over the winter, when pasture is not available, may result in home-raised goslings that are ultimately as expensive as commercial day-olds.

But, as duck and goose eggs usually cannot be bought for any price, those who truly prefer them over chicken eggs probably will not have economics as a top priority. Charles LaRose of Labrador City, Newfoundland, installed what was virtually a waterfowl palace, a brick building for overwintering his layers of exotic duck and goose eggs. Besides, there is likely to be a small local market for them, and at a dollar each for goose eggs and a quarter for duck eggs, a small income is a possibility. If one has good pasture and an incubator or broody females, the whole exercise may be both profitable and satisfying, providing one with a self-perpetuating flock.

In most cases, one will choose to winter more females than males — about five females to every male. If fertile eggs are not an issue, an all-female flock is the best bet. One may choose to buy sexed day-olds or to butcher males in the summer or fall.

Either approach demands that one know which is which. All of the Mallard-type ducks are quite easily distinguished, as the female has a loud, brassy quack while her mate has a muted call. Also, the males possess a "drake feather," a curly feather at the top of the tail. Rouens, like Mallards, are very distinct, with brightly coloured drakes and drab females. Muscovy drakes can often be distinguished by their large size, often twice that of the females.

Geese, except for the sex-linked Pilgrims and some strains of Embden, which produce a lighter grey male gosling than female, are more difficult to differentiate. Ganders are often more obstreperous and are likely to have a more upright carriage and larger bill knob than the female. Vent examination, however, is the only reliable method of sexing. T.H. Canfield of the University of Minnesota describes it thus:

"After the goose is caught, lift it by the neck and lay it on its back, either on a table or over your bended knee, with the tail pointed away from you. Move the tail end of the bird out over the table edge so it can be readily bent downwards. Then insert your index finger (sometimes it helps to have a little vaseline on it) into the cloaca about half an inch, and move it around in a circular manner several times to enlarge and relax the sphincter muscle which closes the opening. Next, apply some pressure directy below and on the sides of the vent in order to evert or expose the sex organs."

The immature gander has spiral-like rings inside the cloaca, while the mature gander has a pointed penis; the female simply does not. Be very careful, in sexing, not to damage the bird and to watch out for its sharp claws.

Birds that are kept over the winter will require better housing arrangements than the summer flock. Allowing six square feet per goose, three per duck, plan for a building that will shelter the birds from draughts, precipitation, predators and very cold temperatures. Although they will require neither insulation nor heat, the walls must be secure enough that the animals' own body heat is contained within the building when the door is closed, which it will likely be at night only. It is a good idea, however, to suspend a heat lamp above the waterer, otherwise the water will have to be replenished whenever the birds are fed. As the birds will spend more time than usual indoors, the litter may have to be changed as often as once a month. Keep a supply of sawdust or straw by the coop just for this purpose, and save the old litter for compost — it is rich in nitrogen.

Chicken "scratch" can be given as winter feed. Adding an extra measure of cracked corn to it will help the birds stay warm. In addition, wintering birds appreciate greens whenever possible. Because snow will limit their grazing, they should be fed such vegetables as chopped kale, cabbage, root crops, carrot tops, leaves and grain or bean sprouts, all of which can be grown or provided especially for the bird. Allow them as much as they will eat.

Ducks and geese are subject to few of the ailments that plague chickens and turkeys, but it is during infancy and the winter months when they are indoors much of the time that they are most vulnerable. If the coop is kept dry and quite clean and if fresh water is always provided for the feeding birds, any disease problem is unlikely. Overcrowding of birds can cause problems, but this is more likely to occur in commercial establishments than in the home situation.

Egg laying will most likely begin with the lengthening and warming days of spring, in February or March. About a month before this, a calcium supplement must be added to the feed; chopped oyster shells (available in feed stores) or recycled eggshells are suitable. The best duck breeds will eventually produce an egg a day, while the best geese will reward their keeper with one every two days during the spring, usually laying for a couple of weeks and then resting for a week or two. Unlike chickens, waterfowl do not require elevated nest boxes. They lay on the ground and will do so wherever it pleases them, usually, if they are given the chance, under the hedge or at the edge of the woods, where a marauding raccoon or jay will be as likely to find it as will the farmer.

DECOY EGGS

To best keep track of the eggs, most of which will be laid in the early morning, drive the birds into their house at night (by now, most keepers will have been doing this for a while, so the birds will be trained to this routine), and release them late the next morning. Provide three-sided wooden nest boxes in the coop, about one for every five females. Goose boxes should be 2½ feet square, duck boxes 1½, and padded with straw in either case. Keep a dummy egg in each box to encourage the birds to lay there — a golf ball works for ducks, a L'eggs stocking package for geese.

Those who have decided to raise their own young will, of course, have kept ganders or drakes over the winter. Mating amongst ducks is often a comical process which, if it takes place in water, sometimes seems pretty dangerous to the female, a near-drowning situation that prompted Chaucer to dub the duck "stroyere of his owene kynde."

Waterfowl mating usually begins in early spring, and those who wish to control it — if, for instance, you are raising more than one breed — should step in during the winter to separate the birds into the desired pairs of groups. Each group will then have to be kept in its own enclosure and can be released into a central area for feeding and drinking twice daily.

In the wild, geese are well-known for forming closely bonded pairs, sometimes for life. For this reason, they have been considered a model and symbol of fertility by various cultures. Less understandable is their association with eroticism — Goosey Gander was, after all, on his way to "my lady's chamber." Pliny believed goose fat to be an aphrodisiac, and the British once had a saying, "the more geese, the more lovers," which apparently alluded to a custom in which a courting gentleman would send his lady a goose at Christmas. Some ladies seem to have received entire flocks.

Despite any reputation they have attained, most domestic ganders will happily mate with up to five geese, and they are often awkward lovers on land, requiring a pond to add buoyancy to their advances. In any case, if one is going to keep waterfowl full time, it is a good idea to provide a pond at least a foot deep for drakes, two feet for ganders. A child's portable wading pond will suffice. Ramps should be provided both for access into *and out of* the water. If the run is small and mud a problem, provide access to the pool only during the mating of geese (except Toulouse, which do not require water), during setting on eggs and as an occasional treat.

Fish culture and waterfowl are compatible only if the pond is large enough that the fowl do not muddy and dirty the water so badly that fish cannot live in it. On the other hand, a diet of too much fish will give both waterfowl eggs and meat an undesirable aquatic flavour.

If one hopes to have the fowl hatch their own eggs, water must be provided for the females, as the eggs must be kept quite damp, and this can only be done if the duck or goose is able to wet herself occasionally.

While some breeds, especially Muscovy, Rouen and banty ducks or Embden geese, are often broody enough to do their own mothering, saving their keeper a great deal of trouble, most ducks and geese are far enough removed from their wild instincts that they have little interest in the consistent setting required to hatch young. In this case, the services of a broody hen or the female of another breed must be enlisted, or the eggs must be artificially incubated. Those who wish to do a fair amount of such incubation, or who have waterfowl-raising friends, should consider an investment in a commercial incubator. The lightbulb-in-a-box system can be made to work, but a great deal of diligence is required to ensure that the proper humidity and temperature levels are maintained — and duck and goose eggs are not plentiful enough that one usually wants to waste them on experimentation.

All duck eggs except Muscovy must be incubated for 28 days; Muscovy take 35, and goose, 30. Because chicken eggs do not take as long, a broody hen may give up on the job before it is done. She will require some help in any case, as she will probably not be able to turn goose eggs (this must be done twice daily) and will not be able to keep the eggs sufficiently damp. (Spray them twice daily.)

Both ducks and geese can be expected to lay well beyond the normal burnout of chickens, usually for at least three years. Geese, in fact, usually lay better in their second year than in their first.

When geese are setting on eggs, the ganders become very protective and feisty; this is the time that has given them a reputation as the crankiest of livestock. Their touchiness is understandable. The females are literally sitting ducks for predators, and the farmer should keep them as well protected and as calm as possible. After the eggs have hatched, the goslings must be kept safe from predators.

Fortunately, with mama's help, these babies are better equipped to face the world than are the commercial day-olds, which have no one but their keeper between them and the elements. Keeping waterfowl full cycle, from egg to egg, as it were, is a most satisfying experience. While it is unlikely that one will discover the mystical goose that lays the golden eggs, the next best thing is possible. One will find domestic waterfowl to be the most companionable and the most self-reliant of poultry, friendlier and more disease-resistant than chickens, prettier and smarter than turkeys. ∎

Sources

Publications

MANAGING A SMALL DUCK FLOCK
Available from Information Services, Agriculture Canada, Ottawa, Ontario K1A 0C7. Publication #1524. Free.

POULTRY NUTRITION HANDBOOK
Available from Ontario Ministry of Agriculture and Food, Information Branch, 801 Bay Street, 12th floor, Toronto, Ontario M7A 1A5. Describes nutritional requirements of chickens, ducks, geese and turkeys at all stages of development. Also describes yields and nutrients of poultry meats. $5.00.

FEATHER FANCIER NEWSPAPER
R.R.5
Forest, Ontario N0N 1J0
(519) 899-2364
Monthly Canadian publication for poultry breeders. Subscription $10 per year. Sample copy $1.50.

RAISING THE HOME DUCK FLOCK
By Dave Holderread
Garden Way Publishing

DUCKS & GEESE IN YOUR BACKYARD
By Rick and Gail Luttmann
Rodale Press
272 pages
125A — paperback, $8.95
Available from Harrowsmith Books, Camden East, Ontario K0K 1J0.

Breeders

BERG'S HATCHERY
Box 603
Russell, Manitoba R0J 1W0
Pekin and Rouen ducklings.

CANADIAN POULTRY SUPPLIES
R.R.2
Lindsay, Ontario K9V 4R2
Hatching eggs, ducklings and mature stock. Khaki Campbell, Aylesbury, Pekin, Cayuga, Magpie, Buff Orpington, Swedish, White Call, Gray Call, East Indie, Mallard and several others.

MILLER HATCHERIES LTD.
260 Main Street
Winnipeg, Manitoba R3C 1A9
(204) 943-6541
Branch offices in Regina, Saskatoon, North Battleford and Edmonton. Rouen and Pekin ducklings.

SPRINGHILL HATCHERY
Box 849
Neepawa, Manitoba R0J 1H0
(204) 476-2778
Pekin ducklings and Embden goslings.

PARDO'S HATCHERY
R.R.3
Blenheim, Ontario N0P 1A0
Rouen and Pekin ducklings.

WEBFOOT FARM & HATCHERY LIMITED
Elora, Ontario N0B 1S0
(519) 846-9885
White Muscovy, White Pekin and Rouen ducklings.
White Embden goslings.

**WILLOW HILL POULTRY FARMS
& HATCHERY**
R.D.1, Box 100
Richland, PA 17087
(717) 933-4606
Ducklings and mature stock. Khaki Campbell, White
Muscovy, Pekin, Rouen, Cayuga, Buff Orpington,
Swedish, Mallard.

Poultry Suppliers

FANCIERS SPECIALTY CO.
Paris, Ontario N3L 3E3
(519) 442-4038

**KETCHUM MANUFACTURING
SALES LIMITED**
396 Berkley Avenue
Ottawa, Ontario K2A 2G6
(613) 722-3451

**COLLEGE PETS, POULTRY
& GARDEN SUPPLIES**
287 College Street
Toronto, Ontario M5T 1S2
(416) 924-5598

COMMUNITY FARM OF THE BRETHREN
R.R.4
Bright, Ontario N0J 1B0
(519) 684-7309
White Embden goslings.

Rare Fare

Reintroducing the overlooked, overcooked and underappreciated lamb

---

By Pamela Cross and Jennifer Bennett

Ernie Sparks

Much to the consternation of the owners of McDonald's restaurants, under a golden-arch logo that includes a very familiar-looking clown, an entrepreneur in India is selling a burger blatantly labelled "Big-Mac," which also happens to be the name of the restaurant that sells it. Although such an exotic infringement of copyright is like a sesame seed caught in the teeth of the American legal profession, McDonald's back home in the United States will probably never sell the sort of Big Mac that draws the crowds in India anyway. Under that special Indian sauce is a lamburger.

Canadians and Americans eschew lamb almost as zealously as they covet all-beef patties or, for that matter, beef in almost any form at all. Canadians each eat about 85 pounds of beef a year, and about a pound and a half of lamb — the equivalent of just one or two servings from a leg of lamb annually. Furthermore, that is less than half as much lamb as Canadians ate a decade ago, and statistics in the United States indicate a similar decline in popularity there. All this despite the fact that sheep are well-suited to the northern climate — certainly better suited than pork, which Canadians consume at the rate of 60 pounds a year. And, as Irene Chernoff of Saskatchewan Agriculture says, "Lamb is a delicately flavoured meat which is easy to prepare and highly nutritious at the same time." It is an excellent source of high-quality protein, and one of the best meat sources of iron, phosphorus and B vitamins.

The villain, it seems, in our lack of appreciation for lamb is its fat. Lamb fat, which burns at a lower temperature than that of most other meats, is classified as "hard" fat. Cooked too long or at too high a temperature, lamb fat has an odour many find unpleasant. The overcooked, fatty mutton eaten by Canadian troops overseas during World War II has been responsible for an entire generation's turning up its collective nose at the same meat that is highly esteemed and deliciously prepared by almost all Mediterranean peoples.

Cooks willing to be reintroduced to lamb should, then, heat the meat gently or cook it quickly. Says Chernoff, "Properly cooked lamb is slightly pink and juicy inside; if it is dry and grey, it is overcooked." If the meat was freshly slaughtered, the cook must remove the papery white membrane, called the "fell," before cooking, as this, too, can produce unpleasant flavours or odours. Sufficient ageing of lamb is also important. Newly slaughtered lamb should be stored in the refrigerator for three to five days before it is cooked. Store-bought lamb will already have been adequately aged.

"Spring" lamb is no longer an appropriate term for young lamb, which is available at all times of the year from all over the world, especially from the major producers, Australia and New Zealand. Nevertheless, lamb termed "spring" describes an animal four to six months old. More precisely, lambs slaughtered between the ages of two and three months are generally called "hothouse" or "milk-fed" and those three to five months old, "baby" or "milk-finished." Animals five months to a year old are simply labelled "lamb," while those at least a year old, and generally less than two years old, are mutton.

Lamb is available in a variety of cuts, several of which are used in the following recipes. The most popular cut, the lamb chop, is available fresh or frozen in most supermarkets and can be prepared simply by being rubbed with garlic and broiled for eight minutes on each side. Served with mint jelly and vegetables, lamb chops make a quick and out-of-the-ordinary meal.

Roast leg of lamb is, of course, one of the most festive ways to serve fresh, young lamb. General roasting instructions include searing the meat for 15 minutes at 450 degrees F, then cooking it at 350 degrees until an internal temperature of 160 degrees for medium-rare (10 to 12 minutes per pound) or 170 degrees for well-done (13 to 15 minutes per pound) is reached. If the meat is boned, the roasting time should be doubled.

Saskatchewan Agriculture recommends this marinade for lamb chops or roasts: Combine the juice of one lemon with salt, pepper, two coarsely sliced onions, four cloves of chopped garlic and a cup of cooking oil. Add chopped parsley, oregano and crumbled bay leaves if desired. Marinate the roast or chops in this liquid at room temperature for at least four hours;

overnight in the refrigerator is best. Remember to turn the meat at least once. When ready to cook it, wipe off the excess marinade and broil, grill or roast.

Although, as Somerset Maugham pointed out, "no one can make yesterday's cold mutton into tomorrow's lamb cutlets," mutton can be substituted for lamb in many recipes. Because it is stronger in flavour than lamb, the cook may wish to use more or different seasoning. And because mutton comes from older sheep, it is tougher than lamb, and so the cooking time should be increased by 5 to 10 minutes a pound.

Ground, either lamb or mutton can be used in place of beef, mixed with beef in lamburgers, or used in any of a number of Middle and Far Eastern specialties such as moussaka, couscous and samosas. It may well be the meat of older animals that finds its way into the counterfeit Indian "Big-Macs." Here at home, however, the fast-food crowd is unlikely to make a dramatic switch from the appeal of baggy-suited clowns to that of the least appreciated of popular meats. According to Jehane Benoit in her recipe booklet *Cooking Lamb for Sheer Pleasure* (published by the Canadian Sheep Marketing Council), a U.S. government survey found that lamb consumers tended to be "intelligent and/or mature."

"The results made me proud as a peacock," says Benoit, who adds with hardly a trace of sheepishness, "I love lamb myself."

HERBED LEG OF LAMB

Work on this dish must begin 24 hours before it is to be served. Once the marinade is assembled and the lamb placed in it, however, no more labour is required until baking time. The herb combination and the cooking method produce a moist, flavourful leg of lamb.

2 cups red wine
½ cup vinegar
1 cup oil
Parsley
Thyme
4 bay leaves
6 cloves garlic
3 onions, finely chopped
Nutmeg
2 Tbsp. sugar
1 tsp. salt
6-to-8-lb. leg of lamb
½ cup finely chopped parsley
1 carrot, finely chopped
1 stalk celery, finely chopped
4 Tbsp. butter
1 cup beef stock
¼ tsp. basil
⅛ tsp. oregano
Salt & pepper

Stir together 1 cup red wine, vinegar, oil, parsley, thyme, bay leaves, 2 cloves garlic (crushed), 2 chopped

onions, nutmeg, sugar and salt. Marinate lamb in this mixture for 24 hours, turning frequently.

On day of cooking lamb, make the herb sauce by sautéing parsley, carrot, remaining onion and celery in butter until soft. Place in bottom of roasting pan along with leftover marinade. Slice remaining garlic into slivers. Pierce the leg of lamb at 3-inch intervals and insert garlic slivers. Roast the lamb at 450 degrees F for 15 minutes.

Meanwhile, combine remaining wine, beef stock, basil, oregano, salt and pepper. Pour mixture over lamb, reduce heat to 350 degrees and continue roasting 15 to 20 minutes per pound. Serve with herb mixture.
Serves 8 to 10.

— *Anne Morell*
Margaree Valley, Nova Scotia

RIVERSLEA SHOULDER OF LAMB

3-4 lbs. boneless shoulder of lamb
1 cup bread crumbs
2 Tbsp. melted butter
1 onion, finely chopped
1 clove garlic, crushed
1 cup dried apricots, chopped and
  soaked in water to soften
1 Tbsp. parsley
1 egg, beaten
Salt & pepper

Have your butcher bone and roll (but not tie) a

shoulder of lamb. Combine all other ingredients, mixing well. Lay the meat out flat and spread the mixture over it. Roll the meat up and tie several times to hold together.

Roast in an open pan at 350 degrees F for about 30 minutes per pound.

Serves 6.

— *Jean Rivers*
Russell, Ontario

SHISH KEBAB

¼ cup red wine vinegar
¼ cup olive oil
4 Tbsp. lemon juice
2 tsp. oregano
1 tsp. basil
2 Tbsp. grated onion
1 clove garlic, minced
1½ tsp. chopped fresh ginger
1 tsp. cumin
Salt & pepper
3 lbs. lamb shoulder, cubed
2 green peppers, cut into large chunks
2 Spanish onions, cut into large chunks
½ lb. mushrooms

Combine vinegar, oil, lemon juice and seasonings. Place meat in bowl and pour marinade over it. Let sit, refrigerated, for several hours or overnight. Drain and place on skewers, alternating with green peppers, Spanish onions and mushrooms. Barbecue over coals, turning frequently and basting with leftover marinade, until meat is cooked through — 10 to 15 minutes.

Serves 6.

MOUSSAKA

3 lbs. eggplant
3 tsp. salt
7 Tbsp. olive oil
½ cup finely chopped onion
⅓ lb. mushrooms, chopped
2 Tbsp. minced green onions
2 cups ground cooked lamb
½ tsp. thyme
½ tsp. pepper
½ tsp. rosemary
1 clove garlic, crushed
½ cup beef stock, thickened with
    2 Tbsp. flour or cornstarch
4 Tbsp. tomato paste
3 cups tomato sauce
Parmesan cheese

Cut eggplant into 1-inch slices, sprinkle with salt and place in a single layer in an oiled casserole dish. Bake at 400 degrees F for 20 to 30 minutes or until tender.

Meanwhile, sauté onions and mushrooms in 2 Tbsp. olive oil until lightly browned. Combine with lamb, thyme, pepper, rosemary, garlic, thickened beef stock and tomato paste. When eggplant is cooked, allow it to cool and remove skins. To assemble moussaka, place one layer of eggplant in bottom of greased casserole dish and top with half of the meat mixture. Pour half of the tomato sauce over this and repeat layers. Top all with Parmesan cheese.

Bake at 375 degrees F for 20 minutes or until heated through and lightly browned.

Serves 6.

SCOTCH BROTH

This soup can make a hearty main course when accompanied by hot crusty bread and a tossed salad.

1½ cups barley
14 cups water
3 lbs. lamb or mutton
2 cups mixed chopped vegetables
    (potatoes, carrots, peas, etc.)
4 Tbsp. butter
Salt & pepper

Soak the barley in 4 cups of water for 1 hour. Place in a large heavy pot with lamb and remaining water. Bring to a boil and then lower to simmer. Cook, covered, for 2 to 3 hours.

Meanwhile, sauté vegetables in butter until they begin to soften.

After two hours, remove the meat from the pot, take it off the bones and dice. Discard bones and return meat to pot. Add vegetables and cook for another half-hour. Season with salt and pepper to taste.

Serves 6 to 8.

ADAIR'S MARINADE

2 cloves garlic
1 small onion
1 tsp. fresh ginger
2 chili peppers
¼ cup brown sugar
2 Tbsp. lemon juice
½ cup soya sauce
¼ cup sesame seeds

Blend all ingredients except sesame seeds in blender or food processor, then add sesame seeds. Pour mixture over a leg of lamb and marinate for 8 hours at room temperature or for 24 hours refrigerated. This marinade is also good with lamb shish kebabs and other cuts of meat.

— *Sue Griggs*
Willowdale, Ontario

LAMB STEW

Mutton may be used in place of lamb in this recipe, provided that a slightly longer cooking time is allowed and that a somewhat stronger taste is acceptable. If a thick gravy is desired, combine 3-4 Tbsp. of flour with a bit of the broth and stir into the stew about 15 minutes before serving.

¼ cup oil
2 onions, chopped
2 cloves garlic, chopped
3 lbs. lamb (shoulder or breast)
2 cups beef stock
1 cup red wine
6 potatoes, peeled and cubed
6 carrots, scraped and thinly sliced
1 cup peas
1 cup corn
Salt & pepper
½ tsp. marjoram

Heat oil and sauté onions and garlic. Cube meat and add to pot when onions are translucent. Cook over high heat, stirring frequently until browned. Add stock and wine and bring to a boil. Lower heat and add vegetables and seasonings. Cover pot and simmer 2 to 4 hours or until meat is tender and vegetables are well cooked. Adjust seasonings and serve.
Serves 6. ∎

Jelly of the Gods

"Come buy my mint, my fine green mint! Let none despise the merry, merry cries of famous London town. . . ."

— *Old London street cry*

Square of stem, rampant of growth, cloaked in folklore, this is the world traveller of the herb kingdom, a native of the Middle East that now grows, cultivated and feral, around the globe. One of the first known plant species transplanted to the New World, mint was not a weedy botanical stowaway but, rather, prized cargo tucked here and there in the colonist's belongings, waiting to be introduced to a continent where it would thrive despite the brittle winters it never faced in its Mediterranean homeland.

Science groups the sages, basils, thymes, marjorams and other familiar herbs such as rosemary, horehound, hyssop, lemon balm and lavender within the mint family, but the true mints — the genus *Mentha* — carry a name and reputation bestowed upon them by the ancient Greeks.

Theophrastus, the philosopher-scientist, is credited with connecting the fragrant perennials to the story of Mintho, the sparkling nymph who enchanted the god Pluto and thereby enraged his captive mistress Persephone. In a fit of mythological jealousy, Persephone is said to have transformed the enchanting young Mintho into an aromatic weed and banished her to the shady fringes of Pluto's underworld domain.

Early Hebrews are said to have scattered mint cuttings on their synagogue steps, to be trod upon and to fill the air with their cool essence, while even today in the hot Middle Eastern countries, bunches of mint are sometimes hung in open doorways to welcome visitors with a fresh scent. The ancient Romans and Greeks carried this one step further and rubbed their tables with the herb just prior to the arrival of especially honoured guests.

"The smell of mint stirs up the mind and appetite to a greedy desire of meat," wrote Pliny the Elder in the first century A.D., bringing Mintho's legacy out of the realm of the storyteller and into the kitchen.

Spearmint or garden mint is so esteemed by cooks that it now grows "wild" throughout the civilized world. Its usefulness is reflected in its myriad of names: lamb mint, green mint, julep mint, spire mint, mackerel mint, sage of Bethlehem, fish mint, yerba buena, Our Lady's mint and heart mint. The gourmets refer to it simply as mint, relegating the dozens of other mints, including the more intensely flavoured peppermint, to the world of teas and chewing gums.

The Elizabethans loved both their *spere mynte* and their medicinal mints, and Culpeper credits this herb with some 40 pharmacological uses:

Government and Virtues — It is an herb of Venus, and has a binding, drying quality; the juice taken in vinegar, stays bleeding, stirs up venery, or bodily lust; two or three branches taken in the juice of four pomegranates, stays the hiccough, vomiting, and allays the choler. It dissolves imposthumes, being laid to with barley-meal. It is good to repress the milk in womens' breasts. Applied with salt, it helps the bites of mad dogs: with mead or honeyed water, it eases the pains of the ears, and takes away the roughness of the tongue, being rubbed thereupon.

The dried powder taken after meat, helps digestion, and those that are splenetic. Taken in wine, it helps women in their sore travail in child-bearing. It is good against the gravel and stone in the kidneys, and the strangury.

Peppermint, *Mentha piperita*, still finds its way into many modern drug preparations, primarily as a flavouring agent to mask the taste of less agreeable components. Nevertheless, it is believed to have a strong positive effect on disturbed digestive systems, and some herbalists argue, with the weight of centuries of use, that it can be used as a tea to treat cramps, flatulence, colic, dyspepsia, diarrhoea and a whole gamut of ailments from the stomach through the intestines.

Both cook and herbalist are blessed by the vigorous growing habits of this family, which does best in rich, moist soil, but which will tolerate all sorts of growing conditions. Some consider it a pernicious weed. It is easily propagated by cuttings of root divisions, but one is well advised to choose a reliable source before establishing a bed of mint that may very well last for centuries.

Mints are notorious cross-pollinators, and an infinity of impure strains exists, none of any distinctive variety and many of questionable value to those who seek the pure spearmint or peppermint effect. Mint will do well in full or partial sun, but it demands moist, well-fertilized earth to thrive. Knowledgeable herb gardeners use various bordering techniques to segregate the mints, lest they spread and overrun less robust plants. Cuttings should be set two feet apart, as runners will quickly infiltrate the intervening spaces. Grasses and weeds must be removed until the mint takes command, and a covering of mulch in the fall will prevent losses due to extreme cold, while providing fresh nutrients for the next season.

Mint is, of course, considered *de rigueur* with roast or broiled lamb, as either a jelly or a sauce, but its great versatility in enlivening vegetable dishes is often overlooked. Fresh chopped mint can be added to the boiling water of peas, spinach, new potatoes, beans, carrots and beets. (Add approximately two tablespoons of minced mint per quart of vegetables.)

Recipes for traditional mint preserves follow, courtesy of young Mintho and the creative wrath of the gods.

FRANCIS LEE'S MINT RELISH

2 cups sugar
2 cups cider vinegar
2 tsp. mustard powder
2 tsp. salt
½ lb. red tomatoes
½ lb. red apples, peeled
1½ cups seedless raisins
1 cup mint leaves, tightly packed

Boil together the sugar, vinegar, mustard powder and salt and then let cool. Meanwhile, put remaining ingredients through a meat grinder or food processor. Add to liquid and mix well. Bring to a boil and immediately bottle in sterile jars. Let stand at least 10 days before using.
Makes 6 cups.

— *Nancy Davidson*
Toronto, Ontario

MINT JELLY

1 cup packed fresh mint leaves
½ cup vinegar
1¼ cups water
1½ lbs. sugar

Wash the mint, chop finely and bring to a boil with water and vinegar. Remove from heat and let stand for a few minutes. Add sugar and bring back to a boil. Boil for 20 minutes or until jelled. Place in jar.

— *C. Majewski*
Pansy, Manitoba ∎

Inspired Harvest

Vegetable medleys for the weeks of bounty

Edited by Pamela Cross

There is a bittersweet tinge to the bounty of summer and fall, moments when we find ourselves overwhelmed with hampers of tomatoes, zucchini and onions that we know will be worth a king's ransom in the supermarket produce section in midwinter. By February, we will be reduced to paying those horrifying prices, each time knowing that we could have grown better quality ourselves, and that just a few months ago, we had more vegetables than we could give away.

Eating well at the height of the harvest season may very well be the best revenge. In fact, other than freezing and canning with tenacity or planning a solar greenhouse, it is the only revenge.

Actually, the salad days are a prime opportunity to exercise one's talents and creativity with vegetable medleys, dishes as tangy, unusual and refreshing as they are free for the picking. All of them taste best when made from freshly picked, sun-ripened produce, and some, such as green tomato curry, are almost impossible to make without home-garden vegetables. Excellent as main courses for warm evenings, the following dishes can also be made in large quantities and frozen for the bleak months ahead, should any of the recipes strike the collective fancy of those around your table.

Ernie Sparks

GREEN TOMATO CURRY

This recipe provides a delicious way to use end-of-the-season unripe tomatoes. It can be frozen very successfully and does not take a great deal of time to prepare.

2 medium onions, chopped
¼ cup butter
4 Tbsp. curry
1 tsp. cumin
1 cup water
8 cups green tomatoes
½ cup brown sugar
2 Tbsp. lemon juice
½ tsp. paprika
Salt

Sauté onions in butter for 10 minutes. Add curry and cumin and cook for 5 minutes longer. Stir in water and remaining ingredients. Simmer for 30 minutes, stirring occasionally, adding more water if necessary. Serve over rice.
Serves 4.

— Leslie Gent
Courtenay, British Columbia

VEGETABLE MEDLEY WITH BEER SAUCE

1 medium eggplant, peeled & cut into ½-inch slices
2 medium zucchini, cut into ½-inch slices
2 eggs
2-3 Tbsp. butter
13-oz. can tomato paste
½ lb. mushrooms, sliced
2 cups peeled tomatoes, stewed
½ cup beer
½ green pepper, diced
1 medium onion, diced
2 tsp. oregano
½ tsp. basil
1 tsp. salt
4 oz. cream cheese, softened or sliced
4 oz. Monterey jack cheese, sliced
4 oz. Cheddar cheese, sliced

Dip eggplant and zucchini slices in beaten eggs and sauté in butter for approximately 5 minutes on each side.
Make the beer sauce by combining the tomato paste, mushrooms, stewed tomatoes, beer, green pepper, onion, oregano, basil and salt in a saucepan. Bring to a boil and simmer for 10 minutes.
Assemble the casserole in a greased 9" x 13" pan as follows: half the eggplant, all of the cream cheese, half the zucchini, one-third of the beer sauce, the rest of the eggplant, half of the Monterey jack and Cheddar cheeses, one-third of the beer sauce, the rest of the zuc-

chini, the rest of the beer sauce and the rest of the cheeses. Bake at 350 degrees F for 45 to 50 minutes.
Serves 6.

— Francie Goodwin-Rogne
Calgary, Alberta

ITALIAN VEGETABLE MEDLEY

This recipe is really just a guideline. Almost any garden-fresh vegetable can be added or substituted — it is the banana pepper and garlic that give the dish its distinctive flavour.

4 medium onions, cut in half & sliced lengthwise
1 banana pepper, sliced
6 cloves garlic, crushed
1 tsp. finely chopped ginger
3 Tbsp. oil
2 Tbsp. curry
2 sweet peppers, thinly sliced lengthwise
8 tomatoes, chopped
Juice of 1 lemon
1 cup bean sprouts

Sauté onions, banana pepper, garlic and ginger lightly in hot oil. Add curry and sweet peppers. When vegetables are cooked, but still crunchy, add tomatoes and lemon juice. Cook over low heat until tomatoes are soft. Add bean sprouts and toss. Serve with pasta or rice.
Serves 4.

— Sandra Hunter
Toronto, Ontario

SPAGHETTI SQUASH SPAGHETTI

1 spaghetti squash
3 cups peeled tomatoes, stewed
1 Tbsp. oil
1 tsp. basil
1 tsp. oregano
1 tsp. marjoram
1-2 cloves garlic, crushed
½ bunch parsley, snipped
1 Tbsp. cornstarch
2 green onions, chopped

Using a sharp knife, cut the squash in half along its width, and scoop out seeds. Remove the flesh, pulling out the pieces by hand. They will separate into spaghettilike strands. Place them in a steamer and cook over boiling water for 20 minutes.
To make the sauce, combine all the remaining ingredients in a large, heavy pot, and simmer for at least 1 hour.
Serves 4.

— Cricket Fox
Sooke, British Columbia

SCALLOPED TOMATOES WITH HERBS

2 medium onions, sliced
½ green pepper, diced
2 stalks celery, diced
¼ cup butter, melted
¼ tsp. pepper
½ tsp. thyme
2 cups coarse, soft bread crumbs
2 Tbsp. chopped parsley
1 tsp. chopped chives
3 cups chopped tomatoes
2 Tbsp. butter

Sauté onions, green pepper and celery in butter with pepper and thyme. Cook, stirring occasionally, until onions are transparent, and remove from heat.

Combine bread crumbs, parsley and chives. Stir half this mixture into onions.

Arrange alternate layers of chopped tomatoes and onion/bread crumb mixture in a greased casserole dish, ending with tomatoes. Sprinkle with remaining bread crumbs, and dot with 2 Tbsp. butter.

Bake at 350 degrees F for 45 minutes.
Serves 4.

— *Cathy Gordon*
Kingston, Ontario

RATATOUILLE

For a satisfying meal with Italian overtones, this succulent vegetable stew can make a complete meal when served with black olives and warm, fresh bread. Another delicious serving possibility is to accompany the ratatouille with Fettuccine Alfredo. Cook fettuccine in boiling water until just tender, then rinse under hot water. Make a rich cream sauce, using whipping cream instead of milk and seasoning liberally with coarsely ground pepper. Stir in Parmesan cheese to taste, add the pasta, and mix well. Serve with additional Parmesan cheese.

½ cup oil
2 large onions, thinly sliced
2-3 cloves garlic, minced
1 eggplant, peeled & diced
4 tomatoes, peeled & diced
1 zucchini, peeled & diced
2 green peppers, cleaned & diced
3 stalks celery, diced
2 tsp. fresh basil
1 tsp. oregano
Salt & pepper

Heat oil in heavy saucepan, and brown onions and garlic. Add eggplant and tomatoes and cook for a few minutes.

Add remaining ingredients, bring to a boil and lower heat. Simmer for at least 1 hour.

Serves 4 to 6.

— *Mrs. E. Imboden*
Uxbridge, Ontario

MOROCCAN TAGINE

The contributor learned how to make this dish while living in Morocco. The word "tagine" refers to the covered clay pot in which the vegetables and tomato sauce were simmered over an open fire.

1 parsnip
1 potato
1 carrot
1 eggplant
1 zucchini
3 tomatoes
1 onion, chopped
1 clove garlic, chopped
2 tsp. cumin
½ tsp. turmeric
½ tsp. cayenne
5-6 prunes
5-6 olives

Chop or slice parsnip, potato, carrot, eggplant and zucchini. Steam tomatoes to remove skins, then mash with fork. In saucepan, sauté onion and garlic; add tomatoes and spices. Layer vegetables over tomato sauce as follows — parsnip, potato, carrot, eggplant, zucchini. Add a little water and the prunes, and top with olives.

Cover and simmer over medium heat for about 30 minutes, or until vegetables are tender.

Serves 2 to 3.

— *Sylvia Dawson*
Manitoulin Island, Ontario
■

Pamela Cross is the food editor of Harrowsmith *and lives in Kingston, Ontario.*

Acetous Juice and Oyl

"Of mordant mustard add a single spoon;
Distrust the condiment that bites too soon
Yet deem it not thou man of taste, a fault
To add a double quantity of salt —
Four times the spoon with oil of Lucca crown
And twice with vinegar procured from town."

By Jennifer Bennett

His talents as a poet may have been modest, but English clergyman Sidney Smith, writing at the turn of the 19th century, did not have today's array of pastel-coloured commercial salad dressings to goad him beyond the muse of awkward iambic pentameter. Smith's recipe for homemade vinaigrette was more or less standard fare of the time. Oil of Lucca was olive oil, something a decent salad could not be without. Where is that ingredient in today's Kraft, Wish-bone or Lawry's, or any of the other sauces that compete for dominion over the modern shopper's cucumbers? And where is the MSG, the BHT, the artificial sweetener, flavour and colour in Smith's homely recipe?

From Smith's perspective, those ingredients were safely ensconced in the vials of the future; for him, the recipe was as it had been since the time of the Romans — vinegar, oil and salt, with other appropriate seasonings added at the discretion of the cook. John Evelyn, another Englishman, had described the basic salad (*salat*) dressing this way a century before Smith's time: "We are by Salats to understand a particular Composition of certain Crude and Fresh Herbs, such as usually are, or may safely be eaten with some Acetous Juice, Oyl, Salt, etc., to give them a grateful Gust and Vehicle."

Indeed. No doubt the irony of today's gardener dousing his organically grown produce in a cacophony of chemicals would not have escaped a perceptive man such as Evelyn, who also noted that salad dressing should be a "discreet choice and mixture, neither the Prodigal, Niggard nor Insipid." Salads should not be overpowered, drowned, glued together or left unflavoured by their dressings; they should, via the wonderfully piquant or sweet-sour combination of dressing ingredients, be complemented. As Beryl M. Marton wrote in *The Complete Book of Salads*, "A good dressing can make a salad and a poor one can ruin it, no matter how fine your greens are."

Vinaigrette dressings, a group that today encompasses such labels as French, Italian, Catalina and Roquefort, are the simple oil and vinegar mixes, distinguished from cooked dressings and from mayonnaise. Vinaigrette dressing is technically known as an emulsion; oil and vinegar do not mix, the oil rising above the vinegar where it rests in a clearly defined layer. The emulsion may, however, be made a colloid — permanently mixed — by the addition of an emulsifying agent such as egg yolk which keeps the oil in suspension within the other ingredients.

Vinaigrettes are usually three to four parts oil to vinegar by volume, though many exceptions exist. Smith's poetic recipe, for instance, calls for a two-to-one ratio. The oil component may be any vegetable oil, although each has its own flavour and weight and is thus best suited to certain raw vegetables and to other seasonings. The "oil" may also be sour cream, mayonnaise or whipping cream, all or in part. Olive oil is the most highly favoured of oils; many gourmet cooks will consider nothing else. It is very expensive, however, and has a heavy and distinct flavour all its own.

The vinegar component of vinaigrette may be any type of vinegar: wine (red or white), cider, malt, white (clear) or flavoured, or even Betsy's dandelion wine that somehow became dandelion vinegar. Commercial wine vinegars are the most highly flavoured, but like the oils, each type of vinegar has its own properties and its own best uses. Lemon juice is often requested as all or part of the acid portion, and wine may be used on some occasions.

The most popular additions to the oil and vinegar emulsion include garlic, mustard, onion, salt and pepper, but virtually every herb and spice will be delicious with the appropriate salad. For instance, string beans are complemented by oregano, savory or tarragon; coleslaw by celery seed, dill or poppy seed; potatoes by caraway seed, chervil, curry, dill or oregano; tomatoes by basil, savory and thyme. Fruit salads are often served with a sweet dressing flavoured with spices such as cinnamon, ginger or nutmeg. M.F.K. Fisher writes in *The Art of Eating* that sometimes she adds a pinch of good curry or minced, fresh anise "to baffle people."

Make any vinaigrette dressing at least three or four hours before the salad is to be served, so that the ingredients may ripen and the flavours marry. Dressing may be served alongside the salad, allowing each diner to add his own, but the idea of offering a selection of dressings for a single salad is frowned upon by most respectable cooks, who will alone know the ingredients of both salad and dressing and whether or not they will suit each other and the rest of the meal. The dressing may be poured into the bottom of the salad bowl, the salad ingredients placed on top and the whole mixed just before serving — a process followed in Parisian households. Rather than ripening the dressing, some cooks prefer to add the ingredients one at a time directly into the salad. In this case, add the oil first, coating the entire salad thoroughly so that it will not wilt when the vinegar is added. Herbs and seasonings are added last. However the salad is dressed, add just enough dressing so that all the vegetables are coated but the dressing does not pool in the bottom of the bowl. When in doubt, start small.

Dressings may be stored in either plastic or glass containers with tight-fitting lids that enable the dressings to be shaken without spilling. Do not use metal or pottery that may have been finished with a lead-based glaze. The standard commercial dressing bottle (the best feature of commercial dressing — it is reusable) takes about one and a quarter cups of dressing.

Unless a dressing contains egg or dairy products, it should not be stored in the refrigerator where the oils will solidify. Dressings should keep several weeks at room temperature. If they are refrigerated, let them warm to room temperature before serving.

Those who are calorie conscious should not turn in resignation from home mixes to the dieter's section of the commercial salad dressing array. Remember that the calories of a dressing are almost exclusively in the oil; vegetable oils contain about 125 calories per tablespoon. Nevertheless, some delightful salads (especially those that already contain an oil ingredient such as tuna, eggs or cheese) can be made without the use of oil at all. The judicious use of good wine vinegar, herbs and a bit of honey can result in a dressing low in calories and far more palatable than the artificially sweetened "low-cal" choices.

It will also probably be less expensive than the store-bought dressing. Olive oil is the most costly dressing ingredient; include it, and it will be difficult to produce a less expensive dressing than the store-bought version; exclude it, and the opposite is true. The fact is, of course, that commercial dressing producers do not use expensive ingredients such as olive oil; they use inexpensive ingredients and bolster them with chemical additives that make their product as comparable as possible to the "real thing."

One ingredient that may keep sweet-tooths returning to commercial dressings is sugar. *Consumer Reports* magazine found that Wish-bone Russian Dressing, for instance, contains 30 percent sugar, a proportion more than three times that of Coca-Cola. The use of sugar in salad dressings, one of the options one has when making dressings at home, has gone in and out of fashion with the times. John Evelyn, writing in 1699, remembered a time when sugar was very often used in dressings, "but now, sugar is almost wholly banished from all, except the more effeminate palates, as too much paling and taking from the grateful acid now in use." (Evelyn himself favoured a dressing of three parts olive oil to one part vinegar, with dry mustard and the mashed yolks of hard-boiled eggs added.)

FRENCH DRESSING

This first dressing does contain sugar, albeit a small quantity, and as such is likely to suit the palate of anyone used to store-bought condiments.

½ cup olive oil
2 Tbsp. wine vinegar
2 Tbsp. lemon juice
1 Tbsp. brown sugar
½ tsp. salt
½ tsp. dry mustard
½ tsp. paprika
Cayenne

Combine all ingredients in a tightly lidded jar. Cover and shake. Shake again just before serving, in three or four hours.

Consumer Reports published the recipe for a similar homemade French dressing, then suggested that for a low-calorie option, tomato juice be substituted for the oil and vinegar. Add ½ tsp. of curry for a little more flavour.

Makes approximately ¾ cup.

ITALIAN DRESSING

This is a spicy, "hot" dressing that is a good accompaniment to baked beans and a salad of tomatoes and strongly flavoured greens.

1 cup olive oil
¼ cup wine vinegar
1 clove garlic, pressed or minced
1 tsp. salt
½ tsp. pepper (white is aesthetically preferable)
½ tsp. celery salt
¾ tsp. cayenne
¼ tsp. dry mustard

Prepare as for French Dressing.
Makes approximately 1¼ cups.

HONEY AND POPPY SEED DRESSING

A nice balance for the tanginess of fruit salads or citrus/green vegetable combinations, this very sweet dressing may also tempt children who are otherwise reluctant to eat their greens.

⅓ cup liquid honey
2 Tbsp. vinegar
1 tsp. salt
1 tsp. Dijon mustard
¾ cup oil
1 Tbsp. finely chopped onion
1 Tbsp. poppy seeds

Combine first four ingredients in a small bowl. Gradually add oil, beating thoroughly until very well blended. Stir in onion and poppy seed. Pour into jar, cover and let sit for several hours before serving.

Makes approximately 1¼ cups.

BLUE CHEESE DRESSING

2 Tbsp. wine vinegar
¼ tsp. salt
Pepper
½ cup olive oil
2 Tbsp. heavy cream
¼ cup crumbled Roquefort cheese
¼ tsp. lemon juice

Combine first five ingredients in a jar and shake. Stir in cheese and lemon juice. Shake before serving.

Makes approximately 1 cup.

PIQUANT YOGURT DRESSING

This dressing has a mustardy bite to it and is especially good on a mixed salad of tuna, tomato, cucumber and lettuce.

¾ cup plain yogurt
1 Tbsp. Dijon mustard
3 Tbsp. vinegar
½ tsp. salt
Pepper
1 tsp. sugar
1 clove garlic, minced

Combine all ingredients in a jar and shake. Shake again before serving.

Makes approximately 1 cup. ■

Simpler Wheys

Making & cooking with ricotta — the most versatile of cheeses

By Pamela Cross

Favignana, the largest of the Egadi Islands off the west coast of Sicily, is a low, rocky, wind-swept plateau more interesting to archaeologists — the island is riddled with grottoes and caves, some of which have been found to contain traces of Palaeolithic habitation — than to tourists. It is not surprising that Favignana was used to hold Italian political prisoners during World War II. The vegetation is sparse, and local farming is therefore minimal; the chief occupation of the island's several hundred inhabitants is tunny fishing.

On a recent visit to the interior of Favignana, however, we came upon an old, blind farmer who, with his son, was busy making what turned out to be ricotta cheese in the barn behind his house. Into a large iron cauldron over an open fire, the two men poured a bluish mélange of milk from their small herd of goats, sheep and cows. When the milk was heated, they added an equal amount of salt water (hauled up from the Mediterranean) and stirred this unlikely mixture with a stick, clockwise, stopping from time to time to let the thickening curds continue to swirl by their own momentum. Then a most amazing thing happened: The cheese mixture stopped turning clockwise, came to a somewhat sluggish halt and reversed itself in a counterclockwise direction. It had, quite literally, "turned"

— a sure sign that it was ready.

The Favignanians ladled the curds into wicker baskets to drain, but the warm, undrained cheese could also be eaten just as it was, in a bowl with fresh Italian bread. A white, smooth cheese with a grainy texture and a slightly sweet taste, ricotta is an important ingredient in a variety of Italian dishes, from appetizers through main courses, like the ravioli and cannelloni recipes provided below, to desserts as exotic as Coeur à la Crème or as simple as a bowl full of ricotta topped with fresh or preserved fruit.

Because it can only be kept for a few days (though it can be frozen quite successfully), fresh ricotta is often difficult to buy outside major centres. But you do not need an iron cauldron and a wind-swept island to make it — just a heavy saucepan, a wooden spoon, a colander and some cheesecloth. The whole procedure takes about two days, but actual working time for the cook is less than 30 minutes. Ricotta is traditionally made from the whey left over from making provolone (the mellow, dried cheese often served with prosciutto sausage as an appetizer), but any kind of milk can be used, from store-bought two percent to fresh, rich Jersey.

However you come by it, you will find ricotta a perfect all-round cheese. *Buon appetito!*

RICOTTA CHEESE

Either fresh whole milk or commercial milk (whole, skimmed or 2 percent) may be used in this basic recipe for ricotta cheese. The richer the milk, the richer the cheese. Once the cheese has been separated from the whey, it can be used in cooking, or herbs can be added to make a delicious spread for crackers or a dip for vegetables.

4 quarts milk
Juice of 1 lemon
1⅓ cups buttermilk or yogurt

Combine milk and lemon juice, cover and let sit in a cold place for two days. Pour into a heavy saucepan, add the buttermilk or yogurt, and cook over medium-high heat, stirring frequently, until it reaches a temperature of 185 degrees F. The milk will begin to turn at this point, separating into curds and whey. Lower heat to medium-low, and continue to cook, stirring, for two or three more minutes. Remove from heat. Strain through triple layers of cheesecloth placed in a sieve. The whey may be preserved for baking or fed to a pet. Allow the curds to cool, and then place in a covered container in the refrigerator. The cheese may be salted to taste. It should be used within a few days.
Makes 3-4 cups.

RICOTTA CUSTARD

1 cup ricotta cheese
3 egg yolks
1 cup milk
⅓ cup sugar
1 Tbsp. rum
Grated orange rind
1 cup whipping cream
Nutmeg

Beat together cheese, egg yolks, milk and sugar. Add rum and orange rind to flavour. Bake at 325 degrees F for 45 minutes or until set.
Whip cream until stiff peaks form. When custard has cooled, garnish with whipped cream and grated nutmeg.
Serves 4 to 6.

— *Elizabeth Templeman*
Heffley Lake, British Columbia

RICOTTA FRUIT FLAN

4 cups ricotta cheese
4 eggs
1 cup yogurt
¾ cup sugar
2 tsp. rum
Juice and grated rind of 1 lemon

½ cup gingersnap crumbs
2 cups sliced or chopped fruit
(for topping)

Combine cheese, eggs, yogurt, ½ cup sugar, rum and lemon juice and rind, and beat until smooth (or process in blender or food processor). Pour into greased 9-inch springform pan. Place in a pan of water, and bake at 375 degrees F for 40 to 50 minutes.
Combine gingersnap crumbs and remaining ¼ cup sugar, and toast lightly in oven.
When flan has cooled, remove from pan. Gently pat crumbs around sides, top with fruit, and serve.
Serves 8 to 10.

SWISS CHARD AND RICOTTA CHEESE QUICHE

Pastry for single-crust pie
5 eggs
1 cup whipping cream
Salt & pepper
Nutmeg
1½ cups cooked, chopped Swiss chard
1 cup crumbled ricotta cheese
⅓ cup Parmesan cheese

Line a pie plate with pastry, and set aside. Combine eggs and whipping cream, and beat until frothy and light. Add salt, pepper and nutmeg to taste.
Place Swiss chard and ricotta cheese in pie shell. Pour custard mixture over, and sprinkle with Parmesan cheese.
Bake at 350 degrees F for 20 to 30 minutes, or until set and golden brown.
Serves 6.

CANNELLONI

Pasta

3 eggs
3 tsp. olive oil
3 Tbsp. water
2 cups flour

Filling

2 cups ricotta cheese
1 cup torn spinach
1 cup grated Swiss cheese
1 cup grated mozzarella cheese
½ cup grated Parmesan cheese
2 eggs
Salt & pepper

Tomato Sauce

2 cloves garlic
Olive oil
1 medium onion, chopped

1 Tbsp. fresh basil
2 tsp. fresh oregano
2 cups puréed tomatoes
13-oz. can tomato paste
Salt & pepper

Cheese Sauce

3 Tbsp. butter
3 Tbsp. flour
2 cups milk
½ cup grated Swiss cheese
½ cup grated mozzarella cheese
½ cup grated Parmesan cheese

To make pasta, combine eggs, oil and water, and work in 2 cups flour to make a soft dough. Continue adding flour until dough becomes stiff. Cover and let sit for 30 minutes. Roll out until paper-thin, or put through a pasta maker to desired thinness. Cut into 2" x 4" rectangles, and stack.

Meanwhile, combine filling ingredients, using salt and pepper to taste.

For tomato sauce, crush garlic and sauté in olive oil with onion, basil and oregano. Add tomato purée, tomato paste and salt and pepper to taste. Cook over low heat, stirring occasionally, for 2 hours.

To make cheese sauce, melt butter in a heavy saucepan. Stir in flour, and cook for 1 minute. Slowly add milk, cooking and stirring until hot and thickened. Add Swiss and mozzarella cheeses, and continue stirring until they have melted. Remove from heat.

To assemble, place 2 Tbsp. of filling on each pasta rectangle, and roll up. Place in greased 9" x 13" casserole. Spoon tomato sauce over cannelloni, pour cheese sauce over this, and top with Parmesan cheese. Bake at 350 degrees F for 30 minutes.

Serves 6.

RAVIOLI

Meat Sauce

1 medium onion, chopped
2 cloves garlic, crushed
2 Tbsp. olive oil
½ lb. ground beef
2 stalks celery, chopped
½ green pepper, chopped
½ lb. mushrooms, sliced
1 Tbsp. chopped fresh basil
2 tsp. chopped fresh oregano
3-4 cups puréed tomatoes
13-oz. can tomato paste
Salt & pepper

Filling

2 cups ricotta cheese
1 cup cooked, chopped spinach
  or Swiss chard
1 egg
Salt & pepper

Pasta

See Cannelloni recipe.

For meat sauce, sauté onion and garlic in oil until limp. Add ground beef and cook over medium-high heat, stirring frequently, until browned. Add remaining ingredients, mix well, and cook over low heat for at least 2 hours.

Meanwhile, combine filling ingredients, mixing well, and set aside.

Make pasta as for cannelloni, but do not cut after rolling out to desired thinness — just leave in strips of the same size.

To assemble ravioli, place one strip of pasta on lightly floured work surface. Spread a very thin layer of filling over this, and top with a second layer of pasta. Using a ravioli roller, roll over the ravioli in both directions, pressing down firmly to ensure the dough is cut right through, and then separate the squares. If cutting by hand, cut into 1-inch squares, sealing edges with moistened fingers.

Cook the ravioli in boiling salted water until it rises up to the top of the pot — 3 minutes. Remove to serving platter with slotted spoon, top with meat sauce, and serve with Parmesan cheese.

Serves 4 to 6.

COEUR A LA CREME

A beautiful, rich and yet light dessert, Coeur à la Crème requires a special heart-shaped mould with drainage holes in the bottom, which can usually be found in kitchen shops.

4 oz. cream cheese
4 oz. ricotta cheese
1¼ cups whipping cream
⅔ cup powdered sugar
1 tsp. vanilla
1 pint strawberries
2 Tbsp. kirsch
Sugar

Whip cheeses and ¼ cup whipping cream with electric mixer. Add sugar and vanilla, and beat until doubled in volume.

Beat remaining whipping cream until firm, then gently fold into cheese mixture.

Wring out a large double thickness of cheesecloth that has been soaked in cold water, and place in a Coeur à la Crème mould, making the cloth as smooth as possible. Fill mould with cheese mixture, and smooth top. Drape cheesecloth over top, place mould on a plate, and weight the top with another plate. Refrigerate overnight.

Meanwhile, sort the strawberries, setting aside the most attractive half. Purée remaining berries with kirsch, and sugar to taste. Unmould coeur onto serving plate, and pour a ribbon of strawberry purée around base. Garnish with remaining berries.

Serves 6 to 8.

■

Making Stock

The steamy essences of great cooking

By Pamela Cross

"To make a good soup," admonished the old French chef, "the pot should scarcely smile." In a country where the evening meal in the provinces is fittingly called *la soupe*, the making of stocks and broths is taken very seriously, indeed. The French, too, are credited with originating one well-known version of the delightful "Stone Soup" fable, in which an itinerant tramp appears on the doorstep of a country cottage and asks to borrow a kettle so as to make himself some soup.

The housewife asks, with some skepticism, what ingredients he has, and the wanderer produces a well-washed stone from a deep pocket. "One cannot make soup from a stone," argues the woman, but the stranger smiles and says he would show her how if she would but lend him her kettle and some water.

He puts the stone in the bottom of the pot and sets the water to heating. "Now, you wouldn't mind letting me have a bit of sage from your herb garden, just to flavour the soup?" he innocently asks. The herbs are plentiful, and the woman does not object. "And a bit of dandelion from the weeds growing by your doorstep?" Again, she sees no harm. The man busies himself, filching the odd leaf here and some dried pods of seeds there. The woman has become very curious, and the tramp now enquires if she might have a small, shrivelled potato he could use, and perchance an old bone. All of this goes into the kettle with the original stone.

"*Voilà*!" he exclaims at last, "My stone soup is ready. Will you share it with me?" The woman, bemused at the turn of events, finds the soup delicious.

From the kitchens of peasants to the banquet tables of kings, soup is one food that crosses all boundaries of culture and status. A hot, well-herbed *potage* "doth comfort many men," wrote one Elizabethan herbalist, "[it] can do lytel displeasure and relaxeth the belly."

"To possess a cook who makes perfect soups is to possess a jewel of great price," huffed P. Morton Shand in 1928. "A woman who cannot make soup should not be allowed to marry." Shand would be horrified today, for the great traditions of soup making have been lost to many: astonishing numbers of cooks — men and women — are ignorant even of basic stock making.

Virtually all good soup is based on stock, a nutrient-and flavour-rich broth slowly simmered at the back of the stove. Unlike most recipes, stock calls not for the youngest, tenderest and freshest vegetables and meats, but rather the fully ripe, even overripe, vegetables and the most aged — often very tough — animals. The stock maker covets a strange array of culinary oddments: fowl carcasses, tomato skins, mushroom stems, knucklebones, chicken feet and fish heads.

Stocks are by no means all based on meat, the vegetarian versions relying on fish and vegetables to produce a broth used in meatless *au maigre* cooking. In contrast, those derived from poultry and red meats are known as *au gras*. Either type allows one to make full use of kitchen by-products that might otherwise have gone to waste, and the resulting stock is the foundation on which great soups, sauces, gravies and stews are built. The kitchen in which good stock can be substituted for water in all manner of dishes is a kitchen with a loyal following.

My own stocks always start with onions, carrots and celery and develop from there, depending on what the vegetable bin and refrigerator yield. Most vegetables are eligible, even those that are definitely past their prime — but not decaying. Leeks are very good, and some cooks always add a clove of garlic. Turnips and cabbage, however, should be used sparingly, as their flavour can become overwhelming. Vegetable skins, onions included, are added to enhance the taste, nutrients and colour.

If making a meat, poultry or fish stock, either raw or cooked carcasses may be used. Do not use organ meats as they will overpower the flavour. If a darkly coloured stock is desired, brown or roast the meat before adding the other ingredients.

Stock must start with cold water to draw the vitamins and minerals — what food writers of past centuries called the "virtue" of the ingredients — out.

To protect them and the essence of the stock, the pot is simmered slowly and not, as the French cook cautioned, allowed to boil or "smile." (Many break this rule slightly by bringing the stock to a boil for an instant at the outset and then letting it cook at a steady, low heat.)

Accomplishing this is no small feat with many modern stoves, especially the electric models, and the cook may wish to use a large double-boiler. A good stock pot should be a part of every kitchen, but avoid aluminum, which can affect the clarity of the final product. The authors of *Joy of Cooking* recommend a pair of clean bricks to elevate the pot above the burner if boiling is a problem.

The cooking time for stocks varies, with beef requiring the longest (up to 12 hours), followed by chicken (up to 8 hours) and finally fish and vegetable stocks. The latter two deteriorate rapidly, and they should be done in less than an hour in most cases.

An albuminous scum will rise to the surface of meat stocks, and it can be skimmed off periodically while the cooking continues. Once it is done and has met with your taste approval, strain the liquid through cheesecloth to remove all solids. Cool at room temperature, cover and refrigerate. If a meat or poultry stock has been made, fat will rise to the top as the fluid cools. This should be removed only when the stock is to be used. Refrigerated stocks will keep for three to four days; freezing preserves them for several months.

The stock recipes which follow are of mild flavour intensity, just right for most soup bases. (They are light and delicious by themselves and make for a low-calorie first course to a formal meal.) To make consommé, aspic or clear chicken broth with more flavour, simply boil down the strained stock until the desired strength is achieved.

Good stock is simple to make, requiring little attention while cooking and using the most economical ingredients found in the kitchen. Once made, it allows the cook's imagination to take over. It can be used in all manner of soups, gravies, sauces, stews and casseroles, or to replace water when making rice and noodles.

Writing in *Simple Food for the Good Life*, Helen Nearing admitted that, "in creating a soup, I find it one-third products on hand, one-third ingenuity and one-third good luck. Sometimes I make a really good soup (usually out of scrap ingredients) and, like the Lost Chord in music, can never find it again." The following recipes are offered to help you enter and lose your own way in the world of creative stocks and soups.

FISH STOCK

6 Tbsp. butter
1 cup chopped onion
½ cup chopped carrots
1 cup chopped celery
8 peppercorns
4-5 cloves
¾ cup white wine
6 cups cold water
Bouquet garni (place 6 sprigs parsley, 1 bay leaf,
  2¼ tsp. thyme, the chopped white part of 1 leek,
  2 cloves garlic & chopped celery leaves in
  cheesecloth bag)
Twist lemon rind
2-3 lbs. washed fish bones, heads, tails, skins
  & trimmings

Melt the butter. Add onion, carrot and celery, and sauté gently for 5 minutes. Add remaining ingredients, and heat until liquid simmers. Cook, uncovered, for 20 to 30 minutes.

Strain stock, discarding vegetables and fish. Cool at room temperature, then cover and refrigerate.

Makes approximately 4 cups.

BOUILLABAISSE

½ lb. haddock
½ lb. sole
1 lb. lobster
12 mussels
¼ cup oil
1 leek, white part only, chopped
1 onion, chopped
1 clove garlic, chopped
1 tomato, peeled & seeded
Bouquet garni (see Fish Stock recipe)
4-6 cups fish stock
Salt & pepper

Cut fish into bite-sized pieces, keeping the haddock and sole separate from one another. Break lobster in shell into pieces, and wash and clean the mussels.

Heat oil in heavy pot, add vegetables, and sauté for 10 minutes, stirring often. Add bouquet garni and haddock, and cook for 7 to 10 minutes. Add sole and lobster, and cover with fish stock. Season with salt and pepper, and bring to a boil. Add mussels, and cook until they open. To serve, place fish in a deep dish and pour hot liquid over.

Serves 4.

CHICKEN STOCK

1 chicken carcass or 1 raw chicken with most of the
  meat removed
2 carrots
2-4 stalks celery, including leafy tops
2 onions
8 cloves
2 Tbsp. salt
1 tsp. coarsely ground pepper
1 bay leaf
12-18 cups cold water

Cut the carcass or chicken, carrots, celery and onions into quarters. Place in large heavy pot, and add
cloves, salt, pepper and bay leaf. Cover with water.
Cover pot and slowly bring to a boil. Lower heat so
that stock continues to simmer gently.

Cook for 4 to 6 hours. Let cool slightly, then strain
stock, and discard vegetables and bones. Cool to room
temperature, cover and refrigerate.

Makes approximately 12 cups.

BEEF STOCK

4-5 lbs. meaty beef bones
2 carrots
2 onions
2 stalks celery, including leafy tops
1 Tbsp. salt
Bouquet garni (see Fish Stock recipe)
12-18 cups cold water

Chop bones into 2-to-3-inch pieces. Brown in heavy
pot, stirring frequently. Quarter carrots, onions and
celery and add to pot. Add salt and bouquet garni.
Cover with water and slowly bring to a boil. As scum
rises to top of liquid, remove with a spoon. Cover pot,
reduce heat, and gently simmer for a minimum of 6
to 8 hours.

Strain stock and discard meat, bones and vegetables.
Cool to room temperature, cover and refrigerate.

Makes approximately 12 cups.

VEGETABLE STOCK

4 carrots
4 onions
1 bunch celery, including base & leafy tops
2 potatoes, including peels
2 leeks
4 tomatoes
6 cloves
2 Tbsp. salt
2 tsp. pepper
1 bay leaf
12-18 cups cold water

Coarsely chop vegetables, and place in heavy pot.
Add cloves, salt, pepper and bay leaf, and cover with
water. Cover pot, and slowly bring to a boil. Reduce
heat so that stock continues to simmer gently, and cook
for 1 to 2 hours. Strain stock, discarding vegetables.
Cool to room temperature, cover and refrigerate.

Makes approximately 12 cups.

VEGETABLE SOUP

12 cups vegetable stock
4 cups chopped potato
4 cups chopped carrots
1 cup chopped green beans
1 cup lima beans
3 cups chopped celery
2 cups peas
1 cup corn
1 Tbsp. soya sauce
2 tsp. Worcestershire sauce
Salt & pepper

Bring stock to a boil while preparing vegetables. Add
potatoes, carrots, green beans and lima beans, and simmer for 15 minutes. Add celery, peas, corn, soya sauce,
Worcestershire sauce, salt and pepper, and simmer for
another 15 minutes, or until all vegetables are tender.

Serves 8.

ONION SOUP

6 Tbsp. butter
3 cups thinly sliced onions
10 cups degreased beef stock
½ tsp. pepper

Melt butter, and sauté onions until well browned.
Add stock and pepper, reduce heat, cover and simmer
for 30 minutes.

Serves 4 to 6.

CHICKEN NOODLE SOUP

10 cups degreased chicken stock
3 carrots, finely chopped
4 stalks celery, thinly sliced
2 tsp. sage
Salt & pepper
2 cups chopped, cooked chicken
2 cups raw flat egg noodles

Bring chicken stock to a boil while preparing vegetables. Add vegetables and seasonings, and simmer for
20 minutes. Add chicken and noodles, and continue
to cook for 10 minutes, or until noodles are tender and
chicken is heated through.

Serves 6 to 8.   ■

Zero-Degree Harvest

Keeping the nutrients on permanent hold: a guide to the intelligent use of a home food freezer

A Harrowsmith Staff Report

Her skin is dark, tufts of reddish hair still attached to the feet, her two-foot-long trunk culminating in what looks like a pair of fingers. In her stomach, there are traces of her mother's milk, of seeds, roots, even soil she consumed in a desperate struggle to survive until, not yet weaned, her mother gone, the baby mammoth died in primaeval Siberia. Found in June 1977, her remarkably intact remains are a testament not only to the baby's last dramatic days, but also to the ability of freezing temperatures to store perishable things. Professor Nikolai Vereschagin of Leningrad told *Moscow News*, "I put my hand on the dark skin and felt the chill of centuries long gone; it was as if I had touched the Stone Age."

Cold temperatures preserve not only mammoths, but anything organic, like food. They do so by slowing the respiration rate of living things and by slowing or even stopping the action of destructive microorganisms and enzymes that would otherwise cause decay. The lower the temperature, the longer and better food keeps. "In five years at minus 20 degrees F, green beans, peas, cauliflower and spinach have shown no measurable or detectable loss of colour or flavour and no measurable change in chemical constituents or physical attributes," according to the *Quality and Stability of Frozen Foods*, edited by Wallace B. Van Arsdel. Dima, as the baby mammoth was called by the Russians, suffered relatively little deterioration in 40,000 years of Siberian cold storage. Refrigeration preserves food for days; freezing keeps it for months and years, perhaps even for centuries.

It is an extremely effective method of food storage, but also a remarkably luxurious one, demanding, in effect, that the climate of the mountains be brought to the valleys, that of the poles to the tropics, that of winter to summer. Although a good deal of energy and insulation are required in the maintenance of the mini-climate we call the deep freeze, the fact that an average North American can eat, in mid-February, the beans he picked from his own garden in July and that he can eat them in almost the same condition regardless of season seems a technological miracle. It has, however, a very simple foundation, resting on principles of refrigeration that have been used for centuries, and on food preparation methods developed only within the last generation.

While it is generally conceded that freezing is easier, less steamy and, in most cases, productive of more nutritious vegetables than the older canning processes, surprising numbers of freezer owners either misuse this particular harvest tool or do not fully understand the rationale or methods used in the preparation of food for freezing.

Although one needn't be a refrigeration engineer to put away a bag of Brussels sprouts, a simple appreciation of the science of freezing may help. Historically, three methods have been used to freeze food or water. The first involves simply placing the substance to be frozen in contact with ice or in a space with below-freezing temperatures.

The second, which has been utilized for centuries, was probably first put into use when man noticed that he felt cool when a breeze blew across his damp skin, drying it. Evaporation causes cooling, a principle that enables East Indians to collect, after a dry, breezy night in which the temperatures do not have to descend to freezing, a skin or even a solid block of ice from shallow pans of water that have been placed on beds of straw.

By the 17th century, the third method was discovered. If snow were mixed with salt or saltpetre and

Bob Suzuki

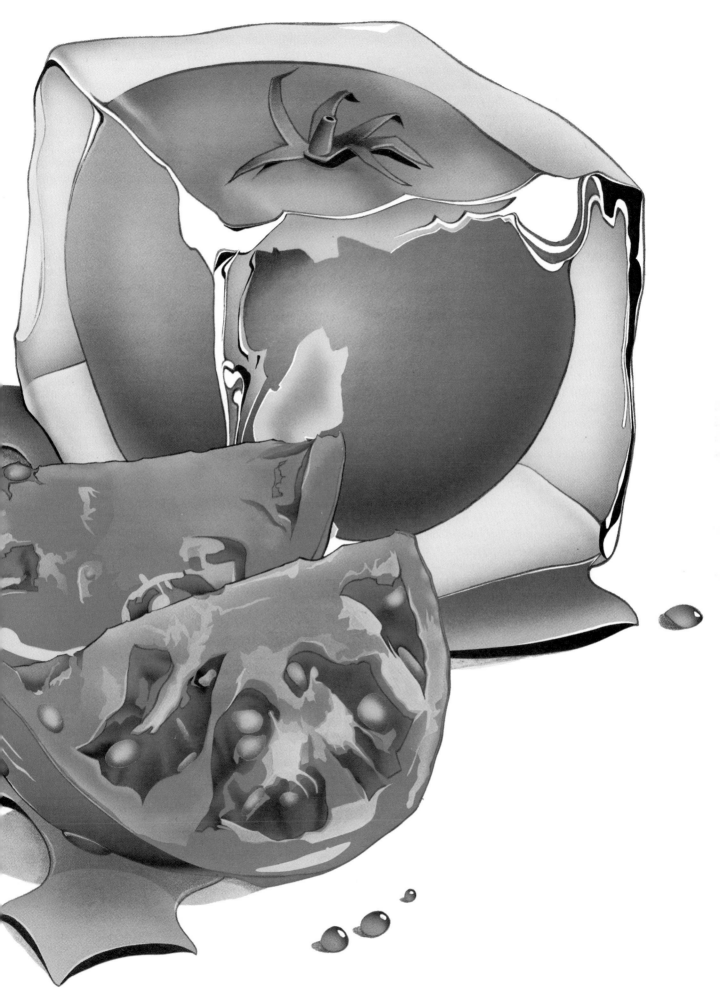

placed next to a vessel of water, the water would freeze. This happens because a solution, such as salt water, has a lower freezing point than its solvent alone, in this case water. (Vegetables, also made up of water and other materials have a freezing point between 25 and 32 degrees F.) If salt and snow were mixed in the proper proportions, the temperature of the mixture dropped without any outside help. Later, scientists would experiment with and use other refrigerants like ether and ammonia, finally developing synthetic refrigerants in the 1920s, substances such as Freon, which is odourless, relatively harmless if leaked, and still in use.

Ether, ammonia and synthetic refrigerants all have a freezing point below that of water. In modern freezers, utilizing what is known as the vapour-compression system, the refrigerant boils and evaporates under regulated gas pressure in an evaporator, absorbing heat from the space to be cooled — the freezer compartment. The refrigerant then passes to the key element of the freezer, the part that requires an external source of power, the compressor, where the vapour is compressed. In the condenser, the heat is dissipated to circulating water or, more often, air, as the refrigerant returns to a liquid state. The refrigerant is then returned to the evaporator to be vaporized, and the cycle begins again. The whole operation is triggered by a thermostat, which can be set at the desired freezer temperature, zero degrees F in a home unit.

FISH AND CHIPS

Truly efficient freezing was, as might be expected, first a commercial venture, but its applications in the food industry inevitably worked their way down to the home food preserver. A surprising spin-off of the application of freezing technology to the fishing industry — one of the first places it was used — was the birth of the British fish-and-chip combo in the 1860s and '70s. The fish were frozen whole, to be cleaned in the shops. It was not until after World War I that an American, Clarence Birdseye, brought forward the idea of marketing food in ready-to-cook form. By the end of the Roaring Twenties, Birdseye, whose name would grace the labels of millions of frosty packages, was freezing Oregon cherries and strawberries on double-belt freezers — one belt froze the fruit from above, the other from below.

Vegetables were not as trouble-free as fruit, whose high acid content lent itself naturally to the new technology, while vegetables were frustratingly apt to continue to deteriorate rapidly, even when frozen. The United States Bureau of Plant Industry finally discovered that if peas were scalded briefly before freezing, almost-fresh quality could be maintained in storage. The process, blanching, introduced in 1930, counteracted the work of proteins whose existence had been established only 80 years before.

These proteins, called enzymes, are present in very large numbers in all living cells — the average human cell contains about 3,000 — where they act as accelerators or catalysts in almost all biological processes. Each enzyme promotes only one type of chemical reaction. For instance, amylase converts starch into sugar, and pepsin in the stomach aids in digestion. Commercially, enzymes are necessary in cheese, wine and bread making, in the tanning of leather and the tenderizing of meat. Because they are protein molecules, they can be damaged, even destroyed, by both high and low temperatures, although the temperature in a home freezer is not sufficiently low to stop their activity. The presence of sugar, acid or salt — all used in various types of food preservation — can, in sufficient quantities, inactivate enzymes.

FIFTH COLUMN DEFEAT

Enzymes are responsible for food's ripening and eventual deterioration; while moulds and bacteria may work from outside, enzymes are the food's own fifth column, acting within it toward its own destruction, withering produce, turning fruits brown. Particularly destructive to vegetables are catalase and peroxidase, both of which can be inactivated by blanching.

Blanching involves exposing the vegetable to a high temperature — by boiling or, preferably, steaming — for a duration long enough to heat all cells, but short enough that little cooking occurs. After sufficient heating, respiration in the vegetable stops — it is now "dead" and the chlorophyll, which gives many vegetables their bright green colour, begins to convert to pheophytin, a dull, olive-green colour, brownish green in the extreme. To stop cooking and to help prevent this colour change, the vegetable must be cooled quickly, most easily done in the home by plunging it into ice water. As soon as it is chilled, the vegetable is removed from the cold bath to drain and is then packed and placed in the freezer.

Once blanching had been introduced, the vegetable-freezing industry burgeoned. Large freezer lockers began to rent space to individual families, while the home freezer unit made its first appearance in pre-Depression homes of the '30s. Although they were banned from manufacture for civilian use during World War II, they boomed in popularity when peace returned, with 200,000 freezers manufactured in 1946, double that in 1947 and one million in use by 1949.

In 1953, Oscar Anderson Jr. wrote in *Refrigeration in America*, "To the farm family, it meant convenience . . . . But, for a city family to save money, it needed access to a supply of low-cost food, either grown in its own garden or purchased on a quantity basis.

"The future of the home freezer depended on certain imponderables. Foremost among these was the extent to which consumers were convinced that the advantages were worth the initial and operating costs. With upper-income groups, convenience rather than economy would be the determinant, but with middle- and lower-income groups, economy would be an important consideration."

Obviously, a good many North Americans decided and continue to decide "that the advantages were worth the initial and operating costs." Today, about half of all Canadian homes possess a freezer. While, in 1947, canned vegetables outsold frozen, pound for pound, by more than twelve to one, this had fallen to only a four-to-one lead in 1978. And in 1982, Statistics Canada reported that Canadians consumed approximately twice as many canned vegetables as frozen.

Although firm figures for home food-preservation habits are not available, it would seem safe to speculate that freezing has superseded canning at least to the same extent as in commercial production. For certain vegetable crops — most notably peas, beans, broccoli, cauliflower, Brussels sprouts and asparagus — freezing has clearly become the method of choice for those who want superior colour, flavour and texture. The number of home freezer units sold annually in Canada has almost doubled in the past decade, perhaps in step with the increased interest in home gardening, farmers' markets and pick-your-own operations.

SOGGY SPECIES

That multitude of freezers, however, may not be keeping food as well as it might. This is partly the fault of freezer maintenance (an American study in 1962 determined that about one-third of all freezers were kept at a temperature above 10 degrees F, rather than at the optimum zero degrees) and partly a problem of improper preparation or poor choices of food for freezing.

Some vegetables simply do not freeze well in a home unit. The main determining criterion is the water content of the vegetable in question: high moisture working against high quality in the finished product. Because slow freezing produces large ice crystals, and the home appliance freezes more slowly than does the commercial processor, some home-frozen vegetables, notably French fries, are pale and mushy imitations of the quick-frozen, store-bought product. Not only potatoes, but also summer squash, celery, onions, tomatoes and cucumbers are high in water content and will be soggy when thawed, although if they are needed only for soups or stews, the final product may be quite acceptable. Frozen tomatoes, in fact, are comparable, when thawed, to canned ones, but take much less time and energy to prepare.

The most successful vegetables are the drier ones, and indeed, if they are properly prepared, they make many of their commercial counterparts seem like so much coloured cardboard. Peas, the most popular commercially — 30 million pounds of frozen peas are sold every year in Canada — are entirely different when picked from the home garden and promptly blanched and frozen, and one has simply not tasted frozen beans until he has tried the home-grown kind. Because commercial processors choose varieties that excel in characteristics like simultaneous ripening and resistance to mechanical damage (in other words, tough), qualities like tenderness, sweetness and good flavour often lose out. Frozen green and yellow beans, picked quite young, high in nutrients and easily prepared and stored, are often a winter staple of families that both garden and freeze.

Beans, whole or shelled, peas, with or without pods,

Burpee's Seeds

broccoli, spinach, chard, cauliflower, kernel corn, asparagus, sliced or shredded cabbage, carrots, beets and parsnips are all delicious if properly blanched and stored. Brussels sprouts and corn on the cob are more difficult, as their mass makes proper blanching hard to attain. All vegetables, with the exception of asparagus, are best cut into relatively small pieces before blanching so that heating time can be kept as short as possible. Tomatoes, peppers, herbs, fruit and any cooked vegetables need not be blanched, although tomatoes are often preferred skinless. To remove skins, dip in boiling water for one minute, then plunge into cold water. Remove core and slip off peel. Cut peppers in half or dice, discarding seeds and membranes.

In freezing, time is of the essence. Those striving for perfection will let no waste time elapse between picking and preparation, blanching, chilling, packing and freezing. A general rule of thumb maintains that best quality is achieved if no more than two or three hours pass between a vegetable's leaving the garden and entering the freezer. If the produce must be held overnight, it should be kept at about 40 degrees F — in the refrigerator in most cases. Harvesting early in the morning rather than in the heat of the day also contributes to better overall quality.

Having all necessary equipment and help lined up beforehand is essential for speed; at least two pairs of hands will make the whole process more manageable, and several more can make for a swift and smooth flow of work (call it Operation Deep Freeze and make an occasion of it).

Unfortunately, despite optimum processing speed, some vitamin loss is inevitable in blanching. While certain authors of magazine articles in recent years have espoused no-blanch freezing — claiming that the food looks and tastes the same — laboratory analyses would clearly show that enzyme action during frozen storage had lowered the nutritional quality of the unblanched food.

Blanching is especially hard on vitamin C; a loss of 10 percent has been attributed to blanching in the com-

PREPARING GARDEN VEGETABLES FOR THE FREEZER

VEGETABLE	SPECIAL PREPARATIONS		BLANCHING TIME IN MINUTES	
			Water	Steam
Asparagus	Sort stalks according to thickness. Cut in 2-inch lengths or leave in spears.	Small Medium Large	2 3 4	3
Beans, Shelled, such as Lima or Soy	If desired, sort according to size.	Small Medium Large	2 3 4	3
Beans, Snap, Green or Wax	Remove ends. Cut as desired.		3	3
Beets	Sort according to size. Trim tops, leave ½ inch of stems. Peel after boiling.	Small Medium	30 45	
Broccoli	Peel stalks and trim. If insect removal is necessary, soak for ½ hour in salt water (4 tsp. salt, 1 gal. cold water).		3	4
Brussels Sprouts	Trim, removing coarse outer leaves. Sort according to size.	Small Medium Large	3 4 5	4
Cabbage	Trim off outer leaves. Shred for tight packing or cut into wedges.	Shreds Wedges	1½ 3	2 4
Carrots	Remove tops. Peel. Leave small carrots whole. Slice others.	Whole Cut	5 2	5 3
Cauliflower	Trim and cut in pieces 1 inch across. If necessary, remove insects as for broccoli. Drain. Blanch in salt water (4 tsp. salt, 1 gal. water).		3	3
Celery	Strip any coarse strings from young stalks. Cut across the rib into 1-inch pieces.		3	4
Corn, Whole-Kernel	After blanching, cut kernels at about ⅔ the depth of the kernels.		4	3
On-the-Cob	Sort according to size.	Small Medium Large	4 5 6	5 6 7
Greens, All Kinds	Remove tough stems and imperfect leaves.		1	1
Herbs	No blanching needed.			
Mushrooms	Use firm, tender, small-to-medium size. Cut off lower part of stems. Alternatively, sauté in butter and freeze without blanching.	Small Large	2 4	3 5
Peas, Green and Blackeye	Shell. Discard tough peas.		1½-2	1½-2
Peas, Edible-Podded	Remove blossom end and string.		2	3
Peppers	Halve, remove seeds and membranes, slice or dice. Peppers do not require blanching.			
Squash, Summer	Select squash with rind still tender. Cut without peeling in ½-inch slices.		3	4
Squash, Winter and Pumpkin	Peel, cut in pieces and remove seeds. Cook until soft. Put pulp through sieve or use a potato masher. Cool by placing pan containing purée into cold water. Stir purée occasionally to hasten chilling.		20	
Tomatoes	Remove skins by dipping in boiling water. Core and cut in chunks or freeze whole. No blanching is necessary.			

Adapted from *Managing Your Personal Food Supply*, edited by Ray Wolf/Rodale Press, Inc.

mercial preparation of frozen peas. However, even greater losses will occur without blanching — up to 40 percent of the vitamin C content of peas has been shown to be lost because of oxidation prior to blanching in commercial operations where the vegetables must stand for long periods in transport vehicles.

Vitamin A is likewise protected by blanching, while the B vitamins, such as thiamine and riboflavin, are also lost because of enzyme action prior to blanching. Nevertheless, a certain amount of trade-off is involved here.

The *Quality and Stability of Frozen Foods* states, "washing, blanching and cooling necessary for the preparation of vegetables for freezing are responsible for appreciable losses of vitamins. Most measurements have been made on vitamin C losses, but it is possible that what can be said about vitamin C would also apply to water-soluble B vitamins present. In this regard, blanching is the worst offender."

The book does go on to state that while there is always some vitamin loss, a high-temperature blanch of short duration followed by rapid cooling will lead to best retention of both vitamins and colour. When blanching is done in boiling water, vitamin loss increases with the time in the water, while if it is done with steam, the loss becomes negligible after the first 60 seconds.

Steam blanching is, therefore, the preferred method, both commercially and in the home, where such steaming can easily be accomplished with a medium-sized lidded pot and a bamboo steamer-basket. Also available are large home steamer units, working on the double-boiler principle, and although quite expensive, these are good for processing large quantities quickly.

When working with a small steamer basket, place it in a pot containing about a half inch of water. First let the water come to a full boil over high heat, and then pour about two cups of vegetables into the basket. Cover the pot and begin timing (see accompanying chart).

Halfway through the timing, remove the lid and turn the vegetables. The blanched portion will appear noticeably brighter in colour, especially with green vegetables. Replace the lid for the remainder of the blanching time.

When the blanching time elapses, remove the basket, dumping the vegetables into a large kettle or sink full of ice water. More prepared vegetables may now be placed in the basket over the boiling water to steam while the first lot chills. Remove the first lot of vegetables from the water before adding the second lot, placing the chilled vegetables in a colander, sieve or on a clean tea towel to drain. An abundance of ice will prove handy, as the colder and faster the chilling procedure, the better the vegetables will turn out. Swirling the vegetables in hand-numbingly cold water will speed things along. Produce should never be allowed to languish and become water-soaked during this step. Chilling will take roughly the same amount of time as the blanching, after which the vegetables should drain for approximately 15 minutes. (During all of this, blanching should continue on the next batch, and the water level in the blanching pot should be checked from time to time to ensure that the pot does not boil dry.)

The purpose of the vegetable container is to keep desiccating freezer air away from the food — which can easily become "freezer-burned" if not properly protected — and to retain the food's own moisture and flavour. Not only should the container material be impervious to air and water, but also air should be removed from around the food itself. Water vapour in the trapped air within the container will cause crystals to form around the food, lowering its quality.

Plastic wrapping, freezer bags, aluminum foil, freezer paper, glass jars and plastic or waxed cardboard containers may all be used for freezing, although air removal may be difficult or impossible with all but plastic bags. If the food cannot be seen through the container, label the contents clearly on the package. (A wax pencil comes in handy here, as does freezer tape, which adheres even in cold temperatures.) All food should be dated and, if possible, used in the order in which it was frozen. The method used at home is, incidentally, called "still freezing," the cheapest and slowest way of freezing food. Commercial processors agitate most vegetables or blow cold air over them to speed the freezing process. George Arbuckle, general production manager of York Farms, says that while various companies have their own "pet processes," York uses a high-velocity wind that blows upward through the free-flowing vegetables on the freezer belt "so the peas look like they are boiling" as they freeze in three to five minutes.

Plastic freezer bags, available in a variety of sizes in most supermarkets, are the most convenient freezing packages for most items. Recycled plastic bags can be put into use during the harvest, but the very thin material sometimes used in sandwich wrapping will not adequately protect vegetables from freezer burn. Vegetables will freeze most quickly if they are loosely packed in their bags, but excess air should be extracted before the bags are placed in the freezer. Using a straw, suck out as much air as possible, and pinch shut the neck of the bag while fastening with a twist tie.

Newly packed food will, of course, raise the temperature inside the freezer, so do not freeze more than three pounds of food per cubic foot of total freezer space at a time, if possible. While the rate of freezing apparently has little effect on vitamin content, it will influence the final texture of the food. Spread the packages out in a single layer, not touching, in the coldest area of the freezer.

FARM-STYLE PORTIONS

How much one should freeze depends entirely upon the family's preferences. Canada's Food Guide lists a portion of vegetables as one-half cup. "In order to serve six portions (three cups) of a frozen vegetable once a week for 26 weeks, the total quantity required would be 26 small freezer bags," states an Agriculture Canada news release. One-half cup seems, however, a very small portion for anyone but a child. As farm-style portions nudge closer to a cup, even an overflowing one, we find that a quart bag of frozen vegetables serves two people for only two meals — hence the frantic scramble to fill a large freezer every fall. Most large families can easily polish off a quart bag of vegetables at a meal.

Frozen vegetables should generally be taken from the freezer and immediately cooked in their frozen state — steaming, stir-frying or adding directly to soups or stews will retain vitamins best.

It should be remembered that frozen vegetables, because they have previously been blanched and somewhat tenderized by the freezing process, need only one-third or one-half the cooking time of fresh produce. A minimum of water — as little as ¼ cup — will suffice to steam most frozen vegetables to perfection. (If frozen in a block or chunk, vegetables should be broken into several lumps prior to cooking to hasten the penetration of heat.)

Recipes calling for fresh vegetables can be carried off using frozen produce, provided the cooking time is shortened. If frozen beans or corn are being included in a stew or chowder, for example, add them only at the very last minute to prevent their becoming overcooked and textureless.

An exception to the general rule is corn on the cob, which is thawed completely, then buttered, wrapped in foil and baked for 20 minutes at 400 degrees. (Frozen fruits are also allowed to thaw before serving, unless they are destined for the cooking pot. They should be left in their unopened container until ready to serve — optimally while a few ice crystals still remain. This state of readiness normally occurs three hours after a pint container is removed from the freezer, longer for larger quantities.)

While zero degrees F is considered the optimum temperature in a home freezer, it is a compromise between good food storage and reasonable power usage. Lower temperatures will store food in better condition for a longer time, but they will greatly increase energy use, and in any case, a year is usually sufficiently long for home food storage, taking the family from harvest season to harvest season. The *Quality and Stability of Frozen Foods* states that vegetables held at zero degrees will be "stable enough to maintain high quality from one harvest season to the next." There will be minor colour and flavour deterioration, it states, but this will be noticeable only if the food is compared directly with fresh. (The small freezer compartment of the average refrigerator, by the way, is not recommended for long-term food storage. Temperatures there usually range from 10 to 25 degrees F.)

SECOND TO WATER HEATER

Every freezer has some warm spots, where the temperature will be above zero, and these should be used for soon-to-be-consumed items. The warm spots will usually be near the top and middle of a chest freezer, or in the upper door shelves of an upright. If the entire freezer were cooled to the point where the warmest part measured zero degrees F, power usage could increase by as much as 50 percent, according to Consumers

Union of the United States. This from an appliance that is in any case a heavy power user. According to the Consumers' Association of Canada, electricity to run a 12-cubic-foot freezer costs about $35 a year, slightly more than the kilowatt consumption of an electric range. But a 24-cubic-foot unit uses about 40 percent more than its half-size counterpart, placing it second only to the water heater as a power user in the average home.

Not only the freezer's size, but also its position will affect power usage. One freezer owner noted what she called a "drastic change" in her home's electricity needs after the freezer was moved to an unheated attached shed from the kitchen, where it had been warmed all winter by the wood stove. Many homeowners choose to place the freezer in the basement, where it can be kept cool year-round. There is, after all, no perfect insulating system. Other factors, too, will affect energy requirements. Every time the freezer is opened, cool air is lost from the interior and must be replaced. Limit openings as much as possible, especially in hot, humid weather. Power usage also increases as the freezer empties — air is more difficult to keep cold than is food. And an inadequately insulated or poorly sealed freezer may lose cold air to the outside even when it is closed, while extra insulation can result in a great saving. "We found that 1.4 cm of extra insulation resulted in a remarkable 30 percent decrease in energy consumption," says *Canadian Consumer* magazine. Freezers in Canada are now sold with an Energuide sticker, an assessment by the Canadian Standards Association of the energy needs of each appliance.

Those who have ready access to vegetables and home-grown poultry and meats may want to follow the recommended practice of keeping two smaller freezers, rather than one larger one. In the boom-and-bust cycle of harvest freezing, both of the freezers are filled to the brim in fall, but by spring, both are half-full, and one can be emptied into the other, the first disconnected during the warm summer months.

The size of freezer a family needs is, like its vegetable preferences, a very individual matter. *Canadian Consumer* recommends from three to seven cubic feet of freezer space per adult, depending on whether the freezer will receive light or heavy use. We find, however, that the family that freezes virtually all of its food requires more than seven cubic feet per adult, even when the food system is backed up by a cool room for root vegetables, as well as considerable canning and pickling.

Freezers are available in upright or chest models. The former offer the convenience of a refrigerator-type layout, but more cold air is lost when the unit is opened, resulting in somewhat higher energy consumption compared with similar-capacity chest models. These are a little more difficult to organize but are a better energy bargain on the whole.

Of course, a freezer of any sort practically extends a hand in invitation to its owner to grow a garden, raise meat chickens, pick strawberries by the gallon, make ice cream and quantities of pies. It is difficult to say which comes first, the freezer or the stuff to go in it.

All that cold empty space, just waiting for the fruits of the harvest. One would have to have the heart of a Confucian gentleman to resist — a heart said to be symbolized by a fine jade vessel packed with ice. ■

Sources

KEEPING THE HARVEST
Home Storage of Fruits and Vegetables
By Nancy Thurber and Gretchen Mead
202 pages
74A — paperback, $9.25
Available from Harrowsmith Books, Camden East, Ontario K0K 1J0. A complete guide to freezing, canning, jamming, pickling, salt curing and grain storage. Every common garden vegetable is covered, and each method of preserving is thoughtfully and fully discussed. Each chapter is illustrated with photographs, and both old and new ways of home storage are compared.

SEASONAL FREEZER COOKBOOK
By Jeni Wright, Caroline Ellwood, Clare Ferguson and Carole Handslip
208 pages
396B — hardcover, $24.95
Available from Harrowsmith Books, Camden East, Ontario K0K 1J0. Divided into Spring, Summer, Autumn and Winter sections, the book explains how to freeze those fruits and vegetables in season, whether bought or from the garden. In addition, there are more than 250 freezer recipes designed to make the most of your produce. Charts provide quick reference for seasonal availability and storage times.

THE BUSY PERSON'S GUIDE
TO PRESERVING FOOD
By Janet Bachand Chadwick
132 pages
292A — paperback, $6.95
Available from Harrowsmith Books, Camden East, Ontario K0K 1J0. With a 9-to-5 job or children to tend, finding time for canning and preserving can be a chore in itself. Chadwick lists her own time-saving techniques, which should be useful to all readers, whether they garden or buy food in bulk or whether they prefer canning, freezing or root cellaring. Recipes are included.

Briny Exotica

Pickles the way grandma — bless her heart — didn't make them

By Anne Borella

My idea of a super morning in early fall is an amble around one of Montreal's open-air markets. As the harvest season draws to a close, there is an air of confusion and cheerful chaos as farmers cram their stalls with locally grown crops, aggressively vying for each shopper's attention with noisy one-liners announcing the daily specials: *les tomates, courgettes, haricots.*

I find it difficult to decide what to purchase amidst all this abundance: huge creamy white cauliflowers, mounds of green and yellow snap beans, sun-ripened tomatoes, beets, celery and peppers, red, yellow and green. Homemakers, anxious to extend the low cost of in-season produce over the winter months, haggle with vendors for special prices on bulk purchases of the goods they will preserve with canners and freezers.

For me, this is pickling time. I love the incredible profusion of fruits and vegetables, so fresh there is an earthy fragrance of sweet, moist soil filling the air. As I meander around the crowded aisles making mental notes of the quality and variety of the produce offered at each stand, I already envision relish trays resplendent with an array of pickled fruits, chutneys mellowed by months of storage, spicy relishes and crisp, tangy vegetables in exotic brines.

I learned to pickle long before I knew how to bake a cake. Butter, sugar and eggs were rationed in Britain during and after the war, so baking was a luxury in which few of us could indulge. But we could make pickles. Everyone, it seemed, had a victory garden or an allotment, a small parcel of land away from the house where the fruit and vegetables were grown during the summer months. Thriftiness was fashionable. Besides, preserving the excess of each crop was a necessity, especially if the family wanted to survive the winter on anything but rationed foods.

Thriftiness may still be fashionable, but today I pickle for pleasure. I love the pungent aromas that permeate the kitchen during preparation, the satisfaction of seeing filled jars gleaming from my cupboard shelves. But most of all, I enjoy the taste of homemade pickles, the cool, crisp texture and tart, salty-sometimes-sweet sensation that shocks my palate and sharpens my awareness of other foods.

Furthermore, pickling is easy. For the canning novice, it is an enjoyable way to become familiar with the equipment, terminology and methodology used in preserving food.

Pickles are not simply cucumbers, whole or sliced and steeped in a spicy vinegar solution; a pickle is any fruit or vegetable alone or in combination that has been preserved primarily in salt and vinegar. Based on the method of preparation and the ingredients, there are actually four types of pickles.

Brined or **fermented pickles** go through a curing process of about three weeks. Dilled cucumbers and sauerkraut belong to this group. During curing, the colour of the cucumber changes from bright green to olive or yellow green. The white interior of the cucumber becomes uniformly translucent. A fine flavour, neither too salty, sour nor spicy, develops during curing. Some connoisseurs feel that pickles prepared this

Ernie Sparks

way develop a flavour that is superior to those prepared with a vinegar solution. They are the most difficult to make, however, as the preparation and storage temperatures must be carefully controlled so that the vegetables can be preserved before spoilage occurs.

Fresh pack or **quick process pickles**, on the other hand, are the easiest to prepare. Vegetables are usually soaked in a saline solution for a few hours or overnight. Excess water is thereby drawn from the vegetables, whose tissues are strengthened so that they remain crisp after pickling. The vegetables are then drained and combined with a boiling vinegar solution.

Fruit pickles are usually prepared from whole fruit and simmered in a spicy sweet-sour syrup. They should be bright in colour and uniform in size. Pears, peaches, grapes and watermelon rinds are some popular fruits for pickling.

Relishes, chutneys and **sauces** are made from fruit and vegetables that have been chopped, seasoned and cooked to a desired consistency. Clear, bright colour and uniformity in size of pieces will produce an attractive relish.

EQUIPMENT

Fortunately, most kitchens are stocked with many of the pieces of equipment necessary in pickle making — bowls, measuring cups and spoons. An important consideration, however, is the material out of which the equipment is made. Only enamel, stainless steel, glass or aluminum containers should be used for pickling. Do not use galvanized iron, copper, brass or even chipped enamel, as the vinegar and salt used in the pickling process may react chemically with these metals to form harmful compounds.

Besides standard kitchen utensils, a few pieces of specialized apparatus are necessary for proper pickle making, equipment that can be used for other canning as well.

Preserving food at home can be a way to economize, but some cooks may carry economizing too far, searching for ways to save money within the preserving process. This may not only be detrimental to the quality of the food being preserved, but may also result in spoilage, which immediately adds to the overall cost.

The first necessity is a canning kettle, or water bath processor, essential for processing packed jars of pickles at a temperature of 212 degrees F and useful for sterilizing empty jars when necessary. A deep kettle that has a well-fitting lid and interior metal basket on which the jars rest should be used. It should be at least 9 to 10 inches deep, so that the jars can be covered by two inches of briskly boiling water, permitting proper heat penetration at the top of the jar. Such heat is necessary for elimination of dangerous organisms within the food.

As well, a very large pot is useful for cooking quantities of pickles, relishes, chutneys and sauces. It can also be used for jam making. The volume should be approximately 10 to 12 quarts, and although I only make jam in small quantities to ensure the best quality, a large pot eliminates any anxiety about the mixture bubbling over the sides.

The key word for me in pickle making is not economizing but preserving, so I am careful to use the right equipment and most up-to-date methods. I prefer the self-sealing Mason-type jars to any others. These are available in half-pint, pint, quart and two-quart sizes and are sold with lids and screw-on rings to hold the lids in place. The smallest jars are offered in decorator styles as well as the traditional plain models. There are also several styles of imported preserving jars on the market, prohibitively priced but excellent, as are the decorator jars, if the pickles are for gift-giving or donation to the school bazaar. Wide-mouthed jars, where they are available, make the packing of whole fruit easier.

One of the most common ways that picklers cut costs is by reusing commercial containers, a hangover from the World War II era when jars, due to necessity then, were tempered so that they would stand up to repeated use. As this is no longer the case, and today's commercial jars made of thinner glass are designed for "one trip only," their use in canning can lead to messy and costly breakage. Some jars, such as those for mayonnaise or coffee, are manufactured specifically as "cold pack" jars and are not designed to tolerate heat at all. Cooks who reuse commercial jars do so at the risk of losing some of their precious preserves.

Likewise, I do not consider reusing lids an appropriate way to cut corners, and always use new lids myself. Again, the cook must realize that he or she risks lower food quality by using old lids. If they do not seal, the food must be used immediately or reprocessed, causing the pickles to be overcooked.

The other most commonly used canning system involves the use of jars that are fitted with glass lids and rubber rings. In this case, the rubber rings can be used several times. These jars are no longer manufactured, but many cooks still use their supply of older jars and lids. Fortunately, the rubber rings are still readily available.

A few other pieces of equipment are optional but can be useful. A large colander with legs for good drainage is helpful in washing produce and allowing it to drain well, although a sieve is a good substitute. A jar funnel is a help when hot mixtures are poured into the jars. These are sold in most stores that stock canning supplies. Jar lifters, again custom-made for canning, help in the easy, safe removal of hot jars from the boiling water bath. The baskets in these baths lift and hook onto the sides of the kettle, however, so it is quite possible for the cook to remove the jars safely by using a pot holder. A bubble freer is another low-cost helper. Made of clear plastic, this simple tool, substituting for the knife of yesteryear, is run down the inside edges of filled jars to release air bubbles without damaging the jar. The magnetic wand is new on the canning scene, a gadget useful in lifting the metal snap lids out of boiling water.

As the interest in home preserving has gained momentum in recent years, even more equipment has been designed to lessen the drudgery involved in the preparation of large quantities of food for canning, freezing or pickling. I am lucky to have a mixing machine with several optional attachments for slicing, mincing or chopping, including a supersonic sieve attachment that has made my preparation of sauces and catsups so easy that I sometimes get carried away and prepare more than I need.

INGREDIENTS

Vegetables and fruits for pickling should be at the peak of perfection. Vegetables should be young and tender, while fruit should be just ripe, perfect for eating out of hand. Overripe but not spoiled fruit or tomatoes can be used for sauces and catsups. As spoilage organisms thrive in dirt, be sure to wash all produce thoroughly, using a vegetable brush to remove soil.

Salt plays an important role in pickling. Used in the correct proportions, it acts as a preservative; dangerous organisms cannot grow in strong saline solutions, which is the reason early sailors subsisted on salt pork during their long sea voyages. Use a coarse, uniodized salt sold especially for pickling. Because of its iodine content or anti-caking ingredients, table salt may cloud the brine and is therefore unsuitable for pickling.

Vinegar, too, is a preservative; bacterial action is inhibited or prevented entirely in an acid mixture of the correct strength. Select a vinegar that has at least four to six percent acetic acid content; most commercial vinegars are prepared to this standard. Although homemade vinegar can be delicious, its use in pickling recipes can be risky because the quality and degree of acidity are undetermined. Use it in salad dressings instead.

Distilled white vinegar is most suitable for pickling light-coloured fruit, while cider, malt or wine vinegars can be used for darker foods or when a more interesting flavour is desired. Do not dilute the vinegar with water unless so directed by the recipe.

Sugar can be white or brown depending mostly upon the degree of darkness desired in the food to be pickled. I prefer to use white sugar when I want to retain the colour of the fruit or vegetable pickle. Honey or corn syrup can be used in place of sugar or to replace half of the sugar specified in a recipe. Remember, though, that honey will contribute its own flavour to the produce being pickled.

Spices add immeasurably to pickled foods, so the cook should take care to see that they are as fresh as possible, since they tend to lose flavour during storage. Whole spice mixtures especially suited for pickling are commercially available, but any cook can mix fresh spices for a more individual flavour.

Whole spices should be tied in a cheesecloth bag before being added to the recipe. Keep a supply of cheesecloth and string on hand for that purpose. This way, the spices can be removed from the mixture readily, and the degree of spiciness easily regulated. Small seeds such as dill, mustard or celery are often added directly to the pickles, however, as they lend a decorative touch to the finished product while adding flavour as well. Powdered spices should be used only in sauces, relishes and chutneys.

Water, too, is an important ingredient in many pickle recipes. Soft water is best. The minerals in hard water can interfere with the pickling process or cause undesirable colour changes in certain foods. If the cook must use hard water, it should be boiled first, and any scum that forms removed. Leave it for 24 hours, and then carefully ladle it from the top of the container, taking care not to disturb the sediment that has accumulated on the bottom. Add one tablespoon of vinegar per gallon of hard water before using it.

Alum and lime, which help retain the crispness of pickled vegetables, were additional ingredients often used by picklers in our grandmothers' era. These additives are not particularly desirable from a health standpoint, nor are they necessary if proper procedures are followed. One old trick used by seasoned picklers involved the layering of cucumbers with grape leaves before brining. Scientific evidence has revealed that the leaves do in fact contain a substance that is helpful in inhibiting the development of an enzyme that can cause softening of pickled vegetables.

PROCESSING

To an experienced pickler, the suggestion that filled, sealed jars of pickles need processing may come as a shock. Because of the high percentage of salt and vinegar in such recipes, it has long been believed that further protection from spoilage organisms was unnecessary. There is the possibility of contamination as food is packed in jars, however, so many authorities now recommend that all pickled foods be given a short heat treatment to ensure full protection against spoilage.

Immediately after the jar is filled and sealed, immerse it in actively boiling water in the canning kettle, making sure that the water covers the top of the jar. Keep a kettle of boiling water handy, and, if necessary, add water to raise the level. Cover the container, and when the water returns to a full boil, start to measure the processing time. For fermented cucumbers and fresh pack pickles, however, start to measure the processing time as soon as the filled jars are immersed in actively boiling water. This method helps prevent a cooked flavour and loss of crispness in the pickles.

Jars that are to be filled, sealed and processed do not have to be sterilized prior to packing, as both the jar and food will be sterilized together during the processing. When processing is not anticipated, however, the jars must be sterilized before they are filled. But always process jars if the recipe demands it; the heat treatment has been included to ensure that the final product will be safe.

GENERAL PROCEDURE
FOR PICKLING

1. Read through the recipe to be sure all ingredients and equipment are on hand. Note that some pickle recipes are prepared in two or three stages, with several hours between each stage.
2. Fill the water bath three-quarters full or to the cor-

rect depth so that overflowing will not occur when the jars are immersed.

3. Check preserving jars for any imperfections in the sealing edge, discarding any that have small nicks or chips that can prevent proper sealing or permit air to enter the jar during storage. Wash jars in hot soapy water and rinse them well.

4. Wash produce thoroughly in cold water, using a vegetable brush to loosen any soil.

5. Prepare the recipe according to the instructions.

6. To sterilize, if necessary, immerse jars in hot water, making sure they are covered by an inch or two of water. Cover the water bath and bring to a boil for 20 minutes. Leave the jars in hot water until ready to fill.

7. Place snap lids or glass lids and rubber rings in a small saucepan, cover them with water and boil for five minutes. Leave in hot water until needed for sealing.

8. Fill half-pint jars to ⅛-inch, pint jars to ¼-inch and quarts to ½-inch from the top edge. Run a bubble freer or clean knife inside the jar between the food and jar to release air bubbles.

9. Use a clean paper towel or damp cloth to wipe the sealing edge and threads of jars. Seal each jar immediately after filling by topping it with a hot flat metal snap lid and securing that with a metal retaining ring. If using glass lids, first apply a rubber ring, then a glass lid and finally, a screw ring. Tighten firmly if using snap lids, but leave them slightly looser if using glass lids.

10. If the recipe does not call for processing, place jars upright, well apart, on a wooden board or rubber mat and leave to cool. Do not set jars in a draught or on a cold, wet surface.

11. If the recipe calls for processing, follow the instructions already given for processing in a water bath. As soon as glass-lidded jars are removed from the bath, their tops should be snugly tightened. Do not touch the tops of snap lids, however.

12. As metal-lidded jars cool, the cook may hear a popping noise, which indicates that the seal has taken effect.

13. When the jars are cool, test the lids to be sure they have sealed. If the flat metal snap lid is down and slightly concave, it is sealed. The lid, in any case, should be firmly attached to the jar; a push with the thumb should not move it. The retaining ring may be removed, the jar wiped, labelled and stored in a dark, dry place.

PICKLED CORN ON THE COB

I always keep a few ears of corn back from the freezer for this pickle. We love the fun of nibbling the spicy kernels off the cob.

3 cups white vinegar
1 cup sugar
½ tsp. coarse salt
3 Tbsp. mixed pickling spice
1-inch piece cinnamon stick
3-4 ears of corn, cut crosswise in 1-inch pieces

Mix vinegar, sugar and salt. Tie spices in a cheesecloth bag and add to vinegar mixture. Bring to a boil, stirring to dissolve sugar. Simmer, covered, for 10 minutes. Remove spice bag.

Cook corn in boiling water for two to three minutes. Drain. Pack into clean, hot Mason jars. Cover with boiling vinegar solution to ¼-inch from sealing edge. Seal with a metal snap lid and screwband. Process in a boiling water bath for 10 minutes.

Makes about 3 pints.

SPICED BLUEBERRIES

This makes an unusual accompaniment to roast lamb.

4 cups fresh blueberries
⅓ cup white vinegar
⅓ cup sugar
⅛ tsp. powdered cloves
⅛ tsp. powdered cinnamon
⅛ tsp. powdered allspice

Combine all ingredients in a large saucepan and bring to a boil. Simmer, stirring often, until mixture thickens — about 10 to 15 minutes. Pour into hot jars, leaving ⅛-inch head space. Seal immediately with a metal snap lid and sealing band. Process jars for 5 minutes in a boiling water bath.

Makes about 1 pint.

SPICY PICKLED GRAPES

These look magnificent in the jar and make an excellent gift. When prepared *en branche*, they make a stunning and elegant addition to a relish or hors d'oeuvre tray. The grapes will be cooked during the processing. As they cook, they will shrink and hang suspended in the jar in a very attractive manner — I love to prepare these just for the pleasure of seeing them in the jar.

2 lbs. firm, ripe seedless green grapes
1-inch piece ginger root, bruised
12 whole cloves
3-inch cinnamon stick
1½ cups white vinegar
2½ cups sugar
2 thin slices lemon

Inspect the grapes carefully, removing any that show signs of spoilage. Leave grapes on the branch or stem and wash carefully. Tie spices in a cheesecloth bag and add to a saucepan with vinegar and sugar. Bring to a boil, stirring to dissolve sugar, then simmer together for 5 minutes.

Pack grapes tightly into a clean, hot pint jar. Tuck lemon slices in between the fruit and the side of the jar. Remove spice bag from syrup. Pour hot syrup over grapes to ½-inch from sealing edge. Remove air bubbles by inserting a bubble freer between the fruit and the side of the jar. Add more syrup if necessary to maintain the head space. Seal immediately with a metal snap lid and screw band. Process for 10 minutes in a boiling water bath. Store for several weeks before using.

Makes 1 pint.

HOT TAMALE

A lovely blending of summer fruits, vegetables and tomatoes. I usually make two batches of this, one with the fruit and vegetables in recognizable pieces and the the other with a smoother consistency.

7 cups peeled, cored and coarsely chopped tomatoes (about 15-20)
2 cups peeled, stoned and coarsely chopped peaches (about 4)
3 cups peeled, cored and coarsely chopped pears (about 3-4)
3 cups peeled, cored and coarsely chopped tart apples (about 3)
3 cups chopped celery
2 cups thinly sliced onion
2 cups cider vinegar
2-3 cups brown sugar
1 Tbsp. salt
½ tsp. cayenne, or to taste
3 Tbsp. whole mixed pickling spice tied in a cheesecloth bag
3-6 small, dried hot chili peppers

Combine ingredients in a large kettle and bring to a boil, slowly stirring, to dissolve sugar.

Simmer, uncovered, for about one hour or until pickle has thickened to desired consistency. Stir frequently as pickle thickens to prevent it from scorching.

Pour boiling mixture into hot jars, leaving ⅛-inch head space. Seal immediately with a metal snap lid and screw band. Process pints for 10 minutes in a boiling water bath.

Makes about 5 pints, depending on the degree of thickness.

INDIAN CHUTNEY

Mention chutney and my mouth waters in anticipation of this smooth, spicy East Indian delicacy. Traditionally, chutney is served with curried dishes, but I find that it is excellent as an accompaniment to chicken, turkey and pork dishes or spooned over cream cheese spread on thin crispy crackers for a simple snack or hors d'oeuvre.

2 cups dried figs, chopped
3½ cups dried dates, pitted and chopped

1⅓ cups raisins
1½ cups chopped green pepper
2 red peppers, seeded and chopped
1 cup chopped onion
3 cloves garlic, crushed and finely chopped
7-oz. jar stem ginger in syrup, diced
5 cups cider vinegar
3 cups brown sugar, firmly packed
2 Tbsp. coarse salt
3 Tbsp. curry
1 tsp. turmeric
½ tsp. pepper
1½ tsp. ground cloves
1 Tbsp. ground ginger
2 cups peeled and coarsely chopped mangoes or papayas
1 cup canned pineapple tidbits
Grated rind and juice of 2 lemons
Grated rind and juice of 2 oranges
½ cup sherry
⅓ cup slivered almonds

Mix dried fruit, vegetables, ginger, vinegar, sugar, salt and spices in a large kettle. Simmer, uncovered, for 1 hour, stirring often.

Add remaining fruit and rind and juice of lemons and oranges. Continue simmering, uncovered, for 1 hour or until chutney thickens to desired consistency. Stir in sherry and nuts and simmer for 10 minutes.

Pour boiling mixture into hot jars, leaving ⅛-inch head space. Seal with a metal snap lid and sealing band. Process pints for 10 minutes in a boiling water bath.

Makes about 6 pints. ∎

Anne Borella is the author of two books and numerous articles on preserving food. She lives in Beaconsfield, Quebec.

Sources

KEEPING THE HARVEST
Home Storage of Fruits and Vegetables
By Nancy Thurber and Gretchen Mead
202 pages
74A — paperback, $9.25
Available from Harrowsmith Books, Camden East, Ontario K0K 1J0. A complete guide to freezing, canning, jamming, pickling, salt curing and grain storage. Every common garden vegetable is covered, and each method of preserving is thoughtfully and fully discussed. Each chapter is illustrated with photographs, and both old and new ways of home storage are compared.

Summer Under Glass

Redolent with ancient tradition, potpourris capture the aromatic essence of the herb garden

By Mary Preus Hamilton

"**T**ake drie Rose leaves, keep them close in a glass which will keep them sweet, then take powder of Mints, powder of Cloves in a grosse powder. Put the same to the Rose leaves, then put all these together in a bag, and take that to bed with you, and it cause you to sleep, and it is good to smell unto at other times."

This benevolent herbal predecessor to the Valium Age is called "a bag to Smell Unto for Melancholy" and was prescribed in *Ram's Little Dodoen,* published in Britain in the year 1606.

It was, then, a time of great olfactory awareness, when fragrant things "to smell unto" — sweet bags and potpourris — were highly esteemed by a population assailed by noxious odours and diseases associated with poor sanitation. Believing strongly in the cheering and curative powers of sweet or sharply scented flowers and herbs, the people of Shakespeare's England are known to have turned frequently to aromatic mixtures both for the sensation and as a cure for lethargy, melancholy and other afflictions of human nature.

Ernie Sparks

After delving into the old herbal literature and being moved to experiment with potpourri blends of my own, I now readily understand why the word "delight" figures so prominently in the ancient titles and recipes. While crushing spices, mixing petals, rubbing herbs between my fingers and tending to all the other pleasant tasks involved in creating a potpourri, I find that unhappiness seems to drift away like a vapour on the breeze. Modern-day research has proved that certain plant oils actually do have sedative and germicidal properties. I also believe that there is something very wise about those old herbalists' beliefs that linked good smells with good cheer. Rousseau called the sense of smell the sense of the imagination, and one good whiff of a finished potpourri conjures up all the scents and colours of a perfect summer's day, caught as if by magic in a jar and preserved for years.

There are two main types of potpourri: moist and dry. Both are mixtures or combinations of herbs, flowers, spices, oils and preservatives. They are often visually pleasing, sometimes useful in repelling insects and always fragrant. The French used the moist method centuries ago and called the finished product *pot pourri* — rotten pot. Half-dried petals were packed in containers with other ingredients, including salt and sometimes alcohol, and the mixture aged until it formed a moist cake and fermented — but still smelled heavenly — apparently keeping its scent for as long as 40 years. Dry potpourris, in which all ingredients are thoroughly desiccated, are easier to make, and although their fragrances are not as long-lived, their colours are usually brighter.

Although the French gave the mixture its name, the art of blending scented plants predated their *pot pourri* by millennia. Over 4,000 years ago, an unknown herbal mixture was placed in the tomb of the Egyptian high priest, Ra Ouer. Found (centuries later) along with a necklace of 4,000 rubies, the potpourri was still diffused with "the delicious scent of flowers, as if sweet-smelling bouquets had only recently been placed there."

The Egyptians were, of course, masters of preservation, but the Chinese, who also explored the use of scents thousands of years ago, had a wealth of spices to draw upon. These treasures would eventually travel westward along the "incense route" through Arabia, and there is mention in the Book of Proverbs of scenting bedclothes with myrrh, cinnamon and aloes.

The ancient Greeks loved scent and used it in religious rituals and secular festivities — revellers wore garlands of flowers and perfumed garments. In the home, they scattered petals and herbs on the floors of their chambers, scenting the air with potpourris. To the Eastern methods of blending potpourri, the Greeks added native herbs which thrived in their sunny Mediterranean climate.

The Romans, however, who carried everything to excess, were history's most lavish users of aromatics. Huge quantities of herbs were strewn at banquets, funerals and other events — participants sometimes actually waded knee-deep in flower petals. Men and women used perfumed cosmetics, unguents, and oils

to such an extent that Rome was in debt to India for, as far as monetary terms can be translated, what seems to have been more than three million dollars a year.

It was the Romans who introduced Oriental aromatics to Western Europe, and the Crusades established their use. Though exorbitantly expensive, the spicy mixtures were valued for everything from combatting plague to correcting imbalances of hot or cold "humours" which caused the lesser diseases. The English herbals tell us that herbs and spices figured in remedies for everything from "griping of the guts" to "worms in the belly and ears" to falling hair and, that old bugbear, melancholy.

Herbs were nowhere more beloved than in England. From Saxon times until the end of the 17th century, in monasteries, palaces and cottage gardens, herbs had a higher priority than ornamentals and were an integral part of daily life.

TUSSIE-MUSSIES

Pungent herbs such as lavender, mint, hyssop and meadowsweet were hung in bunches or strewn "in chambers and places of pleasure, recreation and repose." Herb vinegars were sprinkled to disinfect the rooms. Old herbals tell us that people carried aromatic nosegays called tussie-mussies "both for sight and smell." Ladies and their maids spent hours in the "stillroom," named for the perfumery still where essential oils were distilled from plants. There, using mortar and pestle, bunches of herbs and flowers and boxes of spices and aromatics from exotic places, they concocted medicines, soaps, candles, insect repellents and other preparations for everyday use.

In Elizabethan times, the use of exotic perfumery was the height of fashion — for those who could afford such luxuries. Men and women alike perfumed their bodies, clothing and bedding and indulged in baths scented according to the season. Queen Elizabeth and ladies of the court wore special jewellery containing aromatic substances, while courtiers snuffed an amazing variety of perfumed tobacco powders. Even cardinals were criticized for their extravagant use of expensive perfumes.

The stillroom eventually became part of even the smallest country home, and the collecting of recipes or "receipts" was a fashionable pastime. Many of the court ladies and gallants published "stillroom books" with such titles as *Delights for Ladies, The Toilet of Floria, The Queen's Closet Opened* and *The Secretes of the Reverent Maister Alexis of Piemont*. These contained quaintly phrased instructions for "Howe to gather and clarify maydewe," "To make a speciall sweet water to perfume clothes in the folding being washed," or "Divers sorts of sweet handwaters made suddenly or extempore with extracted oyles and spices." There were also recipes for perfumed powders, pomanders, wash balls, scented ointments, sweet bags, tussie-mussies and, of course, potpourris.

Today, long after the heyday of the tussie-mussie, anything as old-fashioned as a potpourri may seem impractical, but there are many modern uses for the sweet-smelling mixtures. Potpourris can be sewn up in cloth sachets, to be tucked in with clothing and linens. English gentlemen used to frequent a certain inn because, as one said to a friend, "The sheets are scented with lavender." Lightly scented linens are no less pleasant to modern tastes. Another variation on the sachet idea was the "dream pillow," a little bag of fragrance which was said to bring sound sleep and sweet dreams when slipped inside a pillowcase.

Before mothballs were available, ingredients that smelled good to humans but not to insects were blended into special mixtures, which were hung in scent-balls or sachets for insect-proofing. It still works, and the fragrance is infinitely preferable to that of mothballs.

A colourful mixture of flowers, shown off in a sparkling glass jar, makes an unusual display in living room, bedroom or bath, and when the lid is removed, the air soon fills with a delicate perfume. Potpourris also make fine handmade gifts, unusual enough to please even those who "have everything." (How many modern homes can claim to have a sweet jar?)

Because they are unique, potpourris and sachets make excellent barter items — I've swapped sweet jars and bulk potpourri for everything from antiques to zucchini — and, when attractively packaged, can find an enthusiastic market in craft shops.

There is nothing especially complicated about blending a potpourri. Mixtures can be simple, utilizing ingredients from the kitchen or garden and perhaps a few from the local drugstore. They can also be quite elaborate and costly. A good approach is to begin with an easy recipe and gradually increase the complexity by acquiring some of the more exotic ingredients. Be forewarned, however: There's an almost irresistible charm in experimenting with fragrant concoctions, and before you know it, you're likely to find yourself up to the elbows. I started, one summer day, to try a recipe for a quart of potpourri, progressed to gallons, and ended up making whole crocks full of a dozen varieties.

As far as equipment goes, one needs only a glass jar or crock with a good, tight-fitting lid, some newspapers or drying racks, and a mortar and pestle, or, as a substitute, a wooden spoon and bowl. (Never use metal.)

A good supply of flower petals is essential. Rose petals are the all-time favourites. When available, choose the old-fashioned wild or damask types, which have more scent than most of the modern hybrid tea roses. So much the better if there are some perfect buds or slightly opened blooms. Lavender is a herb traditionally prized for both scent and colour. Just these two are enough for a simple potpourri, but delphiniums, marigolds, fuchsia, wallflowers, pansies, violets, bee balm, Queen Anne's lace and almost any flower one enjoys can be used to add colour, fragrance and texture.

"In summertime when roses blowe gather them ere they be full-spred or blowne out," an old herbal instructs, "and in drie weather pluck the leaves." Pick freshly opened blossoms of all types of flowers in the morning when the weather is dry, after the sun's warmth has chased away the dew but not yet released the volatile scented oils. Drying greatly reduces the

quantity, so collect three or four times the amount needed. Dry the blossoms thoroughly on newspapers or racks, away from direct sunlight, which fades their colours. This may take up to two weeks, so find a place where they'll be out of the way, under a bed or in an attic. Turn the petals once or twice a day to speed the process. They are ready when paper-dry. If at all moist, the flowers will become mouldy, spoiling the mixture.

An alternative method, which preserves colour better, is to spread dry sand or a half-and-half mixture of sand and borax two or three inches deep on a tray, place the flowers on it, and carefully sprinkle with sand to cover. Again, they will be ready in about two weeks.

Herbs and spices lend their pungent aromas to a potpourri and sometimes help to preserve the scents of other ingredients. In general, it is preferable to use whole herbs and spices, coarsely ground — they not only mix and look better than powdered material (which tends to cloud a potpourri), but their scents are fresher too.

Bay leaves, rosemary, mint, thyme, rose leaves, lemon verbena, patchouli and scented geraniums are some of the more commonly used herbs. Popular spices include cloves, cinnamon, ginger, coriander, cardamom, allspice and anise, but there are endless combinations and variations.

PRESERVATIVES

Once I have blended petals, herbs and spices, I add a fixative to make the scent last longer. There is no need to use an artificial preservative because nature has provided a variety of substances which will do the job while contributing their own distinctive fragrances. Although some are pretty "down home," the fixative department is where things *can* get exotic — and where I like to browse through herb shops and mail-order catalogues for supplies.

Salt is used in the old-fashioned moist potpourris, a half-and-half mixture of *noniodized* rock and pickling types. Bay salt, made by pounding salt and a few bay leaves together until the crystals have absorbed a light scent, is often used in old recipes.

Orrisroot is an old stand-by for fixing scents. It is the dried, then sliced or pulverized root of the Florentine iris, and its aroma is reminiscent of violets. Many drugstores carry orrisroot, but one can buy starts of the root and prepare it at home.

Tonka beans, which grow in South America, are among the best natural preservatives. They impart a sweet, vanilla-like scent to a floral mixture. The fragrance of gum benzoin and storax, exuded from tropical trees, is heavier, more earthy. All of these are available from specialist firms.

While not absolutely necessary, a few drops of an essential oil will enhance the fragrance of a potpourri and prolong life. These oils are extracted by a variety of methods. The best contain only natural ingredients. Rose, lavender, spice, rose geranium, and bitter orange are popular, while among those with fixative properties are sandalwood, patchouli, cardamom, musk (always a synthetic oil these days since the musk ox is an endangered species) and vetiver, also called khus-khus.

Herb shops, bath shops and some food co-ops stock essential oils, or they are available from several mail-order suppliers. Easy does it with them, though — they are very concentrated, so just a few drops too many can spoil a potpourri.

A potpourri or sachet usually includes one heaping tablespoon of herbs or spices, a like amount of fixative and two or three drops of essential oils per quart of flower petals. If I have a limited amount of petals but want to try several different potpourris, I make a basic mixture of petals and fixative, then separate it into smaller batches and scent each individually with different spices and oils using the above proportions. With a little experience, one can create a pleasant personal blend that is one of a kind.

I assemble the ingredients and place the moist or dried petals in my container, all at once or as they become available. While for a small batch I just sprinkle the petals with the other ingredients, for a large one, I alternate layers, mix well by shaking or stirring and then put the lid on tight. At this point, I can sniff to my heart's content but must reserve judgment as the concoction may be sweet smelling but will be raw. Like quality cheese, fine potpourris take time to ripen. I shake or stir the mixture every few days, making sure the heavier materials don't settle on the bottom. After about six weeks, the individual aromas will have blended and mellowed into a lovely, lingering fragrance, one that will last for months.

I haven't tested out the 40-years-of-fragrance claims, but some of my potpourris are more than four years old and still going strong. If they do start to fade, I'll add a few drops of brandy — alcohol dissolves and releases the aromatic substances and brings new life to a tired mixture.

Potpourris will last longer if they are kept in airtight containers and the lid is lifted only when the perfume is desired. Some people find choosing and decorating containers the most pleasant part of the whole potpourri adventure — and there is certainly no end of things to use — apothecary, "lotus," or antique preserving jars, cut-glass candy dishes, china sugar bowls or ginger jars.

Pretty sachets can be fashioned from scraps of fabric and decorated with embroidery, lace, ribbons and other fancy bits and pieces. Two or three stitched to a length of ribbon can be slipped over a clothes hanger to scent a closet.

CLASSIC POTPOURRI

The combination of bay, rose and lavender has been a favourite for generations. This recipe is adapted from Jacqueline Heriteau's book (the best I've found on the subject but unfortunately out of print) *Potpourris, Sachets, and other Fragrant Delights*. The use of salt and fresh rose petals makes it a moist potpourri so, while colour will fade, the scent is intense and long-lasting.

1 cup coarse salt
3 Tbsp. ground cinnamon
¼ cup dry thyme
¼ cup bay leaves, broken
¼ cup rose geranium leaves
½ cup lavender flowers, dried
3 drops rose oil
6 cups rose petals
Rosebuds

Mix the salt and cinnamon in a gallon jar or crock. Seal and keep the mixture in a warm, dry place. Place the herb mixture in a separate container, add the rose oil, seal and store. As the rose petals become available, add them to the salt mixture, stirring daily. When 6 cups have been added, stir in the herb mixture plus a handful of dry rosebuds. Seal and cure for 6 weeks. Heavenly.

ROSE POMANDER POTPOURRI

Sweet, citrus and fresh, this dry mixture will appeal to just about everyone — and most of its ingredients are readily available.

½ cup dried, crushed orange peel
⅓ cup orrisroot, powdered or sliced
4 cups dried rose petals
½ cup dried rosebuds
2 Tbsp. nutmeg
1 Tbsp. cloves
1 Tbsp. allspice
1 Tbsp. cinnamon
Rose oil

Add orange peel and orrisroot to rose petals and buds. Crush the spices and stir them into the rose mixture, adding two or three drops of rose oil if the petals are not highly scented. Seal and cure for 6 weeks.

HOME & HEALTH POTPOURRI

This delightful recipe appeared in the 1907 edition of *Home and Health,* "Prepared and Edited by a Competent Committee of Home-Makers and Physicians."

"Gather 1 peck sweet rose leaves and spread on blotting paper in the sun. Sprinkle with a pint of salt. Turn them each day while they are drying. If you can obtain them, add carnations, sweet-scented violets, wallflowers, lavender, lemon verbena and, indeed, any sweet-scented thing. When all are dry, put them in a jar, and add ¼ ounce each of Tonka beans, coriander seed and orrisroot. Add a little bergamot (bee balm). Pour on this mixture an ounce of alcohol and a few drops of essence of rose and lavender. Let the mixture rest in the jar 1 week, stirring several times. Then put in the rose jars. A jar filled with this mixture will retain its fragrance for years."

HERBAL MOTH BAGGES

Santolina, also known as lavender cotton, is called *Garderobe* by the French, who prize it for its repellent effect on moths, fleas and other insects. Combined with other strong-scented botanicals, it makes a potent yet fragrant moth deterrent.

1 cup dried southernwood
1 cup dried lavender flowers
1 cup fine cedar sawdust
2 Tbsp. ground cloves
2 Tbsp. ground cinnamon
1 or 2 drops rose oil (optional)

Combine all ingredients; stuff into little "bagges."

If after experimenting with these recipes you find yourself ready for more, there is a surprising variety of books on the subject. Look under "potpourri" or "herbs" in the card catalogue of your local library — several of the popular herb books list half a dozen recipes. You can find one or two in almost any old-time cookbook with a "Household Hints" section too.

I wish you many happy hours mixing fragrant concoctions and an end to melancholy. If that seems strange, ponder the words of John Gerard, most famous of the early English herbalists: "If odours may worke satisfaction, they are so soveraigne in plants and so comfortable that no confection of the apothecaries can equal their excellent Vertue." ∎

Mary Preus Hamilton markets potpourris through a family herbs and aromatics business in Washington State.

Sources

WIDE WORLD OF HERBS
11 St. Catherine Street East
Montreal, Quebec H2X 1K3
Stocks wide variety of natural essential oils in small quantities, although expensive. Catalogue $2.00.

FOLKLORE HERB COMPANY
2388 West 4th Avenue
Vancouver, British Columbia V6K 1P1
A good selection of herbs, botanicals, essential oils and books. Free catalogue.

RICHTERS
Goodwood, Ontario L0C 1A0
(416) 640-6677
Excellent listing of herb seeds. Catalogue $2.00.

CAPRILAND'S HERB FARM
534 Silver Street
Coventry, Connecticut 06238
(203) 742-7244
A wide selection of herb plants and seeds, packaged potpourris and sachets, essential oils and bulk quantity materials for potpourris and sachets, to U.S. customers only. Catalogue free.

See also Sources for "Herbal Homegrowns."

Index